THE
Zagros Streams

THE SYRACUSE GEOGRAPHICAL SERIES is designed to publish distinguished work by scholars associated with the Department of Geography of Syracuse University. The initiation of the series was made possible by a generous bequest from an alumnus, Mr. Donald Lloyd, and its continuation and expansion is supported by the contributions of many other alumni, staff, and friends of the Department.

Inquiries and orders should be addressed to Syracuse University Press, Box 8, University Station, Syracuse, New York, 13210. Standard professional and library discounts are offered. Because of variations in length and illustration each number will be individually priced.

THE
Zagros Streams

*A New Interpretation of Transverse
Drainage in an Orogenic Zone*

THEODORE OBERLANDER (Ph.D., Syracuse)

Assistant Professor of Geography

UNIVERSITY OF CALIFORNIA, BERKELEY ·

Syracuse Geographical Series No. 1   1965

SYRACUSE GEOGRAPHICAL SERIES

Editors

D. W. MEINIG
RICHARD E. DAHLBERG

LIBRARY OF CONGRESS
CATALOG CARD 65-29291

DISTRIBUTED BY
SYRACUSE UNIVERSITY PRESS
Box 8, University Station, Syracuse   13210

Manufactured in the United States of America

Acknowledgments

I would like to express my appreciation to all those whose cooperation and support allowed the completion of this study. First I wish to acknowledge, most gratefully, my obligation to the late Professor George B. Cressey of Syracuse University for his encouragement and help in the early stages of this undertaking and for his efforts in many directions in my behalf throughout my career as a student. Special thanks is likewise expressed to Professor Douglas B. Carter, now at Southern Illinois University, who spent long hours reviewing the manuscript in the minutest detail, and whose criticisms have considerably increased the clarity of this presentation. I am greatly indebted to the United States Steel Foundation for its generous grant awarded through the Geography Department, Syracuse University, in support of this research.

Several individuals in Iran were especially cooperative, in particular: Major William H. Sherman and Colonel Whiteside of the U.S. Army Corps of Engineers; Messrs. H. T. Anderson and M. F. Shepherd of the Geology Department, Iranian Oil Participating Companies; Professors M. H. Ganji and A. Mostafi of the Geography Department, Tehran University; Messrs. H. Hanson and R. Kreiss of the Development and Resources Corporation, Khuzestan Development Service; and especially Mr. Alan Craig of the Khuzestan Water and Power Authority, who, among many other kindnesses, showed me "the ropes" of field work in the Zagros Mountains.

THEODORE OBERLANDER

Contents

Illustrations

Tables

THE
Zagros Streams

General Introduction

The Zagros Highland, which occupies the borderlands of Iraq and Iran from eastern Turkey to the Gulf of Oman, is a most remarkable laboratory for the examination of one of the more perplexing and ubiquitous enigmas of regional physiography: the anomaly of through-flowing drainage that is transverse to the structure of an orogenic system. Some of the world's most spectacular examples of this phenomenon are found in the Zagros, yet these have hitherto received only passing attention by physiographers. A recent opportunity to study this region, which has been truly accessible for little more than three decades, has made possible a detailed analysis of the origin of its anomalous drainage, and the unexpected results challenge a number of common assumptions pertaining to the origin of transverse streams, not only in the Zagros, but generally.

Due to the complexity of tectonic developments and erosional responses in even the younger orogenic systems, such as the Alps and Himalayas, the question of the origin of geologically discordant drainage has almost always been attacked deductively, leading toward conclusions that remain largely within the realm of conjecture. Accordingly, the anomalous stream courses are attributed to a previous tectonic environment, to superposition from hypothetical erosion surfaces or covermasses, or to headward extension under largely unspecified controls. In only the most exceptional instances are there conclusive indications of the precise controls of the location and pattern of streams discordant to their structural environment.

Part of the problem appears to be that geomorphologists have thus far concentrated their efforts upon the outstanding drainage anomalies on their home grounds—the familiar highlands of Europe and North America—in which present complications of structure are so great, or the erosional history so extended, that the initial conditions of deformation and stream development are impossible to reconstruct in detail. The key to the problem of the genesis of all kinds of drainage in orogenic systems would more logically be found in mountain belts that are so young that they preserve the initial conditions created by deformation. Such regions exist, but somehow they have failed to attract the attention of geomorphologists.

A rare example is the outer margin of the Zagros Highland, which overlooks the Mesopotamian Plains and the oil fields of Iran and Iraq. Here there is exhibited as great a discordance between drainage and geological structure as has been discovered in any mountain complex, regardless of age or character. At the same time, the deformational structures transected indiscriminately by the remarkable streams of the region are the youngest major tectonic developments on the face of the earth, and many are clearly in the initial stage of erosion.

In the Outer Zagros the evolution of drainage in a fold mountain landscape may be observed from the beginning; and here it can be seen that, under certain conditions of structure and lithology that are not at all unusual, through-flowing drainage that is transverse and discordant to the deformational pattern evolves in the initial cycle of erosion in the fold structures. Moreover, despite its present apparent discordance to structure, this drainage has developed *in response* to the local geologic situation, and has nothing to do with antecedent tectonic environments, with unconformable covermasses or erosion surfaces, or with random headward penetration.

In both geologic structure and drainage pattern portions of the Zagros Mountains are a remarkable parallel to the folded Appalachians of the eastern United States (Figure 1). In age and lithology, however, the Iranian ranges find a closer analogue in the Franco-Swiss Jura, where a distinctly different drainage pattern has evolved—a consequent-subsequent stream association which might be anticipated among the even younger folds of the Zagros, but which either never developed in that region or has been effaced from it.

The Zagros drainage pattern is distinctive by virtue of its disregard of major geological obstructions, both on a general scale and in detail. Elaborate explanations of similar phenomena have been produced by physiographers working in the Appalachian area and elsewhere, but the most widely accepted

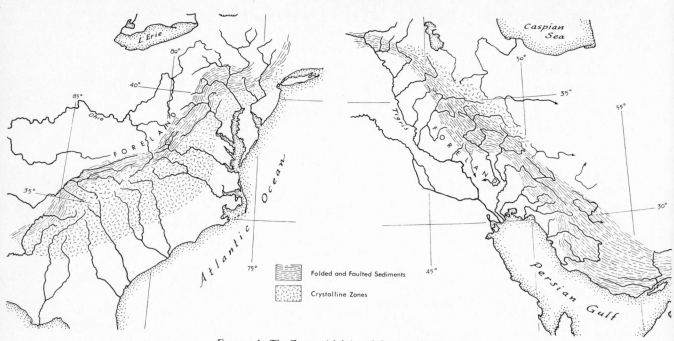

FIGURE 1. The Zagros (right) and the Appalachians (left).

hypotheses derived from study of these regions are beyond verification, for they depend upon erosion cycles, structures, or earth movements whose principal evidence is the very drainage pattern they were invented to explain.

The Zagros streams have remained largely unnoticed by physiographers even though the problem of drainage genesis presented here is a far more spectacular one than the Appalachian drainage enigma, largely owing to the greater scale of the scenery in the Zagros, but also due to the extreme youth of the structures involved. Moreover, the disparities between the structural patterns, geologic ages, tectonic histories, and lithologic characters of the two regions suggest that the present transverse courses of the Appalachian and Zagros streams would not have evolved in a like manner, despite similarities in the patterns and local geological relationships of the two drainage systems.

CLASSICAL HYPOTHESES OF TRANSVERSE DRAINAGE FORMATION

Certain of the theories which have evolved in explanation of drainage that is strongly discordant to its geological environment have become so widely accepted and applied that they have achieved the status of "classic" hypotheses of transverse stream formation.

Virtually all important geologically-anomalous stream systems have been attributed to one or another of five of these hypothetical modes of origin. The writer has yet to encounter the suggestion that a drainage system serving tens of thousands of square miles with uniform disregard for its geological structures could have originated in piecemeal fashion through the simultaneous action of several of these independent processes.

Four of the five classical theories of transverse gorge formation were propounded most extensively in attempts to unravel the Appalachian drainage dilemma, though all were originated at much earlier dates by the nineteenth-century pioneers of geomorphology. On the basis of the most general information concerning the Zagros Highland, there are objections to every one of the classical hypotheses of transverse stream formation as a complete explanation of the discordance between drainage and structure in this region.

The simplest explanation of transverse gorges is that they are merely the surface expression of transverse faults. This is one alternative in the theory of headward extension of streams by progressive piracy in transverse zones of weakness, either structural or lithological. The fault control theory was first advanced to explain the Appalachian problem in

1858,[1] and has been reiterated since by a succession of well-known naturalists and geomorphologists. The most definitive treatment of the hypothesis of headward stream extension in fold zones was that of H. D. Thompson, who believed that the outcrop patterns of various formations were a more vital control than transverse faulting.[2]

Fault control is one hypothesis that can be checked easily in the field, and it suffers accordingly, having been incontrovertibly disproved in the Central Appalachians by A. N. Strahler.[3] In the Zagros, transverse faults have little influence on the drainage pattern; moreover, streams commonly cross the most resistant beds where their surface outcrop attains its maximum rather than its minimum breadth, contrary to Thompson's hypothesis.

Requiring the most ingenuity to follow through to its logical conclusion, but introducing no purely conjectural movements, masses, or structures, is the theory of adjusted consequent drainage, set forth in connection with the Appalachian problem by W. M. Davis in 1909.[4] This remarkable demonstration of Davis's deductive approach to geomorphology traces the evolution of drainage in a fold belt undergoing gradual inversion of relief, plus reversal of drainage. The transverse streams of the Appalachians are seen as originating in transverse structural sags or spillways, with modifications in pattern occurring throughout the denudational history of the region, each of them logically explained. Otherwise convincing, this step-by-step program fails, by Davis's own admission, to account for transverse cuts through the noses of synclinal mountains.

In the Zagros, synclinal mountains are frequently transected near their rising termini. The shifts of consequent transverse drainage postulated by Davis as an accompaniment to relief inversion have not occurred in the manner suggested. Moreover, where relief does correspond to structure, the transverse stream pattern does not.

The hypothesis of drainage antecedence is frequently invoked to explain the situation, common in the Cenozoic mountain systems of the world, in which streams rising in older highlands cut across regions into which there has been a more recent extension of deformation. The suggestion is that streams initially running off from an older highland, or from the initial deformation in an expanding fold system, have been able to maintain themselves through orogenies gradually developing athwart their courses. As the anomalous drainage of the late Paleozoic Appalachian structures flows in a reverse direction, the question of its genesis has provoked a series of alternative hypotheses: among them the regional stream superposition theories, the hypothesis of headward extension by progressive piracy at points of lithological weakness, and the adjusted consequent drainage theory.

Examples of drainage antecedence have been cited in many of the Cenozoic mountain systems of the world; in particular, the Alps, Himalayas, Tien Shan, Cascades, and Pacific Coast ranges of America. The hypothesis of drainage antecedence is favored in the Zagros region, as in the above areas, by the characteristic direction of stream flow outward from the oldest structures in an expanding zone of deformation. However, in the Zagros region the hypothesis is strained by the distribution of unaligned transverse gorges, which occur on both minor streams and trunk drainage lines, and by the fact that many transected structures appear similar in age and magnitude to the structures which originate the transverse drainage.

To explain the seemingly systematic arrangement of windgaps and watergaps in the Appalachian fold belt, the idea of superposition of younger drainage lines onto older structures has been developed in two opposing hypotheses. One of these suggests that the streams were let down on the old folds from the higher parts of overriding structures that have since been removed or greatly reduced by erosion, particularly from a great hypothetical extension of known thrust sheets, or from vanished recumbent folds disharmonic to the underlying folds which are visible today.[5] Stream superposition from allochthonous structures must have occurred extensively in some of the

[1] N. D. Rogers, "The Geology of Pennsylvania," *First Pa. Geol. Survey,* 2 (1858), 895–896.

[2] H. D. Thompson, "Drainage Evolution in the Southern Appalachians," *Geol. Soc. Amer. Bull.,* 50 (1939), 1323–1356.

[3] A. N. Strahler, "Hypotheses of Stream Development in the Folded Appalachians of Pennsylvania," *Geol. Soc. Amer. Bull.,* 56 (1945), 45–88.

[4] W. M. Davis, "The Rivers and Valleys of Pennsylvania," *Geographical Essays.* New York: Ginn and Co., 1909; republished by Dover Publications, 1954, pp. 413–484.

[5] H. A. Meyerhoff and E. W. Olmsted, "The Origins of Appalachian Drainage," *Amer. Journ. Sci.,* 232 (1936), 21–41.

more intensively deformed orogenic systems, but has nowhere been accepted as the progenitor of a regional drainage system. The theory as applied to the Appalachian stream problem seems to be based on some fallacious premises about the evolution of drainage on mobile slablike masses. Its shortcomings are best summarized in Strahler's article.[6]

The hypothesis of regional superposition of streams from an unconformable covermass was applied locally in the Appalachians by Davis,[7] and elaborated by D. W. Johnson in 1931 as a solution for the entire drainage problem there.[8] The superposition theory in general does not demand the marine transgression invoked by Johnson. It requires only denudation followed by the deposition of a thin covermass to completely eliminate structural influences—to "float" drainage lines away from their rock-cut channels and out over beveled structures upon which they will descend in the next regional uplift. The covermass could as well be continental as marine.

Johnson's explanation has gained general acceptance as the simplest way out of the Appalachian puzzle, but it is beyond proof, for no scrap of the hypothetical covermass in the Appalachians has ever been found, or ever will be, in view of the presumed degradation of the region since the supposed deposition of the covermass.

Stream superposition is normally associated with erosional planations, which require significant intervals of tectonic stability, while antecedent streams are considered to be most likely in young unstable mountain belts that lack evidence of well-developed regional erosional surfaces. Hence it has become a general practice to attribute transverse drainage lines in pre-Pliocene mountain systems to regional stream superposition, while those in the late Cenozoic orogenic systems are most often regarded as antecedent, superimposed, or the product of headward extension. In this regard it must be emphasized that even in the vast majority of the Cenozoic deformational zones there is a different landscape today than that resulting from the initial deformation and from that present at the inception of presently anomalous transverse drainage. Ac-

cordingly, there is seldom any clear evidence in existing landscapes of the detailed controls which might have fixed the disharmonic drainage pattern inherited from prior landscapes.

The Zagros Highland, on the other hand, is almost unique in that parts of it have been formed so recently that they are virtually untouched by erosion. The survival to the present of the original geological conditions and landscapes created by intense deformation makes the Zagros Highland ideally suited to an investigation of drainage origins—particularly to a search for concrete evidence of the true genesis of a drainage pattern of the type normally attributed to regional drainage antecedence or superposition.

ORGANIZATION OF THE STUDY

This investigation into the origin of the Zagros drainage anomaly began from the hypothesis that different transverse streams and separate transverse reaches on individual streams in the Zagros have been developed by different geomorphic processes. This conflicts with more generally accepted hypotheses in explanation of transverse drainage in regions of Appalachian structure, for these hypotheses imply the comprehensive application of one or another of the drainage-fixing processes on a regional scale, rather than the concurrent operation of several of them.

The study is divisible into two complementary parts, one being the background for the other. Part I, including Chapters I through VI, consists of a physiographic description of the Central Zagros and its drainage anomaly. These chapters consider the region's general character; its significant structural divisions and their relation to the drainage pattern; the historical development of the higland and the geomorphic significance of the various elements in the generalized stratigraphic column, including their bearing on the problem of through-drainage origins; the physiographic regions of the highland, with emphasis upon the varying manifestations of the drainage anomaly in each region; and, finally, the hydrography of the Central Zagros, concluding with an account of the problems created by the specific paths by which the runoff of the high ranges escapes to the sea.

Part II, composed of Chapters VII through XI, is an investigation of the various means by which discordances between drainage and structure have developed in the Zagros High-

[6]Strahler, *op. cit.*, 71–78.
[7]Davis, *op. cit.*, 1954 ed., 469–473.
[8]D. W. Johnson, *Stream Sculpture on the Atlantic Slope.* New York: Columbia University Press, 1931, 142 pp.

land. The problem is attacked by evaluating the most familiar mechanisms of transverse drainage formation in terms of their structural and lithological prerequisites, their distinctive physiographic effects, and their applicability to the problem of stream development in the Zagros. The portions of the total drainage pattern of the problem area attributable to each of these processes are established and mapped sequentially, thereby isolating a residual drainage anomaly.

The residual drainage anomaly is discovered to be the effect of a simple geomorphic process not normally considered to be an originator of spectacular discordances between drainage and geological structure. The ubiquity of the structural and lithological prerequisites of this process suggests that it is responsible for much transverse drainage which has hitherto been attributed to regional drainage antecedence or superposition.

The objective throughout the study has been to search in the existing landscape for the processes that have originated the present pattern of discordances between drainage and structure, and to avoid dependence upon hypothetical structures, events, and processes in explanation of the Zagros drainage anomaly. Indeed, the principal aspiration of the present work is to explain the genesis of a large-scale drainage system which is spectacularly discordant to its geological and physiographic matrix without deducing a solution that is impossible to verify, no matter how ingenious or comprehensive it may be. It is the preservation in the Zagros Highland of original landscapes created by deformation that makes this possible.

Part I

THE SETTING OF THE PROBLEM

Introduction

The broad belt of well-watered highlands interposing between the arid plains of Mesopotamia and the desert plateau of Iran, and constituting a more or less effective buffer zone between the Semitic and Aryan peoples of Asia, has long been known to the Western world as the "Zagros Mountains." A great sheaf of strongly dissected fold and fault structures, the Zagros Highland reaches 1,000 miles southeastward from Lake Van in easternmost Turkey to Bandar Abbas at the mouth of the Persian Gulf, occupying significant portions of both Iraq and Iran.

Since ancient times an intransigent island rising amid the swirl and contest of civilizations, the Zagros Highland has been a seldom passive backdrop for some of man's greatest ventures and most significant achievements. While its ranges separated ancient Media from Sumer, Assyria, Babylon, and Susiana, its robust inhabitants contributed to the vitality of the populations on either hand. In its foothills the remains of the world's oldest settled cultures have been found, and here some of our basic agricultural commodities, both plant and animal, appear to have been domesticated.

Crossed by the armies of Darius and Xerxes, Cyrus, Xenephon, and Alexander—traversed by caravans for thousands of years—studded with archaic monuments and inscriptions— the mountain system itself seems somehow to have remained nameless through history. Since the time of Polybius these important ranges have been known to the West as the Zagros, a Greek appellation of uncertain origin that has lately been accepted by contemporary scholars of the lands in which the ranges are situated. But to the pastoral people who have possessed these mountains since antiquity, and to those living all around their perimeter, the word *Zagros* is meaningless and unfamiliar. The mountains and their people are regarded as one. Thus a tribesman on the banks of the Sehzar River refers to the snowy heights to the south as the "Bakhtiari," and to the lower serrate ranges to the north as the "Lur." Far to the south, beyond the Karun River, is "Kuhgalu," and then "Fars," while the land north and west of the Saidmarreh River and the Lur territory is the "Kurd"[1] (Figure 2). These traditional ethno-geographic divisions of the Zagros Highland have real significance, for the lands of the various tribal groups are different. Each has a character of its own. Accordingly, Kurdistan, Luristan, the Bakhtiari, Kuhgalu, and Fars are distinctive geographic entities in a physical as well as an ethnic sense. The human consequences of the climatic and physiographic peculiarities of the various adjacent regions are well known; the Lur tribes, for example, lead a marginal existence in the winter when the Bakhtiari are in their best pastures, while the most trying season for the Bakhtiari falls during the most salubrious portion of the Lur year, the relative conditions of the neighboring transhumant tribes being reversed with the change of seasons.[2]

In all of these regions of widely varying aspect the most exceptional features of landscapes frequently distinguished by the spectacular are the unusually precipitous defiles created by southwest-flowing streams and their tributaries, large and small, whose courses appear to be developed in almost uniform disregard of their physiographic and structural matrix. Indeed, the extreme insularity for which the Zagros people are famed is traceable to this characteristic of the terrain. Communications in these mountains are unusually difficult, for riverine routes are disrupted by bottlenecks where rock walls rise vertically out of boiling torrents that are frequently impossible to negotiate. Impassable gorges together with steep mountain walls and serrate crestlines so compartmentalize the country that trunk streams occasionally have different names above and below a single defile, and the annual transhumant migrations of certain tribes were, until recently, planned and executed as a military campaign.

The transverse defiles, known locally as

---

[1] Henceforth, the regional toponymy that has become standard in literature relating to the Zagros will be adopted. In some cases regional names have been "Persianized" (e.g., "Kurdistan" meaning the country of Kurds), in some cases Anglicized (e.g., "Bakhtiari Country" or "Bakhtiari Mountains"), and in some cases the area remains known by its simpler tribal-geographical designation (e.g., "Kuhgalu" and "Fars").

[2] For a graphic and well-illustrated account of the difficulties presented the Bakhtiari by their habitat, see Merian C. Cooper, *Grass,* New York: G. P. Putnum, 1925.

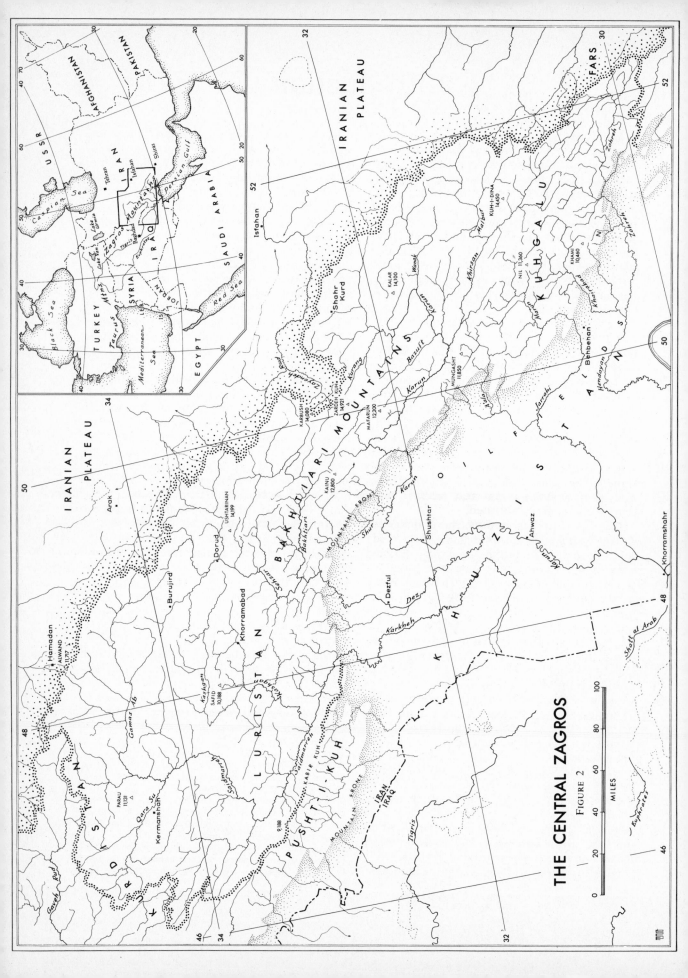

THE CENTRAL ZAGROS

FIGURE 2

tangs, have been explained as tensional cracks resulting from the "cooling" of the mountain masses, as fissures produced by direct tectonic movements, as the result of stream superposition from undefined "surfaces," and as effects of drainage antecedence. The most venerable hypothesis in explanation of these unique clefts was developed locally. Iranian folklore asserts that the great hero Rustam hacked the mountains to pieces with his sword.

Chapters I through VI, which follow, outline the structure, historical development, physiography, and hydrography of the Central Zagros Highland, providing background for the analysis of the problem of transverse stream development that occupies Chapters VII through XI. Part I is not a comprehensive description of the Central Zagros, rather it focuses on phenomena relating to the drainage anomaly in the region. All of the material in these chapters is original with the exception of the statistical data relating to hydrography and the facts of historical geology gleaned from the files and publications of the Iranian Oil Exploration and Production Company and its employees. Information and interpretations relating to physiographic developments were derived in the field and from maps and aerial photographs.

Chapter I

The Zagros Mountains

GENERAL DESCRIPTION OF THE ZAGROS MOUNTAINS

The Zagros Mountains are an important sector of the Tethyan Dinaride mountain system, whose primarily calcareous arcs may be traced from Morocco to Indonesia. This major earth lineament is welded onto the Alpide chains to the north in several syntaxial knots between which lie comparatively inflexible blocks: one of them the mountainous plateau of Iran. These intermediate masses are denuded shields of complex structure that seem to have been formed by the accretion of successively folded zones developing from the earlier orogenic spasms in the Tethyan geosynclinal belt. Radial expansion of the intermediate masses by the outward migration of the fold fronts of the Dinarides and Alpides is continuing today, and will ultimately extinguish the Tethyan mobile belt.

On their equatorward margins the Dinaride arcs step upward from subsiding troughs where either marine or continental sediments are accumulating. These tectonic foredeeps are the final peripheral remnants of the vast Tethyan belts of subsidence from which the intermediate masses and the younger Alpides and Dinarides gradually emerged. The great border troughs still surviving beyond the Dinarides are a reflection of the comparative youth of the southern arcs and of the amount of orogenic work still undone along this line of crustal weakness.

The Zagros Mountain sector epitomizes the tripartite array of the Dinaride landscape. Backed by the 5,000-foot Iranian Plateau, and pushing into the mobile half-submerged geosyncline of Mesopotamia and the Persian Gulf, the Dinarides have expanded in this region in an unusually powerful display of fold tectonics, producing a sheaf of calcareous ranges from 100 to 200 miles in breadth and essentially undeviating in direction for a distance of 1,000 miles.

In elevation, geological structure, and apparent age, the Zagros ranges ascend northeastward by gradual steps from the intact anticlinal domes of the Mesopotamian border-lands to a crestline of imbricate slabs and permanent snowfields between 11,000 and 15,000 feet above sea level. The greatest peaks immediately overlook the lesser mountains of the high Iranian Plateau, so that the Zagros is an asymmetric range, aptly characterized by the ancient Greeks as "The Persian Ladder."

Morphology

Apart from the conglomerate cuestas and mesas fronting the range on the southwest and reappearing among the imbricate structures of the interior, all important positive features in the Zagros Highland are composed of limestone. The external ranges are composed of essentially intact anticlines, while the mountains of the interior are sculptured from homoclines, synclines, resurrected anticlines, imbricate fault slabs, and overthrust structures. Deep dissection of the closely jointed limestone domes, chevron folds, and overturned structures has given the inner ranges a particularly wild aspect, with shark-fin or saw-toothed skylines characteristic of many areas (Figure 3). There are any number of commanding peaks composed of joint-bounded vertical slabs, but no horns in the usual sense since glaciation was never strongly developed in these subtropical mountains. Where glacial evidence is seen, on the ranges surpassing 14,000 feet, it is in the form of shallow, laterally coalescent cirques, holding small tarns and compact moraines. These cirques retain snowfields throughout the year.

The maximum local relief in the mountain belt is in the neighborhood of 8,000 feet. This occurs in longitudinal canyons in the headwaters of the Karun and Dez rivers and occasionally at the sites of transverse chasms through anticlinal ranges. More representative differences in elevation between crests and longitudinal valleys would be 3,000 to 6,000 feet. Transverse gorges in the fold belt commonly attain depths of 4,000 feet, their lower walls being nearly perpendicular and in some cases overhanging.

As shown in Figure 4, the summits are highest in the Bakhtiari Mountains of the northern

FIGURE 3. Topography resulting from denudation of an anticline composed of Cenomanian limestones. Bakhtiari Mountains east of the Sehzar River below Tang-i-Haft.

half of the Karun River Basin, where a number of crests exceed 12,000 feet for many miles. Several individual peaks rise above 14,000 feet; and Zardeh Kuh, at 14,920 feet, is the culminating point in the mountain complex. The gradual rise from the northwest and southeast toward the Bakhtiari Mountains merely reflects the longitudinal structure of the Central Zagros, and appears to be related to broad warping of the fold surface, which may still be in progress.

Drainage

The Zagros Mountains are transected by a series of roughly parallel and equidistant streams that rise near the northeastern margin of the highland and pass completely through it on their way out to the Mesopotamian-Persian Gulf trough. The runoff of the east slope of the snowy ridgepole of the asymmetric mountain sheaf follows longitudinal valleys for short distances and then turns back westward to break through its own watershed and the succession of ranges to the

west with but a few puzzling changes in direction, until the alluvial foredeep of Mesopotamia is reached. Thus the Zagros Hydrographic Basin overlaps the edge of the Iranian plateau, with the divide between endoreic and exoreic drainage located along a line of subdued desert ranges inferior in elevation to the Zagros ridgepole by 2,000 to 5,000 feet.

North of the thirtieth parallel the main drainage lines of the Zagros Highland are transverse to its structure. Eleven major streams cross the orogenic system with amazing disregard for geological barriers, and eight of the drainage basins serving this half of the highland have their longer dimension across the structural grain. Within each of these watersheds is a multitude of short tributaries whose courses are as arbitrary as those of the trunk streams.

The gorges created by these transverse streams are striking in form, many of them being near-vertical slits thousands of feet in depth. These defiles, or *tangs*, have attained wide notoriety since their first description in

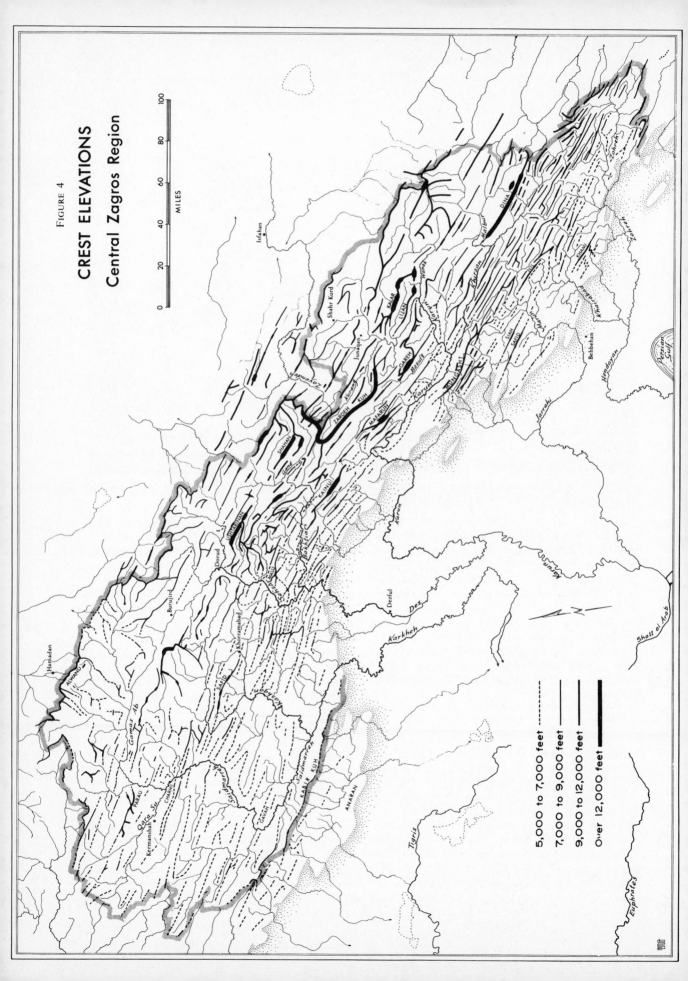

FIGURE 4

CREST ELEVATIONS
Central Zagros Region

MILES

5,000 to 7,000 feet
7,000 to 9,000 feet
9,000 to 12,000 feet
Over 12,000 feet

1855,[1] frequently being attributed to some "catastrophic" mode of formation.[2]

South of the thirtieth parallel, longitudinal drainage becomes characteristic of the mountain complex. Accordingly, the southern watersheds are elongated along the strike. It might be supposed that greater aridity here accounts for the loss of vigor in the mechanism that drove the drainage of the north directly across the highland. However, even in the south anticlines have been transected in spectacular chasms. The cleft domes of the dry Zagros, though few in number, are as puzzling as those of the north, for the folds of the south are shorter and far more widely dispersed—a vast field of isolated domes providing easy consequent paths for surface water moving in any direction.

Climate

The Zagros region has a Humid Mesothermal climate, with extreme seasonality in precipitation.[3] The summer half of the year is totally rainless, but from November to April cyclonic depressions moving eastward from the Mediterranean and warm fronts associated with the Arabian anticyclone affect the Zagros, bringing cloudy weather and as much as 100 inches of precipitation in the northern section. Twenty to 40 inches would be a figure more representative of precipitation in the mountain complex as a whole, north of the thirtieth parallel. Precipitation decreases progressively in a southeastward direction, so that the uplands of Fars receive 10 inches of rainfall or less on the average. Annual totals are everywhere quite variable. Isohyets are thought to be closely related to contour lines, but local orographic effects and the almost certain presence of rain shadows in basins produce an extremely complex picture characteristic of mountain climates. South of the thirty-fourth parallel, agriculture dependent

upon rainfall is almost everywhere marginal, and irrigation is practiced in valleys throughout the highland.

Nevertheless, it must be emphasized that the Zagros Mountains rise from the surrounding deserts of Iraq and Iran as an island of moisture, the rainfall here being sufficient to support parklands and groves of both deciduous and evergreen hardwoods as far south as Kuhgalu.

PREVIOUS STUDIES OF THE DRAINAGE ANOMALY

The mountain region of southwest Iran remained unfamiliar to geographers well into the twentieth century due to a traditional lack of security as well as to physical inaccessibility. In the last thirty years, however, the country has been brought under more effective control by the central government, and has been explored and mapped by the geologists of petroleum companies, and photographed from the air for military and engineering purposes. The new accessibility of this most interesting region, culminating in the rail and road construction of the war years, has already attracted archaeologists and social geographers to the Zagros Mountains, but, along with other aspects of physical geography, the geomorphology of the area has hardly begun to be investigated. This is remarkable when it is realized that the Zagros Mountains present two unique geomorphic attractions: first, an unparalleled display of the sequential development of erosional landscapes in fold structures that are so young that many remain totally unmarred by denudation, and, second, a degree of discordance between drainage and structure which is probably unmatched on the earth.

As the oil fields of southwestern Iran lie in the Zagros foothills, the enigma of the Zagros streams is quite familiar to petroleum geologists who have served in the area, and is frequently mentioned in their writings on other subjects, though it has never been discussed in an analytical fashion. J. V. Harrison, the distinguished geologist of the Anglo-Iranian Oil Company, a veteran of twenty-eight years in this region, has been the source of the majority of the published information on the transverse streams of the Zagros Mountains. In three valuable reports between 1932 and 1946 Harrison presented descriptive transverses of many tribal routes through the

---

[1] W. K. Loftus, "On the Geology of the Turko-Persian Frontier, and of the Districts Adjoining," *Quart. Journ. Geol. Soc., London,* 11 (1855), 247–344.

[2] G. N. Curzon, *Persia and the Persian Question,* 2 vols., London, 1892; Sir A. T. Wilson, *The Persian Gulf,* London: Oxford University Press, 1928; W. B. Fisher, *The Middle East,* New York: Dutton, 1957, p. 263.

[3] For more complete discussions of the climate of western Iran, see H. H. Boesch, "Das Klima des Nahen Ostens," *Vierteljahresschr. d. Naturforsch. Ges.,* Zurich, 86 (1941), 8–61; and H. Bobeck, "Beiträge zur Klimaokologischen Gliederung Irans," *Erdkunde,* 6 (1952), 65–84.

mountains between Kermanshah and Shiraz.[4]
It was his tentative hypothesis that the present
transverse streams were "superimposed" from
"surfaces" now raised 3,000 to 5,000 feet
higher, with several of today's highest ridges
being "monadnock" survivals of a period of
planation. The problem, he admitted, would
bear considerable investigation. Harrison did
not hazard a guess at how these "superimposed" streams adopted their original courses
transverse to the structural grain of the highland.

Apart from the descriptions and incidental
comments of Harrison and others interested in
the economic potential of the country, the
only specifically physiographic investigations
attempted in the Zagros have been those by
Cesar Voute, who was interested in the effects
of climatic change, concerning himself largely
with the ubiquitous valley terraces,[5] and Ar-
dito Desio and H. E. Wright, Jr., each of
whom studied the effects of glaciation in the
higher ranges.[6] Both Voute and Wright con-
ducted their studies in the Iraqi portion of the
Zagros.

THE PROBLEM AREA

Some form of anomalous transverse drainage is found in every sector of the Zagros
Highland, and continues to be seen westward
through the Taurus Mountains of southern
Turkey, which are the structural extension of
the Zagros system. However, the drainage
anomaly is most remarkable in the central portion of the highland in western Iran. Here
major streams utilize longitudinal valleys to a
minimum degree, despite the presence of the
greatest structural barriers to be found in the
orogenic system. At the same time the central
portion of the Zagros Highland has the appearance of a discrete physiographic region:
unified by a centripetal drainage system, and
somewhat set off from regions to the north-

west and southeast by differences in structure,
morphology, climate, and vegetation.

The ranges of the Central Zagros ascend
from a great transverse depression which
crosses the mountain system in eastern Iraq,
and which is both a structural and a relief
feature. This sag, drained by the Diyala River,
creates a deep embayment in the mountain
front where the frontier between Iraq and Iran
crosses the highland transversely. From it
there is a general rise, entering Iran, to a
folded plateau draining southeastward toward
a second important recess in the mountain
front. This opening, centered on the old town
of Dezful, is a drainage node for a high mountain region of about 40,000 square miles. It
attracts three great rivers of the Zagros, draw-
ing in the Karkheh from the northwest, the
Dez from the east-northeast, and the Karun
from the southeast. Thus waters from opposing directions and environments—185 miles to
the northwest and 220 miles to the southeast
—approach to within 13 miles near the city of
Ahwaz, before diverging on the Plain of Khuzistan to take separate paths to the Persian
Gulf. The drainage of the high mountain area
west of the Karun catchment is also drawn
toward the Dezful drainage node, by the
Marun and Zohreh rivers, and enters the gulf
only after a long northwestward detour.

Southeast of the Zohreh catchment the
mountain region changes character. Tight
folding disappears and the landscape opens
into a vast area of widely separated desert
ranges drained directly into the Persian Gulf
by short streams of insignificant volume, and
by longer intermittent drainage lines which
wander back and forth along the trend as
though fearful of meeting the sea.

Within the region drained toward the Dezful Embayment tight folding is superimposed
upon a series of broad structural "waves."
The folds on the crests of these waves have
been denuded to a great depth while those
corrugating the structural troughs have been
preserved in a nearly intact state. In these extreme situations, and in the transitional areas
between, nearly all stages in the evolution of
erosional landscapes in fold structures may be
observed. The widely differing landscapes
within this area provide a complete inventory
of the drainage-forming processes which have
operated in the Central Zagros. Thus, within
the area draining into the Dezful Embayment
there is the possibility of the use of regional

[4] J. V. Harrison, "The Bakhtiari Country, South-Western Persia," *Geog. Journ.*, 80 (1932), 193–210; "Kuhgalu: South-West Iran," *Geog. Journ.*, 88 (1936), 20–36;
"South-West Persia: A Survey of Pish-i-Kuh in Luristan,"
Geog. Journ., 108 (1946), 55–70.

[5] C. Voute, "Climate and Landscape in the Zagros Mountains (Iraq)," *Proceedings*, 21st Internat. Geol. Congr.,
1960, Copenhagen, Part 4 (1960), 81–87.

[6] A. Desio, "Appunti Geographia Geologia Sulla Catena
Della Zardeh Kuh in Persia," *Memoir Geologiche Geog.
Rafichi di Giotto Dianelli*, 14 (1934); H. E. Wright, Jr.,
"Pleistocene Glaciation in Kurdistan," *Eiszeitalter und
Gegenwart*, 12 (1962), 131–164.

comparison to elucidate mechanisms and stages of transverse drainage formation that would otherwise be obscure and impossible to verify.

Accordingly, the area delimited for investigation in this study comprises the drainage basins of all streams tributary to the Dezful Embayment. This area, which includes the basins of the Karkheh, Dez, Karun, Marun, and Zohreh rivers, will be referred to hereafter as the Central Zagros Region. The drainage of this region accomplishes more than 300 complete transections of anticlinal structures, most of which are individual mountain ranges.

The following study, based on field research and the study of aerial photographs,[7] geologi-

cal maps and cross-sections,[8] and topographic maps,[9] is a description of the drainage anomaly in the Central Zagros Region, and an analysis of its origin.

---

[7] The aerial photographs utilized (1:60,000) were made for the Army Map Service, Corps of Engineers, Washington,

D.C. However, their dissemination, reproduction, and publication cannot be undertaken without the authorization of the Imperial Iranian Army. This authorization could not be obtained, though use of the photography was permitted within Iran. Accordingly, these valuable pieces of evidence cannot be reproduced in this report. Where evidence from aerial photography is of great importance photo references have been given in the following form: Aerial Photograph, Geraldine (Shoran) Project Number 158, strip number: photo number.

[8] British Petroleum Company, Ltd., *Geological Maps and Sections of South-West Persia.* London: E. Stanford, 1956. Maps 1:1,000,000, sections 1:250,000.

[9] USAF Aeronautical Approach Charts, 1:250,000; with both altitude tints and plastic shading; contour interval 1,000 to 3,000 feet. Published by USAF Aeronautical Chart and Information Center, Air Photographic and Charting Service, St. Louis, Missouri.

Chapter II

Geological Structure of the Central Zagros

As a large proportion of the Zagros Highland is of extremely recent formation, its high mountain zone exhibits less structural complexity than those of most orogenic systems of similar extent. In particular it seems to lack the digitated nappe edifice that made the interpretation of the structure of the Alps so difficult, and which is only now being worked out in the Himalayan region.

The Zagros orogenic system may be divided longitudinally into the Inner or Older Zagros and the Outer or Younger Zagros. The Inner Zagros comprises the northeastern half of the highland and is essentially a zone of thrust faulting. The structures of this zone have been developed by several periods of compression beginning with the strong movements of late Cretaceous time. The Inner Zagros may be subdivided longitudinally into a zone of horizontal overthrusts, which will be called the Thrust Zone, and a belt of high angle thrust faulting, which will be termed the Imbricate Zone. Within the Thrust Zone an area of igneous and metamorphic rocks may represent the protaxis of the Zagros Highland.

The Outer Zagros, the southwestern half of the orogenic system, is a zone of strong folding produced for the most part by late Pliocene orogeny. This zone is characterized by a repetition of broad wavelike structures on which the individual anticlines and synclines are superimposed. The Outer Zagros may therefore be subdivided both longitudinally and transversely into structural culminations, depressions, and plateaus, all of which are strongly corrugated.

In the following paragraphs the major structural zones of the Zagros Highland are described, and the effect of broad warping in the Fold Zone is discussed and related to the anomalous drainage pattern of the region. The discussion concludes with an attempt to establish the location of the protaxis of the Zagros Highland, a fact which must be known before certain hypotheses of drainage development may be tested in this area.

TRANSVERSE STRUCTURE

The Fold Zone

Figure 5 presents a series of profiles of the oil-bearing Asmari limestone formation carried across the Simply Folded Zone to the first thrust in the zone of imbricate faulting. This Oliogocene-Miocene formation is the uppermost horizon folded conformably with the bulk of the geosynclinal sedimentary column, and its emergence at a steep angle from beneath the covering detrital-evaporite series of the foothill zone is everywhere taken as the "Mountain Front." A gradual northeastward increase in the intensity of the folding is well illustrated by these profiles, as is the general rise along the strike toward the structural and topographic culmination in the Bakhtiari section (profiles 4 to 16).

If a line be drawn in each profile of Figure 5 smoothly connecting the synclinal troughs in that profile, it will be seen to rise steadily and at some points steeply northeastward until a corrugated plateau is reached, as in Luristan (profiles 1 to 4) and Fars (profiles 17 to 25), or else a broad crest beyond which there is a gradual decline toward the Imbricate Zone, as in the Bakhtiari Country (profiles 6 to 16). The individual folds are seen to be superimposed upon these broad undulations. It is important to note that some of the individual arches which underlie the present foothill zone with almost no surface expression closely approach in amplitude the greatest flexures in the high mountain zone. In the foothill zone a barely perceptible structural trough temporarily intervenes between the Mountain Front and the gently undulating stable area that extends southwestward into Iraq. This local basin is presumably responsible for the concentration of petroleum in the anticlinal structures of the foothill belt.

The longitudinal persistence of the folds transected by the profiles is quite variable (Figure 6). The fold axes are straight to slightly curved, locally having *en echelon* dis-

18

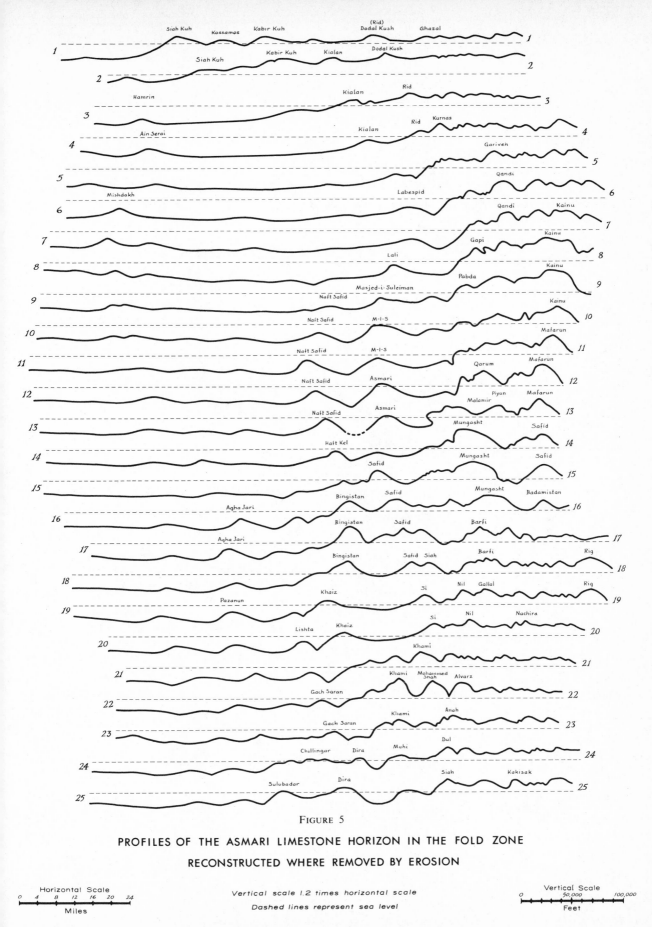

FIGURE 5

PROFILES OF THE ASMARI LIMESTONE HORIZON IN THE FOLD ZONE
RECONSTRUCTED WHERE REMOVED BY EROSION

Horizontal Scale
0 4 8 12 16 20 24
Miles

Vertical scale 1.2 times horizontal scale
Dashed lines represent sea level

Vertical Scale
0   50,000   100,000
Feet

Based on N.L. Falcon, "Evidence for Large-Scale Flexuring
in the Southwest Persian Mountain Zone", IOEPC Geol. Dept.
Report 797 (1950).

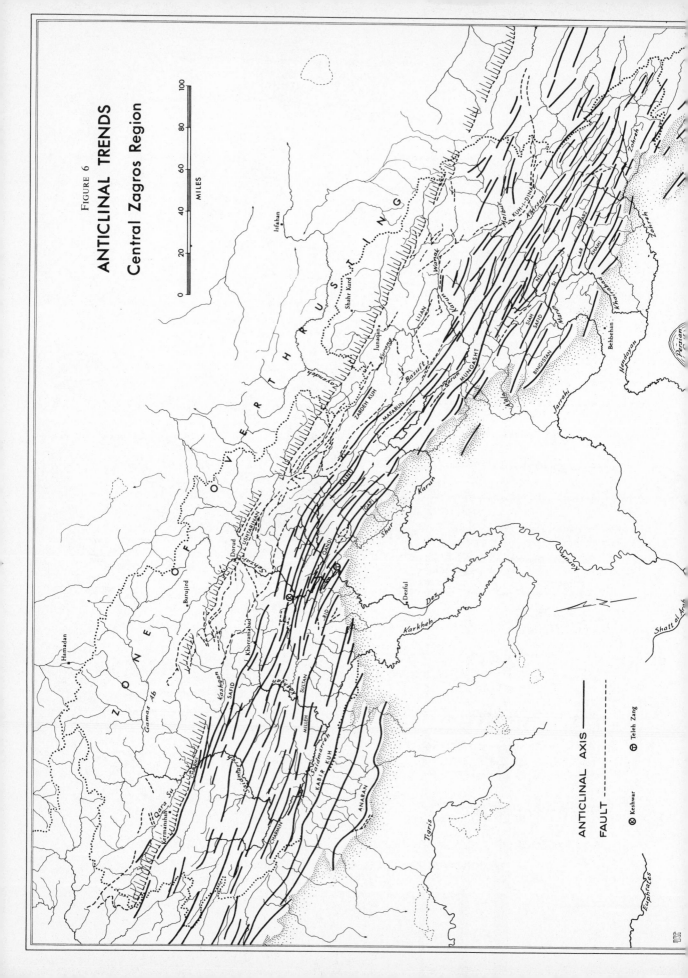

FIGURE 6

ANTICLINAL TRENDS
Central Zagros Region

ANTICLINAL AXIS ———
FAULT - - - - - - -
⊗ Keshwar   ⊕ Teleh Zang

positions. In Luristan, anticlines range in length from one or two miles to the immense outer barriers of Kabir Kuh and Anaran, whose uniquely sinuous axes extend over 140 miles along the strike of the orogen. Occasionally, even-crested anticlines pitch out with remarkable abruptness, so that their noses are quite blunt. More commonly they rise gradually at either end, assuming a smooth whaleback silhouette where not strongly dissected. In a surprising number of instances plunging fold noses are crossed by engorged transverse streams although open valley paths pass the ends of the ridges less than a mile away.

Southeast of the Kashgan River, throughout the Dez Basin, the folds are more crowded, and synclines are V-shaped. Here the folds are usually asymmetric. Anticlines are frequently sheared at their crests, and adjacent pairs may be overturned in opposing directions. The plasticity of the thin-bedded limestones in this section is remarkable, and many anticlines are composed of a steep anticlinorium of miniature nearly isoclinal folds. In the Bakhtiari Country the synclines are more tightly pinched than the anticlines.

The *en echelon* array of the Luristan folds is intensified in the high Bakhtiari Mountains, where there is, in addition, a striking parallelism of the major anticlines. Many of the higher structures pitch out at either end along seemingly significant transverse lines possibly controlled by unknown basement structures. The areas between these master folds are packed with anticlines of lesser longitudinal persistence.

South of the Dez Basin—in the Karun watershed, Kuhgalu, and Fars—the folds become more widely dispersed once more. In this region the general structure resembles that of Luristan: a corrugated rise to a rumpled plateau. As far south as the thirtieth parallel the folds are greater in number and more even in distribution than in Luristan, but beyond this line, in the dry Zagros of Fars, the structure becomes even more open than in the northwest. Here the folds are elliptical domes, short, broad, and often quite high, but widely separated by flat synclinal depressions.

Aside from impersistent crestal thrusts, longitudinal faulting is not well developed outside of the Imbricate Zone, where it is the dominant feature of both structure and landscape. Transverse faulting occurs throughout the fold belt, but on a relatively small scale.

The transverse faults in the Zagros region have little effect on the landscape. They are usually marked by erosional vales but are seldom followed by streams of any kind. Even where transverse faults have caused the nose of an anticlinal mountain to be set down in successive slices in a "telescope" fashion, there has been no significant erosion in the fracture zones.

The Imbricate Zone

South of the Dez River the Simply Folded Zone passes northeastward into a zone of imbricate faulting. Geological cross-sections (Figure 7) indicate that this "shingle" structure originated by the shearing of anticlines similar in magnitude to those of the fold belt. These are presumably somewhat older folds which have been broken by the renewed compression responsible for the youngest structures in the outer part of the orogenic system. The faults are all high angle thrusts, most of which dip toward the interior of Iran. Some of the vertical displacements are in excess of 20,000 feet.

Though these faults bring Paleozoic rocks to the surface, the bulk of the relief in the Imbricate Zone is carved in Middle and Lower Cretaceous limestones. Where the faults displace Middle Cretaceous and older rocks significantly the effect on the landscape is great, for huge escarpments are the result—some of them as much as 8,000 feet high. On the other hand, large areas in the Imbricate Zone now at high elevations appear to have been planed and occasionally covered unconformably by Pliocene and later sediments (Figure 7, sections EE, II, and JJ).

The Imbricate Zone has not been recognized in Luristan, where overthrusts lap directly against the innermost folds, but south of the Dez River it is from 18 to 30 miles wide. It is conceivable that an erosionally beveled Imbricate Zone is completely overridden by the flat thrusts in the area northwest of the Dez River. However, the intensity of the folding in Luristan is considerably less than in the regions to the southeast, and it seems more probable that a zone of steep folding and imbricate faulting never developed in this area.

The Thrust Zone

The Zagros Highlands northeast of a line along the strike of the orogen from Kerman-

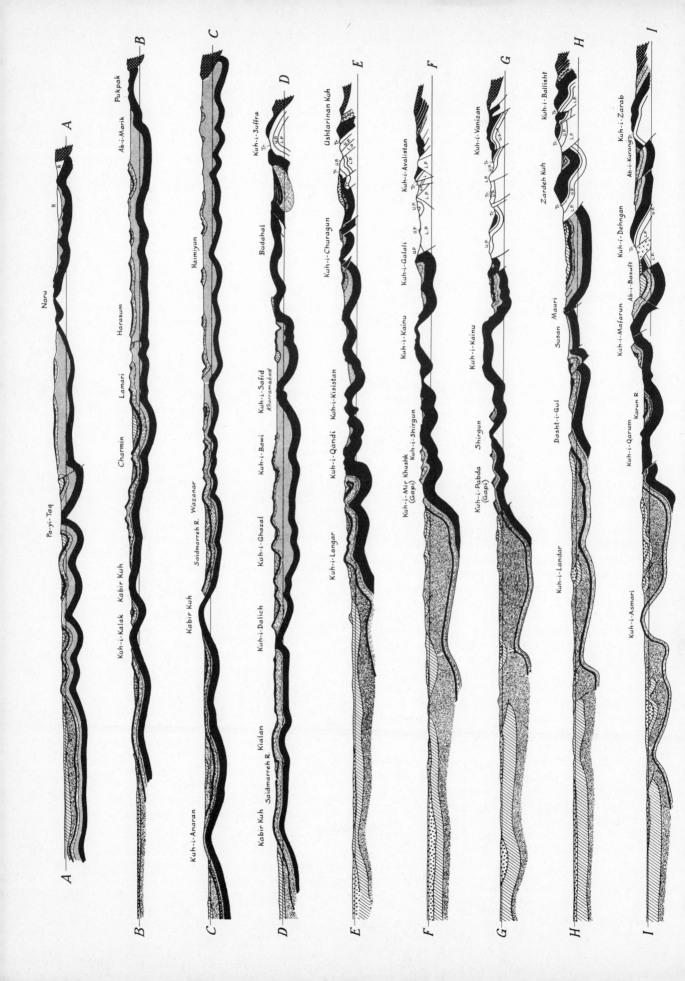

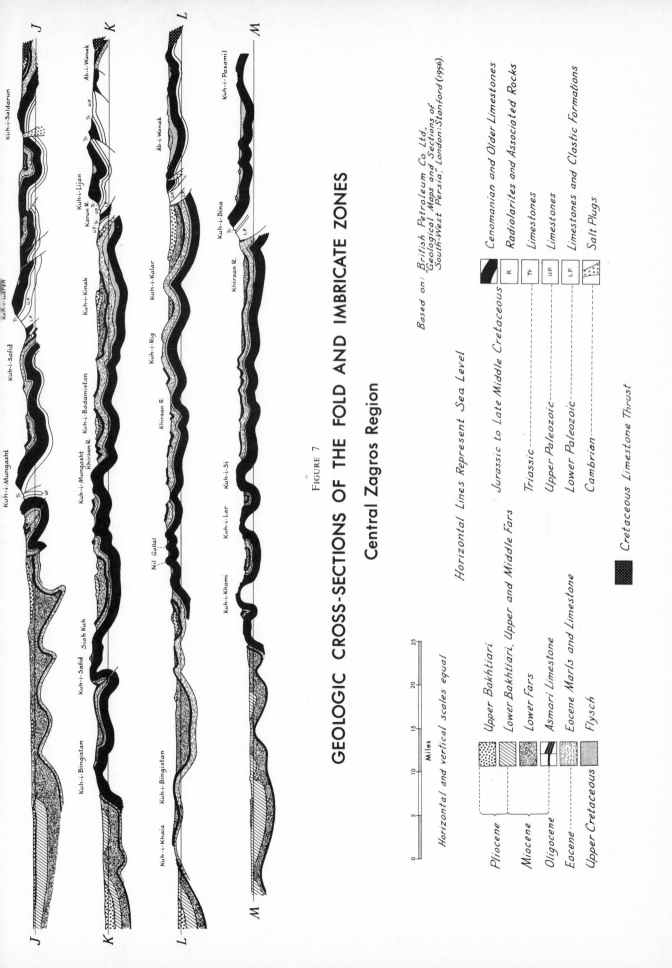

GEOLOGIC CROSS-SECTIONS OF THE FOLD AND IMBRICATE ZONES

Central Zagros Region

FIGURE 7

Based on: British Petroleum Co. Ltd.,
"Geological Maps and Sections of
South-West Persia," London-Stanford (1956).

Horizontal Lines Represent Sea Level

Horizontal and vertical scales equal

Miles

Pliocene
  Upper Bakhtiari
  Lower Bakhtiari, Upper and Middle Fars
Miocene
  Lower Fars
Oligocene
  Asmari Limestone
Eocene
  Eocene Marls and Limestone
Upper Cretaceous
  Flysch

Jurassic to Late Middle Cretaceous
Cenomanian and Older Limestones

R — Radiolarites and Associated Rocks
Tr — Triassic Limestones
u.P — Upper Paleozoic Limestones
L.P — Lower Paleozoic Limestones and Clastic Formations
Cambrian — Salt Plugs

Cretaceous Limestone Thrust

shah to Junaqan are sculptured in at least two thrust complexes whose detailed structure is at present little known. The thrust slices are assumed to have been derived from the axis of the Cretaceous geosyncline by the later overturning and shearing of folds formed in the first Zagros orogeny. Wide differences of opinion remain on the age of some of the beds composing the structures, and on the age and dimensions of the thrusts, some of which are known to have moved a minimum of five miles horizontally.[1]

It is clear that as far south as Isfahan a crystalline overthrust composed of Paleozoic metamorphic and intrusive rocks has been superimposed upon a thrust mass of Cretaceous limestones. The limestone thrust is folded and continues the length of the Zagros system. Serpentinized radiolarite masses found beneath the limestone thrust and in a broad outcrop in front of it in the area of Kermanshah have been a source of controversy. They were formerly believed to have been a nappe which was similar to a structure in corresponding formations in other portions of the Dinaride mountain system,[2] but it has more recently been suggested that they merely lubricated the sole of the limestone thrust, and were partially dragged forward with it.[3]

Some geologists have surmised that the Thrust Zone may have originated in a series of great geanticlines which were transformed by later pressures into *plis-failles* on a gigantic scale.[4] In such a case only the frontal part of the geanticlines would form the thrusts, with their hinder portions passing conformably into the Iranian Plateau. It was further suggested that the older rocks (the radiolarites) are exposed in the farthest advanced and thereby crestal portions of the moving geanticlines, with progressively younger rocks encountered toward their plunging ends. Accordingly, the areas where the radiolarites are missing might correspond to saddles between the geanticlines.

Though the maximum elevations presently found in the Thrust Zone are surpassed in both the Imbricate and Fold zones, the headwaters of all major drainage lines of the mountain complex rise in this structural province. When the transverse drainage lines of the orogen are related to the supposed geanticlines and saddles of the Thrust Zone, they are found to have established courses across both.

BROAD WARPING IN THE FOLD ZONE

The positions of structural culminations and depressions along the strike of an orogenic system are of great importance in the understanding of its hydrology. Logically, synclinal runoff should be drawn toward transverse sags in structure, and should be led out of the highland transversely through them. Thus streams could cross anticlines in gorges and still be consequent—if these anticlines merely corrugate a transverse syncline that rises on either side into a structural culmination. That such "spillway drainage" seldom exists is attested by the multiplicity of theories having been evolved in explanation of transverse drainage in fold belts. Despite the unique correspondence between structure and relief in the Zagros region, its transverse drainage shows as little conformity to variations in longitudinal structure as does the transverse drainage of most other highlands.

The map of anticlinal trends (Figure 6) reveals that the Zagros Mountain Front is sinuous despite a lack of corresponding sinuosity in structural trend lines. This is the result of the pattern of culminations and depressions in the fold complex. Though there is some inflection in structural axes around the head of the Dezful Embayment, this opening is primarily the effect of a major structural sag, a downward plunge of the outer ranges of Luristan on the northwest and Kuhgalu on the southeast. As a major structural depression the Dezful Embayment should be a natural drainage node, and does function as such, attracting three great transverse streams otherwise little affected by structural considerations. Accordingly the Karkheh,[5] Dez, and Karun rivers, which drain 33,880 square miles of the central mountain complex, are drawn together here, to be separated by only 13 miles a short distance above Ahwaz. The Karkheh

[1] British Petroleum Company, Ltd., *Geological Maps and Sections of South-West Persia.* London: E. Stanford, 1956, p. 1.

[2] H. de Bockh *et al.,* "Stratigraphy and Tectonics of the Iranian Ranges," in *The Structure of Asia,* ed. by J. W. Gregory. London: Methuen, 1928, p. 135.

[3] Raoul C. Mitchell, "The Tectonic Foundation and Character of S. W. Asia," *Egyptian Journ. Geol.,* 3 (1959), 22.

[4] H. de Bockh *et al., op. cit.,* 135.

[5] Below the confluence of the Kashgan River the stream previously known as the Saidmarreh is called the Karkheh.

then swings westward to the marshes bordering the Tigris, and the Dez and Karun unite to pass directly unto the head of the Persian Gulf.

Tectonic Divisions of the Fold Zone

In the unfaulted portion of the Zagros Highland the exposures of older rocks mark the zones of maximum uplift and erosion. Where the youngest formations are preserved the uplift has been least. The simply folded portion of the Central Zagros Highland is divisible into five tectonic regions on this basis (Figure 8). These divisions are important because they provide the basis for the regionalization of landforms which has facilitated comparative studies of drainage evolution in the fold belt.

The front of the Luristan salient, the Pusht-i-Kuh region, is a structural culmination composed of three broad anticlines of exceptional longitudinal persistence. This culmination descends on the northeast into the spacious Saidmarreh Syncline, beyond which rises the fold plateau of Luristan. Inner Luristan is actually a rumpled basin, with gentle anticlinal warps on the northeast and somewhat sharper folding along the southwestern margin adjacent to the Saidmarreh Syncline. The folding becomes more intense toward the southeast although there is a general depression of the fold surface in this direction. Structurally, the region crossed by the Kashgan River is a transverse ridge in the sinking fold surface. This ridge is created by the tangency of seven compact anticlines which are arranged in a file across the breadth of the Fold Zone northeast of the Saidmarreh Syncline. Southeast of this transverse welt the fold sheaf continues to sag, forming a transverse syncline extending from Khorramabad to the Saidmarreh Syncline. This feature will be referred to henceforth as the Luristan Saddle. Surging out of this depression, on the southeast, is the Bakhtiari Culmination.

The Bakhtiari Culmination is an anticlinorium composed of several *en echelon* fold groups occasionally dominated by an immense arch of far greater magnitude than adjacent folds. Sections EE to KK in Figure 7 illustrate the intensity of the folding in the Bakhtiari Mountain sector. South of the great range of Kuh-i-Mungasht the anticlinal crests become more or less accordant once more, though the folding remains strong. This area is the Kuhgalu Fold Plateau. In the latitude of Kazerun

another structural saddle crosses the fold belt. Beyond it compact domes are well separated from one another, and a closer adjustment of drainage to structure is evident.

With the exception of the deflecting effect of the Pusht-i-Kuh Culmination and the attraction of the Dezful Embayment, the pattern of structural culminations and depressions in the fold belt is ignored by the streams that cross the region. The best-developed transverse spillway does not function as such, and greatly upheaved areas are crossed by several important drainage lines.

The corrugated Luristan Basin is crossed obliquely by one major stream, the Saidmarreh River, which cuts through many broad anticlinal structures, now unroofed, before being deflected into a longitudinal path by the Pusht-i-Kuh Culmination. The Pusht-i-Kuh area originates drainage lines, but is not crossed by any coming from the interior. Oddly enough, the second major transverse stream, the Kashgan, follows the axis of the narrow transverse welt which separates the Luristan Folded Basin from the Luristan Saddle.

The Luristan Saddle, which could be expected to function as a natural spillway for drainage coming out of the fold belt, is utilized by a small transverse watercourse in its lower section only. The next sizeable streams encountered are the Sehzar and Bakhtiari rivers, which traverse the Bakhtiari Culmination by cutting through the axes of several *en echelon* fold groups.

The Karun River, farther to the southeast, is channeled into the Bakhtiari Culmination by a syncline, then cuts out of it transversely by a path that is incised into a rising anticlinal structure of major proportions. The Kuhgalu Fold Plateau is crossed by three rivers which zigzag from one anticlinal transection to another.

It is a pertinent question whether the broad warps producing the major structural culminations and depressions, and having an amplitude of some 40,000 feet, were formed simultaneously with the individual folds which corrugate them. In the opinion of Falcon the individual folds were formed first, with only the latest phase of movement producing the major flexures, including the steep rise of the

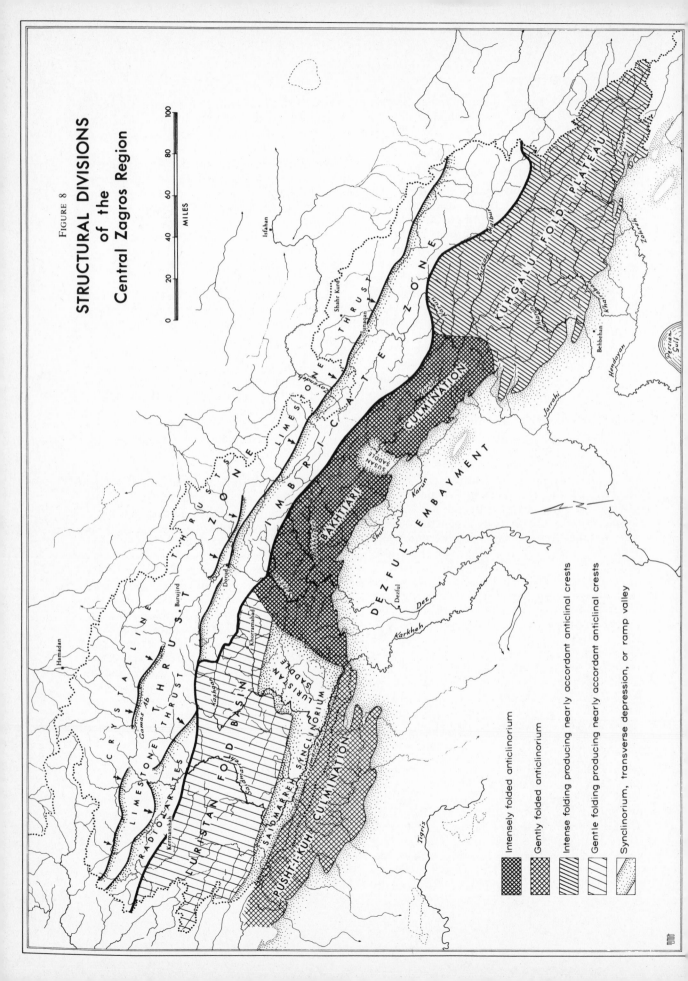

FIGURE 8

STRUCTURAL DIVISIONS
of the
Central Zagros Region

MILES

0   20   40   60   80   100

Intensely folded anticlinorium

Gently folded anticlinorium

Intense folding producing nearly accordant anticlinal crests

Gentle folding producing nearly accordant anticlinal crests

Synclinorium, transverse depression, or ramp valley

CRYSTALLINE THRUST

LIMESTONE THRUST

RADIOLARITES

LIMESTONE THRUST ZONE

IMBRICATE ZONE

KUHGALU FOLD PLATEAU

CULMINATION

SUSAN SADDLE

BAKHTIARI

DEZFUL EMBAYMENT

LURISTAN FOLD BASIN

LURISTAN SADDLE

SAIDMARREH SYNCLINORIUM

PUSHT-I-KUH CULMINATION

Hamadan

Gamas Ab

Kermanshah

Kashgan

Saidmarreh

Burujird

Khoramabad

Dorud

Shahr Kurd

Isfahan

Karun

Shut

Dez

Dezful

Karkheh

Tigris

Jarrahi

Behbehan

Hendijan

Persian Gulf

Mountain Front.[6] Falcon concluded that the broad warping has been episodic, and is still in progress, as shown by the complex terrace systems of the present river valleys. He surmised that the anomalous drainage pattern of the mountains was developed originally on open plains amid the initial folds, becoming "superimposed" when the broad warping began. This "superimposition" is taken as primary evidence of recent major flexuring.

The question of the relationship between the individual folds and broad structural waves and their relative development in time is quite significant to the problem of the origin of transverse drainage in the Zagros Highland. It will be considered at more length in the analysis of the inception and later history of the through-flowing streams of the northwestern Zagros.

THE ZAGROS PROTAXIS

In any investigation into drainage origins in a fold mountain region it is important to determine the whereabouts of the protaxis of the present highland—the locus of the initial deformation within the geosynclinal belt, and presumably the source of the first streams to develop during the gradual emergence of the region. When an orogenic zone is transected by streams flowing from older to younger structures it is necessary to investigate the possibility that the runoff of the highland's protaxis was antecedent to those portions of the mountain belt that were more recently formed, thus creating discordances between drainage and structure in the younger fold zones. In the absence of detailed geologic studies of the Inner Zagros the location of the protaxial zone must be deduced from structural and lithological relationships, and from general principles which have been discovered in studies of tectonic units of similar character elsewhere in the world.

The northeastern divide of the Central Zagros watershed lies on a line of granitic peaks culminating in Kuh-i-Alwand (11,717 feet) immediately southeast of Hamadan. Northeast of this range, in the area of interior drainage, an erosionally battered fold complex reappears, displaying transverse drainage phenomena similar to that of the more youthful Outer Zagros. The age and origin of the granitic line is not established, but it is involved in the thrusting that characterizes the inner part of the Zagros orogenic system. In the Himalayan region a similar crystalline core has been recognized in the nappe complex, with a clear facies difference in the sedimentary sequences on either side of it. This crystalline axis is thought by Indian geologists to have emerged as the first geanticline in the Tethyan geosyncline subsequent to the Karakorum upheaval, and is assumed to be the source of the first Himalayan thrusts.[7] As such, the Himalayan crystalline axis would be the counterpart of the Orobic Zone of the Alps. The similarity between the Hamadan crystalline zone and the Alpine Orobic zone is apparent with DeSitter's description of the latter.

It is important to note that in both the Alps and the Appalachians, and to a certain extent in the coastal Cordilleran system also, the geosynclinal development exhibits a phase where a barrier is warped up between the ocean and the geosynclinal basin. This barrier, the Orobic zone in the Alps, the central zone of the Piedmont province, and the coastal ranges in the Tertiary Cordilleran system, is steeply inclined towards the continent and has at its foot the deepest part of the asymmetric geosyncline [usually thought to be the radiolarian zone]. In the orogenic period this steep face becomes a zone of high angle thrusting accompanied eventually by gliding structures [lubricated by the incompetent radiolarite beds, as are the thrusts of the Zagros region].[8]

The similarity between the Orobic and Hamadan crystalline zones is undeniable, the more so as there seems to be no other structural element in the Zagros Highland which could be the parallel of this seemingly characteristic feature of geosynclinal evolution.

The earliest tectonic activity in the Zagros geosyncline occurred in Jurassic time. This disturbance is reflected in the sedimentary

[6]N. L. Falcon, "Evidence for Large-Scale Flexuring in the Southwest Persian Mountain Zone," Iranian Oil Expl. Prod. Co., *Geol. Dept. Report* 797 (1950), 3.

[7]D. N. Wadia, *The Geology of India.* London: Macmillan, 1961, pp. 420, 426–427, 429.

[8]L. U. DeSitter, *Structural Geology.* New York: McGraw-Hill, 1959, pp. 480–481. The Mesozoic radiolarites of the Alps were assumed to have been deep water deposits by Heim, Escher, Andree, and Horn, but Ph. H. Kuenen has disputed this conclusion, implying that geoclines were never truly deep sea troughs (Ph. H. Kuenen, *Marine Geology,* New York: Wiley, 1950, p. 245). In both the Alps and Zagros thrusting nevertheless was facilitated by the presence of the incompetent radiolarite accumulation, which "lubricated" the movement of the thrusts developing above them.

column by a limy shale facies found in the thrusts north of the Dez River[9]—a marked contrast to the limestone succession which is characteristic of the geosynclinal sequence both above and below this horizon from Permian until Middle Cretaceous time. The exact location of this initial disturbance and the nature of the structures created by it are not certain. Concurrently with this development the Orobic zone was beginning to form as a geanticline in the Alpine geosyncline, and the first orogenic sediments were appearing in both the Alpine and Himalayan sectors of the Tethyan sea in a facies comparable to that seen in the Jurassic of the Zagros.[10]

Though it may have formed and become briefly emergent in the Jurassic, the protaxial geanticline in the Zagros geosyncline appears to have been submerged again until late Middle Cretaceous time when clastic sedimentation was renewed in the geosyncline. At this time the protaxis emerged once more and was thrust southwestward along the newer Cretaceous limestone and Mesozoic radiolarite geanticlines. This tectonic ensemble originated the consequent drainage into the geosyncline that indirectly filled it with detrital Upper Cretaceous flysch beds.[11]

The Upper Cretaceous depositional basin is centered on the area northwest of the Dez River, the logical foredeep of the Hamadan crystalline zone. Though the great thrust sheet of Cretaceous limestones borders the entire fold belt and Imbricate Zone on the northeast, and is presumed to have originated in Upper Cretaceous time,[12] the Upper Cretaceous detrital beds are nowhere so well developed as in the zone fronting the thrust complex southwest of the Hamadan crystalline zone. Therefore the crystalline zone of the thrust complex must be tentatively accepted as the protaxial zone of the Zagros orogenic system.

---

[9]British Petroleum Company, Ltd., *op. cit.,* 1.

[10]H. de Terra, "Himalayan and Alpine Orogenies," 16th Internat. Geol. Congr., Washington, 1933, *Report* 2 (1936), 862, 863–865, 868. Also, D. N. Wadia, *op. cit.,* 252–254, 256.

[11]The flysch sedimentary facies is presently thought to have been deposited by turbidity currents which originated in submarine slumps from an unstable continental shelf; thus it is not a primary deposit of continental streams. See DeSitter, *op. cit.,* 293–295; F. J. Pettijohn, *Sedimentary Rocks,* New York; Harper and Brothers, 1957, pp. 615–617; J. Goguel, *Tectonics,* San Francisco: Freeman, 1963, pp. 26–29.

[12]The thrusts have moved over Cenomanian (Middle Cretaceous) and Senonian (Upper Cretaceous) beds, but are covered by marine Maestrichtian (late Upper Cretaceous) deposits, themselves later folded *with* the thrusts. See K. W. Gray, "A Tectonic Window in Southwestern Iran," *Quart. Journ. Geol. Soc. London,* 105 (1949), 189–223.

Chapter III

Historical Development and Stratigraphy of the Central Zagros

Despite the youth of the Zagros Highland, its geological structures and existing landscapes, like those of all orogenic systems, are the result of events which were episodic in nature and drawn out over a great period of time. Certain aspects of the historical geology of the region are vital to an understanding of its present physiographic problems. Among these are the progression in time and space of the orogenic movements creating the Zagros system, the lithologic succession which influences the scenery of the region, and the facts of stratigraphy indicative of the character of ancestral landscapes in the problem area.

TECTONIC HISTORY
OF THE CENTRAL ZAGROS

As basement rocks are rarely exposed in the Zagros, the Paleozoic history of western Iran is not well known. The limited stratigraphic record at our disposal indicates that marine or lagoonal conditions were prevalent from Cambrian to Carboniferous time, with no orogenic activity having occurred in the region, such as that preparing the frame of the Tethyan geosyncline in both Europe and northern India.[1]

The Tethyan geosyncline became clearly established in Iran during the Permian, and throughout the early Mesozoic marine limestones, homogeneous from the Alps to the Himalayas, accumulated in the vast subsiding trough. In the latter part of the Cretaceous (Senonian) an orogenic convulsion seized the entire Tethyan belt, causing intensive folding poleward of the trough axis, accompanied by intrusions and extrusions of ultra-basic magma.

In Iran the northeastern border of the geosyncline was thrown into strong folds, and ultra-basic magma was injected into the older rocks and also into the new masses of clastic sediments concurrently accumulating in the orogen. The unfolded portion of the geosyncline was arched upward enough to become emergent and subject to erosion for a time,[2] subsiding at last to be deeply submerged by the encroaching debris of the orogeny to the northeast. The axis of the geosyncline was shifted southwestward by these movements— the first of a long series having a similar effect.

Instability continued through the Eocene in the Iranian sector, and isopach maps show that during this period certain anticlines in the present Mountain Front region of the Zagros were already forming as submarine ridges. Throughout the Eocene the axis of the geosyncline continued to migrate slowly southwestward toward the submerged stable area, then located on the site of the present oil fields of Iran and Iraq.

The Eocene closed with a brief emergence and denudation of the axial portion of the Zagros geosyncline, and was followed in the Oligocene by a long period of submergence characterized by continued instability in the axis of the geosyncline. During this period an uneven veneer of limestones was deposited over the clastic Upper Cretaceous and Eocene accumulations. Evidently the folds and possible thrusts created by the late Cretaceous orogeny had been completely reduced by erosion during the Eocene.

In Miocene time the Zagros geosyncline underwent significant changes. Initially there was a marked shallowing of the geosynclinal tract, which was transformed into one or more immense lagoons essentially cut off from the rest of the Tethyan sea. Calcareous deposition ended and a lagoonal evaporite series was laid down uniformly over a belt occupying much of the width of the present Outer Zagros. In the area of the present Dezful Embayment the

[1]British Petroleum Company, Ltd., *Geological Maps and Sections of South-West Persia.* London: E. Stanford, 1956, p. 1.

[2]F. C. P. Slinger, L. E. T. Parker, and J. F. Watson, "The Mountain Front Geological Survey 1948/49 (Pabda to Behbehan)," Iranian Oil Expl. Prod. Co., *Report* 772 (1949), 54.

axis of the Miocene trough lay southwest of the present Mountain Front, but to the northwest and southeast the early Miocene depositional basin covered great areas presently incorporated into the mountain complex. The distribution of these deposits has a considerable effect upon the scenery of the Outer Zagros.

In the middle to late Miocene a final marine invasion concluded the lagoonal phase. This submergence was ended by pronounced uplift of the geosynclinal belt, accompanied by sharp folding of its sediments. All ensuing deposits were syn-orogenic, accumulating in either closed or anastomosing structural basins in an emergent landscape. The intensity of the orogeny increased through the early Pliocene, culminating in an especially violent upheaval of the entire mountain belt in the late Pliocene, when as much as 15,000 feet of molasse conglomerates accumulated in local tectonic basins.

Dunnington believes that near-planar base levels of deposition limited the entire late Miocene-Pliocene clastic sequence.[3] Thus isopachs on the thickness of these materials would give a rough measure of the subsidence of the folded belt and each of its parts during the late Tertiary compression. In a general map that eliminates the attenuation of the formations over each rising fold, Dunnington derives a subsidence of over 13,000 feet in the Iraqi Zagros along an axis extending from Kirkuk to Qasr-i-Shirin on the Iranian frontier. The greater subsidence occurs toward the southeast, with the center of the Pliocene basin being located at Lali oilfield in Iran.

The upper Pliocene conglomerates, deposited concurrently with the most intensive mountain building in the history of the orogenic system, are less deformed than the underlying Lower Pliocene beds, but are still occasionally inclined 20 degrees or more from the horizontal. As the Lower Pliocene is unconformable on the Miocene and the Upper Pliocene is unconformable on the Lower, so is the Quaternary unconformable on the Upper Pliocene. In addition, Quaternary terraces are commonly warped or tilted, and are stranded high above present stream profiles.

Clearly the area is still in the vise of the Cenozoic orogeny, for differential movement is continuing at a measurable rate even well beyond the Mountain Front. Strips of badlands appearing in the desert plains of Khuzistan mark active local uplifts, while submerged townsites at the head of the Persian Gulf indicate instability in the axis of the present foredeep.

The most graphic evidence of the current rate of deformation along the orogenic front comes from a pair of Sassanian irrigation canals cut some 1,700 years ago across an erosionally beveled anticlinal strip on the Khuzistan Plain at Shaur. One canal still carries water, but has cut twelve feet below its original bed. The other, a qanat, has been disrupted by a rise across its course of sixty feet over a horizontal distance of two and a half miles:[4] a local escalation of more than one foot in every thirty years.

LITHOLOGY AND LANDSCAPE

The processes of sedimentation in the Zagros geosyncline have produced six lithologic units which control the development of erosional landscapes in the Zagros Highland.

The long Permian to late Middle Cretaceous submergence produced an accumulation of limestones of variable character, the most important of which are the Middle Cretaceous (Cenomanian) formations. The dark Cenomanian limestones, both massive and thin-bedded, compose the great peaks throughout the Zagros (Figure 3). Outcrops of this formation invariably produce positive landforms whose slopes are joints or bedding planes. Complete erosional transections of the Cenomanian formations are quite rare and older rocks, with few exceptions, appear only where exposed at the base of fault scarps.

Overlying the Middle Cretaceous limestones is an immense clastic flysch accumulation, upwards of 5,000 feet in thickness, which is found in synchronous development from one end of the Tethyan geosyncline to the other, bespeaking its first world-wide orogenic paroxysm. This mass of marls, limestones, chalks, shales, and red beds, laid down in the Upper Cretaceous and Eocene, forms a second vital element in the Zagros landscape. Erosional exposure of the deep flysch mass results in the rapid excavation of subsequent valleys. Thus

[3]H. V. Dunnington, "Generation, Migration, Accumulation and Dissipation of Oil in Northern Iraq," *Habitat of Oil,* publ. by Amer. Assoc. Petrol. Geols., Tulsa (1958), 1219.

[4]G. M. Lees, "Recent Earth Movements in the Middle East", *Geol. Rundschau,* 43 (1955), 223.

outcrops of the Upper Cretaceous flysch produce negative relief features (Figure 9). The Eocene formations are an alternation of limestones and marls, which create a more intricate landscape of minor homoclinal ridges and valleys (Figure 10).

The Oligocene submergence produced the second important cliff-forming horizon in the Zagros landscape: the 1,000 foot-thick Asmari limestone. Though it is the dominant oil-bearing horizon in Iran and Iraq, the Asmari is a massive and extremely resistant formation. It forms the carapaces of the intact anticlines

of the Mountain Front and produces imposing hogbacks and synclinal peaks in the interior ranges (Figure 11).

The transition to lagoonal conditions in Miocene time developed the most colorful and interesting geologic formation to be seen in the Zagros. The interbedded salt, anhydrite, gypsum, and marls of this series comprise the world-famous Lower Fars formation. These rainbow-hued beds, which bespeak great aridity during the early Miocene, are important in two respects. They are the barrier to free upward movement of oil from the Asmari reser-

FIGURE 9. Principal feature-forming stratigraphic units in the Fold Zone. In the foreground two unroofed anticlines expose Cenomanian limestone cores (C), annular subsequent valleys in the Upper Cretaceous and Eocene flysch (Fl), elliptical hogbacks composed of Asmari limestone (As), with an overburden of Lower Fars beds (LF) preserved in synclines. The anticline to the right is Kuh-i-Pabda. In the distance, left and center, are major Cenomanian arches, Kuh-i-Mafarun and Kuh-i-Kashan. (Photo by Aerofilms and Aero Pictorial Limited.)

FIGURE 10. Passage of the Sehzar River through Upper Cretaceous and Eocene formations in an unroofed anticline at Cham Sangar. The Eocene flysch here includes a large number of limestone intercalations, producing a less erodable mass than the characteristic flysch of the Bakhtiari Mountains.

FIGURE 11. Asmari limestone eminence in the Fold Zone east of the Sehzar River: the southwest-dipping flank of the unroofed Churagun anticline. The hills in the foreground are composed of the Upper Cretaceous flysch.

voir, and they are mobile under pressure. Thus the present folds of the Fars evaporite series are markedly disharmonic to those of the underlying competent limestones, a factor greatly complicating the search for oil-bearing structures in the lower beds. In addition, where exposed by erosion in anticlinal structures, the Lower Fars has bulged out in radial or linear thrusts, being extruded by the weight of overlying sediments in the adjacent synclines.

The Lower Fars outcrops are the fourth major element in the landscape of the folded Zagros, particularly in Luristan and along the Mountain Front south of the Karun River. Everywhere they form intricately dissected badlands, which, though colorful, make overland travel by any means extremely tortuous (Figure 12).

Above the Lower Fars evaporite series are encountered progressively coarser clastic de-posits associated with the onset of the orogeny in late Miocene and early Pliocene time. These beds, the Upper Fars and Lower Bakhtiari series, range from marls to conglomerates, and are characterized by many internal breaks, overlaps, and facies changes. Some of the beds are deltaic, others pedimentary, all being deposited in depressions undergoing constant to intermittent deformation. The Upper Fars and Lower Bakhtiari formations are best

FIGURE 12. The Lower Fars formation in the vicinity of Masjed-i-Sulaiman oil field. These are the characteristic landscapes of the oil field region of western Iran. The Lower Fars beds acted as an incompetent mass during the Pliocene orogeny, their deformational pattern being disharmonic and much more intricate than that of the subjacent oil-bearing limestones.

preserved beyond the Mountain Front and in the deeper longitudinal troughs within the highland, where they form complex and occasionally chaotic homoclinal landscapes.

Massive conglomerates everywhere overlie the Lower Bakhtiari formations along a strong angular uncomformity. Both the unconformity and the nature of the succeeding deposits —the Upper Bakhtiari formation—indicate a violent upheaval of the entire mountain belt in the late Pliocene.

The Upper Bakhtiari formation is the local product of the violent denudation of a near-homogeneous orogenic system reaching from the western Alps to the eastern Himalayas. Thus it is hardly distinguishable from the *nagelfluh* molasse of Switzerland or the Siwalik beds of India. The Upper Bakhtiari beds vary widely from basin to basin in both thickness and composition. Their character depends upon the circumstances affecting the immediate locality; thus they may be composed of anything from siltstone to conglom-

erate containing rounded boulders three feet in diameter. The materials of the Bakhtiari conglomerate cuesta facing the Mountain Front are well-rounded limestone cobbles firmly cemented by calcareous selenite, a variety of gypsum. Their most typical diameter is from one to four inches, but a significant proportion are many times larger. In depth the local range may be from inches to 15,000 feet.

The Bakhtiari conglomerate filled basins, flooded through cols, blanketed the plain in front of the orogen, and at present stands before and amid the fold belt in commanding pink escarpments, buttes, and mesas, having vertical faces frequently 1,500 feet high (Figure 13). It seems impossible that a load of such tremendous bulk, lacking the rudest semblance of stratification, could have been delivered by streams operating under the present climatic regime. It is believed by geologists familiar with the area that the period of conglomerate deposition, the late Pliocene, was one of much greater rainfall than the present, perhaps as a

FIGURE 13. The Dez River canyon through the Upper Bakhtiari conglomerate cuesta facing the Mountain Front. The gorge is some 1,500 feet in depth at this point. The Dez Dam, under construction at the time of the photo, is just out of sight behind the projecting wall on the right. The lower half of this canyon will be occupied by the resulting reservoir.

result of the world-wide climatic disturbances culminating in the Pleistocene glacial epochs.

In summary, the scenery of the Outer Zagros may be understood in terms of six relief-forming lithologic elements. The greatest positive relief features in the Zagros are composed of scarps and bedding-plane slopes of the resistant Middle Cretaceous (Cenomanian) and Oligocene (Asmari) limestones. These two horizons are always separated by a body of Upper Cretaceous and Eocene flysch that creates level to hilly country between the limestone domes and hogbacks. Above the Asmari is a great depth of mobile marl and evaporite beds, the Lower Fars series, which forms badlands of vast extent both among and beyond the mountains. The Lower Fars badlands often border intricate homoclinal landscapes composed of siltstones and sandstones. These are in turn overlooked by cuestas and mesas of the heavy Upper Bakhtiari conglomerates, which form imposing cliffs wherever encountered.

STRATIGRAPHY AND DRAINAGE GENESIS

Certain facts deduced from stratigraphy bear upon the problem of drainage genesis in the Zagros region.

On one hand, the southwestward migration of the Mountain Front from late Middle Cretaceous to Pliocene time would appear to favor the development of through-flowing antecedent drainage lines originating in the Cretaceous orogenic zone and becoming transverse to structures formed at successively later dates as the folding spread outward. On the other hand, emergence of the anticlinal structures as islands separated by marine straits would defeat the possibility of their transection by through-flowing drainage lines of antecedent origin.

Isopach maps indicate that submarine anticlines were forming on the outer edge of the present mountain sheaf as early as the Eocene.[5] These primal features should not be regarded as mountains, but as barely perceptible swells pushed above the level of marine sedimentation, and only occasionally above sea level. As the highest parts of these folds

are now stripped down to the Middle Cretaceous limestones, the precise situation of their crests during earlier epochs cannot be deduced. But a possible emergence of these folds and their continued maintenance as islands would be of primary significance to drainage theory, as such islands could not have been crossed by antecedent streams.

The great barrier of Kabir Kuh appeared in at least an embryonic state during the Oligocene, probably well before the lesser folds of the Luristan Basin, whose drainage it now deflects so uniquely. The possibility of the emergence of Kabir Kuh as an island, at least in its long and severely stripped crestal region, is supported by its strong deflecting effort on the drainage that moves toward it from the interior of the highland.

The constituents of the early Pliocene Upper Fars and Lower Bakhtiari formations have given rise to an important controversy over the development of transverse streams in the Zagros. The abundant sandstone layers of the Lower Bakhtiari formation, as compared to the siltier Upper Fars, indicate increasing relief in the emergent orogen. The pebbly beds contain limestone and chert components that are clearly derived from the interior mountains, and also a significant percentage of quartzite and other metamorphic siliceous rocks that can only have come from sources *behind* the mountains derived from the Mesozoic geosyncline. The significance of these beds could be great, for it seems possible that some of them might have been deposited by persistent streams flowing through the orogen from the region of the chert thrusts and the crystalline zones far to the northeast of the Fold Zone. Far-traveled conglomerates of radiolarian cherts and Jurassic rocks from the Thrust Zone have also been recognized in the earlier Fars series in the area of the present transverse Saidmarreh River. Shepherd and Slinger have expressed a tentative belief that these deposits are those of Miocene through-flowing antecedent streams.[6] However, V. H. Boileau long ago emphasized that secondary sources for the materials were present in the nearer mountains, and that it was not necessary to assume that the great rivers had already *headed back* through the mountains even

[5] A. Allison and F. C. P. Slinger, "The Dezful Embayment Mountain Front Survey 1947–48," Iranian Oil Expl. Prod. Co., *Expl. Dept. Report* 723 (1948), 13 and map supplement.

[6] M. F. Shepherd and F. C. P. Slinger, Geol. Dept. Iranian Oil Expl. Prod. Co., Interview, January 1962.

in Lower Bakhtiari (early Pliocene) time.[7]
Boileau concluded that the radiolarite and
metamorphic debris was only indirectly derived from the interior zones, having come
more immediately from the rising Eocene red
beds of Luristan and the Bakhtiari Country.
He thus recognized an exotic detrital facies
in the Eocene of these regions which is absent

eastward of the present Lower Karun River,
where at present direct and deeply penetrating
transverse streams are also absent.

In addition to an important disagreement
on the derivation of the far-traveled materials
of the early Pliocene beds, and on the date of
inception of the through-flowing drainage, we
have expressed here a fundamental difference
of opinion on the process originating the
present transverse streams—Shepherd and
Slinger being proponents of drainage antecedence, while Boileau raises a lone voice in support of the hypothesis of headward extension
of the transverse drainage systems.

---

[7]V. H. Boileau, A. K. Dashti, and L. G. Milliward, "Report on the Dezful Embayment Survey (1937-38)," Iranian Oil Expl. Prod. Co., *Geol. Dept. Report* 584 (1938),
21.

Chapter IV

Physiographic Regions of the Central Zagros

The zonal arrangement of the structural and historical divisions of the orogenic system combines with the presence of broad structural "waves" in the Outer Zagros to create several distinctive erosional landscapes in the mountain complex. As a result the Central Zagros may be divided into more or less homogeneous morphological regions, in each of which the problem of anomalous transverse drainage has its own peculiar manifestations.

Since the structural surge out of the Mesopotamian Plains exceeds the actual rise in surface elevation moving northeastward into the Zagros, a line may be drawn along the strike of the mountains to separate the landscape of undissected folds on the southwest from the farrago of hogbacks, scarps, and resurrected arches of erosionally breached structures on the northeast. Due to the presence of transverse deformations in the fold surface, this line will not be straight. Where the fold belt is relatively depressed, intact anticlines are found well in the interior of the mountain system; and where the folded surface is itself arched, severe denudation is characteristic even at the Mountain Front.

The geomorphic effect of the discordance between the general denudational and structural slopes is reinforced by the sequence of folding, which has established young ranges, only briefly subject to erosion, on the southwestern margin of the orogen—ranges of progressively greater age and more extended denudational history being encountered toward the interior of the highland.

Figure 14 is a geognostic map of the Fold and Imbricate zones in the Central Zagros. This map combines information on lithology, structure, and surface configuration in a diagrammatic manner, and is a graphic portrayal of the variety of landscapes produced by denudation acting on the broad structural waves in the folded surface. Figure 15 delineates nine distinctive physiographic regions which I recognize on the basis of the contrasting effects of erosion on the various structural

waves. The remainder of this chapter is a description of these physiographic regions and of the general nature of the drainage anomalies occurring in each.

THE OUTER ZAGROS

The Outer Zagros is a region of simple folding in which different erosional landscapes have been created by variations in the intensity of the folding, by the presence of broad structural waves in the fold surface, and by variations in the thickness of the erodable flysch formations between the upper and lower limestone groups. On the southwestern margin of the area is a skirt of detrital materials, the Mountain Front Detrital Apron, which is succeeded on the northeast by a discontinuous zone of variable width in which the folding is rather open: the Frontal Fold Region. The remaining physiographic divisions in the Outer Zagros succeed one another along the trend of the fold belt from northwest to southeast; these regions are the Luristan Folded Basin, the Luristan Saddle, the Bakhtiari Mountains, and the Kuhgalu Fold Plateau.

The Mountain Front Detrital Apron

In moving northeastward from the alluvial plains of Khuzistan, the first positive landform encountered is the backslope of a conglomerate cuesta composed of the molasse-like Bakhtiari formation. This immense mass of detrital materials was derived from the erosion of the rising mountain mass in Pliocene time, and has been stripped back from the Mountain Front in some areas as a result of post-Pliocene uplift. The conglomerate cuesta facing the Mountain Front is best developed in the Dezful Embayment, particularly where crossed by the deeply engorged Dez and Karun rivers. The portal of the Dez River canyon through the cuesta is shown in Figure 13.

The cuesta scarp in the Dez River area is indented by several obsequent canyons, and the steep backslope has been maturely dissected by consequent runoff. The Dez canyon

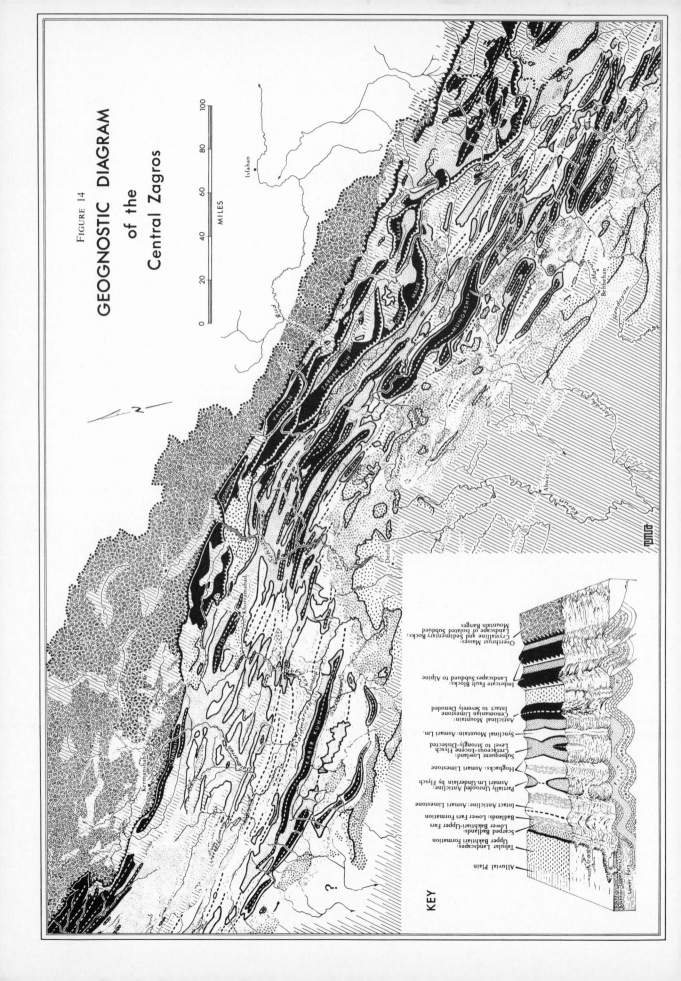

FIGURE 14

GEOGNOSTIC DIAGRAM
of the
Central Zagros

MILES
0   20   40   60   80   100

KEY

Alluvial Plain

Tabular Landscapes:
Upper Bakhtiari Formation

Scarped Badlands:
Lower Bakhtiari–Upper Fars

Badlands: Lower Fars Formation

Intact Anticline: Asmari Limestone

Partially Unroofed Anticline:
Asmari Lm. Underlain by Flysch

Hogbacks: Asmari Limestone

Subsequent Lowland:
Cretaceous–Eocene Flysch
Level to Strongly-Dissected

Synclinal Mountain: Asmari Lm.

Anticlinal Mountain:
Cenomanian Limestone
Intact to Severely Denuded

Imbricate Fault Blocks:
Landscapes Subdued to Alpine

Overthrust Masses:
Crystalline and Sedimentary Rocks:
Landscape of Isolated Subdued
Mountain Ranges

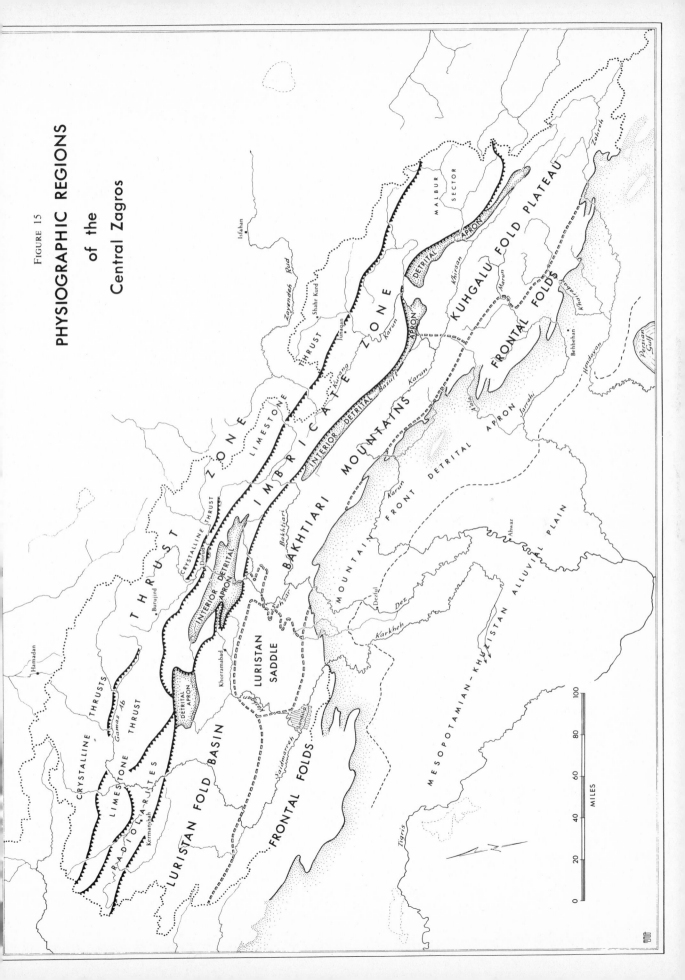

FIGURE 15

PHYSIOGRAPHIC REGIONS

of the

Central Zagros

THRUST ZONE

IMBRICATE ZONE

CRYSTALLINE THRUSTS

LIMESTONE THRUST

RA·DIOLA·R·ITES

LURISTAN FOLD BASIN

FRONTAL FOLDS

DETRITAL APRON

Crystalline Thrust

INTERIOR DETRITAL APRON

LIMESTONE

INTERIOR DETRITAL APRON

LURISTAN SADDLE

BAKHTIARI MOUNTAINS

KUHGALU FOLD PLATEAU

FRONTAL FOLDS

DETRITAL APRON

MALBUR SECTOR

MOUNTAIN FRONT DETRITAL APRON

MESOPOTAMIAN-KHUZISTAN ALLUVIAL PLAIN

Persian Gulf

Hamadan

Kermanshah

Buruird

Khorramabad

Isfahan

Shahr Kurd

Junaqan

Dezful

Ahwaz

Behbehan

Karkheh

Tigris

Dez

Karun

Karun

Karun

Khirsan

Jarrahi

Khairabad

Zohreh

Hendijan

Zayendeh Rud

Kurang

Bazuft

Gamas Ab

Saidmareh

Sehzar

Bakhtiari

MILES

0   20   40   60   80   100

itself appears to have been initiated as an obsequent gully, and a major diversion of the river at this point seems clear, with the old course of the Dez having led westward, parallel to the scarp, into the present Bala Rud. The latter stream crosses the Bakhtiari conglomerates where they have been less affected by post-Pliocene uplift.

East of the Bala Rud the cuesta terminates in a vertical escarpment, occasionally 1,500 feet high, that overlooks a broad belt of colorful badlands on the underlying Lower Bakhtiari and Upper and Lower Fars formations. The scarp has retreated well into the highly ramified gully systems of the cuesta backslope.

Northwest and southeast of the Dezful Embayment the Bakhtiari formation becomes thinner and is inclined at a lower angle, often being gently folded. In these areas the cuesta and scarp are missing and the landscape is one of less conspicuous tablelands and mesas. Just north of the final longitudinal reach of the Karun lie snakelike ridges of the Bakhtiari formation. These mark Pliocene valley fills in less permeable Fars beds which have been reduced more rapidly by Quaternary erosion. A related inversion of relief is seen in the Gach Saran area, where a series of Pliocene landslides peeled from the Mountain Front to fill an ancient river channel, which is now represented by a line of knolls standing above the erosionally reduced foothills.

Between the Bakhtiari cuesta and the Mountain Front in the Dezful Embayment, and in the beveled anticlinal strips in the detrital apron to the northwest and southeast, the Lower Bakhtiari and Upper and Lower Fars formations are exposed, forming badland areas that evidence several erosional rejuvenations. The Lower Fars formation, composed of marls and evaporite beds, is mobile under pressure. In the oil field region, strips of the Lower Fars mass have been exposed by the erosion of shallow anticlines in the Bakhtiari beds, and the underlying material has been extruded under the weight of overlying sediments, in places moving out and over the younger beds in thrustlike masses such as that shown in Figure 16. In these situations the mobility of the Lower Fars formation far exceeds the erosional power of its runoff, so that its surface sculpture is quite superficial in relation to the mass of the landform created by the extrusion. Figure 12 illustrates a typical landscape on the Lower Fars formation, and is indicative of the trafficability of areas in which this material is widely exposed.

The detrital Bakhtiari and Fars formations terminate on the northeast against steeply inclined limestone faces, which are the flanks of

FIGURE 16. Extruded Lower Fars mass overrunning younger formations in the Masjed-i-Sulaiman area. Erosional sculpture of the extrusion indicates stability in the western (left) portion with strong movement proceeding in the eastern (right) half.

cleanly stripped arches or hogbacks of the oil-bearing Asmari formation. The emergence of these limestones from beneath the detrital cover marks the Mountain Front.

The Frontal Folds

Along the outer margin of the Zagros Highland northeast of the Mountain Front is a zone in which the landscape is one of essentially intact limestone anticlines that form ridges or elliptical domes separated by open synclinal lowlands. In Luristan the Pusht-i-Kuh salient extends the width of the zone to fifty miles, while at the head of the Dezful Recess it pinches out altogether. The zone of youthful open folds reappears in the vicinity of Lali oil field, and may be traced continuously southeastward from this point to Tahiri on the Persian Gulf.

Typically, the limestone anticlines of the Frontal Fold Region rise out of extensive badland plains on the Lower Fars formation. Northeast of the inner margin of this zone large outcrops of Lower Fars beds are rare, as synclines are either tightly pinched by strong folding or form mountains through inversion of relief, the result in either case being a distinctly different landscape.

The Frontal Fold Region of the Zagros Highland is one of the few areas in the world in which structures created by strong tectonic activity may be seen in an intact state, their surfaces almost completely unmodified by erosion (Figure 17). The folds of this area are not only young but were protected during their formative stages by the mobile covering medium of the Lower Fars mass, which maintained a near-planar surface over the substratum of limestone during its deformation. It is probable that Quaternary denudation exhumed the majority of the anticlines of this region from beneath thick accumulations of the mobile covermass in essentially their present state. In the Saidmarreh synclinorial belt the crests of buried anticlines are at present being exposed by runoff that is dissecting the Lower Fars overburden.

The anticlinal mountains of the Frontal Fold Region are composed of both the Asmari (Oligocene-Miocene) and Cenomanian (Middle Cretaceous) limestones. The Cenomanian is exposed where the amplitude of the folding is greatest and the intervening Upper Cretaceous flysch horizon is weakly developed, as in the Pusht-i-Kuh salient and Kuhgalu. In these regions the Cenomanian limestones form immense even-crested barriers buttressed by upturned plates of the Asmari Limestone.

In the open landscape of the Frontal Folds, anticlines seldom coalesce or impinge upon one another, yet the trafficability of the country remains poor due to the badland matrix commonly surrounding the domes. The available saddles between the noses of plunging anticlines are rarely utilized as passes by drainage lines, and even the synclines seldom direct any significant runoff. Instead there is a puzzling repetition of watergaps cut through the pitching anticlinal noses themselves. The folds only rarely have a strong deflecting effect upon drainage coming from the interior, or even from the adjacent range to the northeast. Kabir Kuh, the immense barrier rising 6,000 feet over the Saidmarreh Valley, and its lower northern flankers, Kalak-i-Arab and Kuljar, are the only structures having a marked effect on the drainage pattern.

Many of the Mountain Front anticlines are in the most youthful state of erosion imaginable, as Figure 17 indicates. Apart from the abrupt transverse chasms of through-flowing drainage lines, such as that shown in Figure 18, weathering and runoff have only begun to nick the arch-bends of large parts of these folds, removing small triangles of material along intersecting joint systems without marring the naked lower flank of the structure. The eventual enlargement and coalescence of adjacent triangles leaves flatirons between them. This process unpeels the dome, layer by layer, with flatiron superimposed upon flatiron, until the crest of the arch is consumed and its long profile is controlled by the figure of the last line of flatirons to be formed, buttressed outward by the continually shrinking forms of all the flatirons produced previously. This stage is occasionally seen in a ridge which is almost totally undissected a few miles away. Such variations must result from the prior exhumation of the most denuded portions of the fold.

Denudation of the Asmari and Cenomanian limestone anticlines is guided by bedding planes and joint systems. Intersecting shear joints fix the figures of the flatirons produced by down-stripping of the anticlinal arches, and occasionally extension jointing is spectacularly displayed, facilitating the dissection of the fold by closely spaced lateral gullies. Longitudinal joints and boudinage are also seen in the

FIGURE 17. Youthful anticline of Kuh-i-Kialan, rising from the Saidmarreh Valley. Kabir Kuh lies to the south-west (left) and Milleh Kuh to the northeast (right). The synclinal valleys are clogged with Lower Fars masses whose degradation has exposed the Asmari limestone carapace of Kialan. The transverse gorges are Tang-i-Fanni (in the distance) and Tang-i-Lailum. In the middle distance the Saidmarreh landslip covers the nose of the fold, and is trenched by the Saidmarreh River close to the foot of Kabir Kuh. The gorge wall in the foreground reveals that the surface of the arch is an exact reflection of its structure. (Photo by Aerofilms and Aero Pictorial Limited.)

Frontal Folds, but have much less effect on their denudation. The anticlines being stripped under joint control give way bed by bed. Thus the onionlike structure of the domes is always apparent, particularly at their pitching noses, and also around the deep transverse cuts from which "waves" of spalling spread outward along the fold flanks.

In the Frontal Fold Region many of the Asmari limestone anticlines reach similar elevations because they are structural equals. The Cenomanian arches, however, frequently command neighboring Asmari anticlines by thousands of feet, with the crests of their Asmari limestone flatirons surpassing the crests of the intact Asmari arches, as shown in sections AA, BB, and CC of Figure 7.

Quaternary deposits are conspicuous among the Frontal Folds only in the Saidmarreh Valley, where immense landslides from Kabir Kuh have in the past 10,000 years produced one or more large lakes. Wherever the easily eroded Upper Cretaceous flysch is widely exposed, as at Ilam, alluvial plains have also developed.

FIGURE 18. Tang-i-Lailum, a transverse gorge through the Asmari limestone anticline of Kuh-i-Kialan. The central portion of the gorge has expanded into a small axial basin by sapping at the limestone-marl contact. In the distance the arch has been unroofed by both transverse and autogenous streams. (Photo by Aerofilms and Aero Pictorial Limited.)

The Luristan Folded Basin

Northeastward from the Saidmarreh Syncline the amplitude of the folding decreases, while the flysch mass interposed between the Asmari and Cenomanian limestones increases vastly in depth. The combined effect is to elevate the shallower Asmari limestone synclinal troughs above local base levels of denudation. At the same time, the axis of the Lower Fars depositional basin is left behind, so that the limestone anticlines of this region were not protected by a deep covermass during their formation. As a result the anticlinal structures have been unroofed by erosion and the relief of the area is the inverse of its structure.

The landscape of Inner Luristan may thus be described as a scattering of remnant concave slabs of Asmari limestone, supported by plinths of Eocene limestones and marls, resting on a deep groundmass of the Upper Cretaceous flysch.

Due to the great depth of the Upper Cretaceous flysch accumulation in this area, Cenomanian limestones are exposed in the cores of but four anticlinal structures in Inner Luristan, and in none of these situations is their outcrop large enough to create a significant landform. However, along the northeastern margin of the Luristan Basin a local intensification in the amplitude of the folding does bring Cenomanian beds to the surface on a large scale, where they form the great anticlinal mountain ranges Kuh-i-Charmi and Kuh-i-Safid.

The subsequent lowlands that dominate the landscape of Inner Luristan are frequently veneered by Quaternary alluvial and lacustrine deposits in which the present drainage is incised a few tens of feet. The lacustrine plains, such as those at Hulailan, Kuh-i-Dasht, and Mahidasht, offer the best agricultural possibilities to be found within the Central Zagros; accordingly, they are heavily populated in comparison with the rest of the region, and around their margins evidence of prehistoric cultures has been discovered.

There is some degree of summit accordance over portions of Inner Luristan. This appears to be evidence of a similar rate of denudation of nearly equal structures rather than of a regional planation by erosion. The general elevation lies between 3,000 and 4,000 feet, with the synclinal mountains rising 3,000 to 5,000 feet higher. The highest crests are found on the rims of the broadest synclinal mountains. Commonly, though there are notable exceptions, the maximum elevation on a synclinal mountain is found at its nose—at the junction of the flanking homoclines. Well-preserved pinnate drainage systems occupy the high synclinal bowls. Scarp recession has eaten into these relict gully systems, leaving them beheaded and truncated on all sides.

In the Luristan Folded Basin the discordance between structure and drainage is less obvious than in the Frontal Fold Region. In the basin proper (which excludes the Cenomanian arches of the extreme northeast) the only transverse gorges are those through synclinal mountains, for the anticlinal structures are all unroofed and the streams transecting them flow across open lacustrine plains. Five drainage lines cross significant portions of Inner Luristan transversely: the Cham Rawand, the Saidmarreh and its right bank tributary the Jazman Rud, the Kuh-i-dasht Basin drainage, and the Lower Kashgan River. All of these streams link successive anticlinal basins, thereby transecting successive anticlinal structures.

The Luristan Saddle

Southeast of the Kashgan River the fold belt sags briefly, forming the Luristan Saddle. This transverse syncline separates the Luristan Basin from the Bakhtiari Mountains, and has a landscape of its own which is transitional between the neighboring Luristan Folded Basin, Frontal Fold Region, and Bakhtiari Mountains. The change in landscape is effected by the deepening and pinching of the Asmari limestone synclines as the more powerfully folded Bakhtiari Culmination is approached. Thus the table mountains of the Luristan Basin to the northwest pass eastward into serrate hogbacks and homoclinal ridges preserving narrow and highly contorted bundles of Lower Fars beds between them. The axis of the Luristan Saddle is marked by the appearance of intact anticlines rising from a heavy accumulation of Lower Fars beds.

The relief of the Luristan Saddle is distinctly Appalachian in plan, with looping ridges and many fine watergaps. The resemblance is limited, however, by the massive nature of the resistant formations in the Zagros. The numerous concentric ridges of Pennsylvania are the result of the erosional exposure of a succession of strong and weak formations, including some six feature-forming horizons. In the Zagros only two strongly resistant series are exposed, both of which are relatively homogeneous for a thousand feet or more vertically, being separated by a weaker formation—The Cretaceous-Eocene flysch—which is upwards of a mile in thickness.

This transitional region has much wilder scenery than the neighboring Luristan Basin or the structurally similar Appalachian Ridge and Valley Province, due on the one hand to the increased scale of its dislocations, and on the other to the predominance of angular mechanical weathering on its near-vertical hogbacks. Traversing the region along the Kashgan River, one is struck by the isoclinal nature of many synclines, in which the radius of curvature of a foot-thick bed may be less than a foot and a half. The relief effects of such folding are striking. Some tributaries of the Kashgan rising on broad synclinal highlands carry toward the main stream along gradually pinching synclinal aqueducts perched a thousand feet above extensive subsequent lowlands to either side. Figure 19 shows the lower portion of one of these steep-walled troughs.

The Kashgan River and its left bank tributaries drain all of the Luristan Saddle. The Kashgan in this section cuts through the As-

FIGURE 19. Tightly compressed syncline of the Luristan Saddle. View southeast from the Kashgan River at Tang-i-Kalhur. The walls are composed of the Asmari limestone.

mari limestone hogbacks of six major anticlines in a course marked by unusually tight
meandering and the frequent utilization of
trend valleys for short distances. The river
neatly links a series of oval basins in unroofed
anticlines (as shown in Figure 14), the basins
being tangent at the successive hogback watergaps. The broad alluvial and lacustrine plains
of the Luristan Basin are absent from this
region. There are no great expanses of the
erodable flysch in the lowlands of the saddle,
which are, like those of the Frontal Fold
Region, highly dissected and underlain by the
Lower Fars formation and smaller oval outcrops of the flysch.

The Bakhtiari Fold Mountains

From the Luristan Saddle the entire folded
surface rises strongly to the southeast, where
the intact anticlines of the saddle are truncated
by a great cuspate hogback. Beyond this looping scarp the Cenomanian cores of the folds
push to the surface, initiating the Bakhtiari
Mountains.

In the local usage the "Bakhtiari Mountains" are the high ranges lying southeast of
the Sehzar River and extending throughout
the northern half of the Karun River Basin.
This is the home of the transhumant Bakhtiari
tribes. As a morphological region, however,
the Bakhtiari Mountains begin with the appearance of the Cenomanian limestones southeast of the Luristan Saddle. The lithologic and
morphological line separating the Cenomanian limestones from younger beds extends
across the orogen in a direction somewhat
north of east, and crosses the Sehzar River
diagonally. Thus an area of almost 300 square
miles of tight Cenomanian folds lies north and
west of the Sehzar in Lur territory, but is indis-
putably a part of the geomorphic region lying
south and east of the river.

The Bakhtiari Mountains are the surface expression of the great anticlinorium that rises
steeply at the head of the Dezful Embayment.[1]
The first relief culmination southeast of the
Luristan Saddle is a line of 9,000-foot peaks
that lie some ten to fifteen miles northwest of
the Sehzar canyon. This crest is the sharply
upturned Asmari limestone rim around the
Cenomanian core of the Bakhtiari Mountain

anticlinorium. Each of this great cuspate hogback, a portion of which is shown in Figure
20, is a deeply dissected band of flysch, some
two to eight miles wide, beyond which the
Cretaceous limestones ascend steeply to an elevation of about 7,500 feet. This upward surge
is interrupted by the spectacular 4,000-foot
gorge of the Sehzar River. The southeastward
ascent out of the Sehzar canyon is over longer
slopes which reach to a line of 8,000 to
10,000-foot peaks at a distance of five to ten
miles from the stream. From this point southeastward for some 250 miles the higher ridges
continuously approach 10,000 feet, with maximum elevations frequently exceeding 12,000
feet. These simple anticlinal ranges are overlooked on the northeast by the 14,000-foot
peaks of the Imbricate Zone.

The Bakhtiari Mountain morphological
region comes to the very front of the highland
at the head of the Dezful Embayment. Here
the anticlines are similar to those of the
Frontal Fold Region in their state of preservation, but they express a lower horizon in the
sedimentary column, and are so tightly packed
as to present a totally different landscape. The
synclines throughout the Bakhtiari Mountains
are tightly crushed, V-shaped in fact, and in
the vicinity of the Lower Sehzar this characteristic carries all the way to the Mountain
Front. The anticlines of this region are also
frequently of the chevron type, with occasional
thrust-faulting at their crests.

The Bakhtiari Mountain landscape is a
seemingly endless expanse of sharp-crested
Cenomanian anticlines whose straight or convex slopes commonly rise some 5,000 feet from
extremely constricted trend valleys. The narrow synclinal troughs all carry runoff down
the strike, often in tightly meandering and
deeply incised channels that now and then
bite into the plunging dip slopes to either side.
A surprising number of streams also cut diagonally across the mountain complex in canyons which attain depths as great as 8,000
feet. The most notable of these are the Sehzar,
Bakhtiari, Rahmat, Sorkh, Qiyad, Balut, Baba
Ahmad, and Karun.

In the Bakhtiari sector the Asmari limestone is rarely preserved, but occasionally
appears in a great hogback flanking a Cenomanian peak, as in Figure 9, or as a synclinal range interposed between Cenomanian
domes, as in Figure 21.

There is no summit accordance in the Bakh-

---

[1]The southeastward rise of the Bakhtiari Mountains from
the Luristan Saddle is graphically illustrated on the
USAF Aeronautical Approach Chart 428 D-II.

FIGURE 20. Backslope of the Asmari limestone cuspate hogback created by the rise of the Bakhtiari Culmination. The depth of the Upper Cretaceous-Eocene flysch in this area is so great that, despite the tightness of the folding, the subjacent Cenomanian fold cores are not exposed between facing Asmari scarps that are four miles apart.

tiari Mountains. Almost every area is dominated by some individual peak, either a homoclinal plate or a huge partially stripped arch, rising above a welter of jagged buttressing crests. Though the structural trend is definite, the relief is prevented from becoming conspicuously linear by the effects of plunging folds, by wide variations in fold breadth, and by diagonal gorge systems. As hogbacks and scarps face in every direction, the area is one of endless scenic variety. The declivity of the slopes in the region is graphically portrayed in Figure 3.

Open valleys are almost nonexistent in the Bakhtiari Mountains. Thus Quaternary alluvial deposits are found most often in terraces, some of great persistence, perched at various elevations up to a thousand feet above present stream levels. In the dry season streams display ephemeral point bar deposits along their channels.

The Kuhgalu Fold Plateau

Southeast of the Ab-i-A'ala the great dislocation of Kuh-i-Mungasht sinks and spreads out in digitations to initiate a fifth structural and physiographic province in the Outer Zagros. In both structure and surface configuration the area southeast of the Bakhtiari Country is a strongly corrugated plateau, its relief being fine in texture—by comparison with the areas to the northwest—and extremely linear along the strike of the folding. A relatively high degree of summit accordance characterizes this region, for practically all crest lines over an area of 4,300 square miles lie between 8,500 and 9,100 feet. A few domes rise as much as 2,000 feet above this horizon to dominate the surrounding ridges.

This rasp-like country, the domain of the Kuhgalu tribes, is unlike Luristan in that its folds continue the Bakhtiari pattern of close packing. As in the Bakhtiari region, there are no open valleys nor any extensive deposits of Quaternary materials.

The mountains composing the Kuhgalu Fold Plateau continue to be interrupted by transverse gorges. Although they are not so deep as those of the Bakhtiari Mountains, the defiles of Kuhgalu are equally precipitous and

FIGURE 21. Kuh-i-Gariveh, a synclinal range in the Bakhtiari Mountains. An exceptionally deep trough in the Bakhtiari anticlinorium here preserves a strip of the Asmari limestone, the majority of which has been removed from this structural culmination (see also Figure 62).

quite as spectacular due to their constriction and convolution. The trunk streams of Kuhgalu are the Marun, Khairabad, and Zohreh, all of which are structurally discordant, though in a manner unlike that of the through-flowing streams to the northwest. The Kuhgalu streams zigzag from one anticlinal transection to another, making frequent use of synclinal paths. The drainage pattern is of the trellis type, developed with a homogeneously fine texture over an area of several thousand square miles.

Strangely, the greatest deflections of Kuhgalu drainage lines occur *beyond* the Mountain Front. Both the Marun and Zohreh rivers exit from the highland by splitting the centers of Asmari limestone anticlines without deviation. They then swing to the northwest along the trend to follow shallow synclines in the Bakhtiari formation for some forty miles before turning into the Khuzistan Plain. The Karun River, to the northwest, behaves in like fashion upon crossing the

Mountain Front. When the courses of the Dez and Karkheh are observed, coming from the opposite direction, but similarly turned by gentle warps in the detrital apron, it appears that the structural swells presumably most recent in development and least well expressed topographically have a greater effect in directing drainage than do the great dislocations of the high mountain region.

In the latitude of Kazerun and Shiraz the fold belt sags again, and the rough linear terrain of Kuhgalu is succeeded by more open landscapes developed on a wide expanse of the Lower Fars formation. Southeast of this saddle is a region of isolated domes rising from flat alluvial or lacustrine synclinal plains. This is the area traditionally known as Fars or Laristan. Though outside the region delimited for close investigation it must be noted that in this area the occasional discordances between geological structure and drainage paths are hardly less striking. The disregard of consequent transverse paths by some parts of the drainage pattern is even more enigmatic than in the regions to the northwest where the continuity of structural barriers seldom allows easy egress from the orogen, and where some transection of structures by runoff might be expected.

THE INNER ZAGROS

The longitudinal belt of simple folding which includes the Luristan Basin and Saddle, the Bakhtiari Fold Mountains, and the Kuhgalu Fold Plateau is succeeded northeastward by the Inner Zagros, a zone of great vertical and horizontal dislocations along thrust faults which dip toward the Iranian Plateau. A new landscape is ushered in by the first imbricate slab in the faulted zone, and in it are developed the greatest heights found in the Zagros Mountain complex.

The front of the faulted zone is neither straight nor as sinuous as the Mountain Front. Whereas broad warping of the fold surface prohibits the Mountain Front from truly reflecting the strike of the folding, the frontal faults of the Imbricate Zone are almost perfectly parallel to the structural trend of the fold belt. Thus the Pusht-i-Kuh salient and the Dezful Embayment are poorly expressed along this line. The frontal faults depart radically from the trend of the fold belt in one area only—a salient bulging southwestward south of Zardeh Kuh, followed by a recess along the line of the Ab-i-Wanak north of Kuh-i-Rig. These inflections are the result of the dispositions of the anticlines from which the outer imbrics developed.

The faulted zone is composed of two parts, each of them in turn made up of several components. Southeast of the Sehzar gorge at Dorud a belt of imbricate slabs extends along the strike of the orogen for 270 miles to Kuh-i-Dina, disappearing beneath basin fills beyond this range. The Imbricate Zone is succeeded by the horizontal overthrusts that comprise the remainder of the mountain complex. North of the Sehzar the Thrust Zone pinches out the imbricate belt and overlooks the fold belt directly, though occasionally across areas of molasse-like Pliocene beds, which also blanket the interior of the Fold Zone along its contact with the Imbricate Zone.

The Interior Detrital Belt

From Firuzabad southeastward to the source of the Ab-i-Khirsan the terrain of the Imbricate Zone is separated from that of the belt of simple folding by a nearly continuous band of the Bakhtiari formation. The Bakhtiari conglomerates accumulated in a great longitudinal depression in the Pliocene mountain belt, but now appear at an elevation of 8,000 to 10,000 feet where they are carved into imposing table mountains. The Pliocene masses occasionally overlook the dissected arches of the fold belt in thousand-foot escarpments. On the northeast the conglomerate heights are in turn dominated by the great southwest-facing escarpments of the Imbricate Zone.

The conglomerate accumulation immediately southeast of the Sehzar gorge at Dorud overlies a zone of thrust faults of low displacement, and is technically entirely within the Imbricate Zone, though the latter is weakly developed here. The principal imbric thrust in this region lies behind the detrital mass and results in the great massif of Ushtarinan Kuh (14,200 feet). Southeastward from this point the Pliocene clastics disappear for some thirty-five miles. When they are encountered once more it is along the foot of the frontal imbric slabs, generally occupying synclines in the fold belt. Thus Bakhtiari conglomerates or sandstones are found all along the front of the older structures, interposing between the arches of the Fold Zone and the first escarpments of the sheared zone.

The Bakhtiari sandstone and conglomerate heights are crossed diagonally by through-flowing streams and are also trenched longitudinally by drainage lines following the strike of the fold belt. Notable among the transverse crossings are those of the Sehzar below Dorud and the Karun below the Wanak confluence. The gorge of the Bazuft, on the other hand, follows a narrow conglomerate-filled trough along the trend for some eighty miles. All of these streams flow through canyons 3,000 to 5,000 feet in depth.

The streams issuing from the imbric slabs to the east of the Interior Detrital Belt are presently hanging on the brinks of the V-shaped canyons of streams that follow the Bakhtiari strips longitudinally, such as the Bazuft and Lower Khirsan rivers. Lateral tributaries join the longitudinal drainage by an extreme convexity in their lower profiles, often entering by a series of steep cataracts which may extend over a distance of several miles. The lower courses of such streams are profoundly engorged, with their upper valleys being quite open. Many dead drainage systems may be seen on the Bakhtiari surface, having been disrupted by cliff retreat along the longitudinal gorges.

The Imbricate Zone

The walls rising northeastward from the Bakhtiari conglomerate strips are in all cases fault or fault-line scarps. Where longitudinal streams have worked down along the trend faults, as the Wanak has done prior to entering the Karun, the greatest relief figures in the Zagros Mountains are obtained. The rise from the Wanak to Kuh-i-Lijan exceeds 8,000 feet, the slope being continuous, slightly concave, and inclined at about 30 degrees. The longitudinal valleys show considerable accumulations of landslide debris, though this area has not been an earthquake epicenter in recorded time. Several points along the marginal thrust have been invaded by ·Cambrian salt intrusions, and gaseous emanations rising along the fracture zone from deep sources seem to contribute to the Ab-i-Wanak (the "Water of Vile Odors").

The Imbricate Zone is comprised of a series of overlapping scales. At least six major slices may be seen in the widest part of the zone immediately west of Junaqan. All of the slices dip toward the Iranian Plateau, and each presumably originated in a large asymmetric fold overturned in a southwesterly direction. Not all of the thrusts have a strong surface expression, and the major scarps are not found in a consistent position in the imbricate belt. For example, the thrust creating Ushtarinan Kuh (section EE, Figure 7) is at the rear of the belt, with the outer fractures often obscured by erosion and masked by Pliocene detrital sediments. Sections FF and GG show that in some areas none of the thrusts produce large relief features. Section HH indicates that the highest mountain in western Iran, Zardeh Kuh, is the crest of the outermost thrust slice, with those behind it also creating significant positive elements in the landscape. In section II it is seen that, while one of the outer thrusts creates a large mountain, those to the rear are entirely lacking in surface expression. Section KK, crossing the Karun and the great fault-line scarp of Kuh-i-Lijan, shows a series of erosionally beveled backthrusts behind this mountain, which is, on a vast scale, synclinal.

Aerial photographs reveal that there are extensive erosion surfaces in the portion of the Imbricate Zone crossed by sections FF, GG, and HH, though they are hardly apparent in the cross-sections. Very commonly the present drainage of this region is engorged thousands of feet below erosional straths of varying widths, with the greatest eminences rising from these bevels along clearly defined slope breaks which cannot be related to lithology. The bevels are themselves often maturely dissected.

The Imbricate Zone may itself be subdivided. Northwest of the penetration of the endoreic Zayendeh Rud system into this zone, the landscape is one of maturely dissected mountains and V-shaped canyons. There are neither structural nor erosional plains in this region. Thus the northern portion of the Imbricate Zone continues the inhospitable landscape of the Bakhtiari Fold Mountains, which are immediately adjacent to the southwest, and is, indeed, an integral part of the "Bakhtiari Mountains" in the general usage of the term.

Southeast of the Zayendeh Rud penetration the structure of the Imbricate Zone opens out, as shown on the geognostic diagram (Figure 14), and both structural and erosional basins of wide extent become an important part of the landscape. In the drainage basin of the Malbur River a large area of open folding is found behind the frontal fault scarp, as indicated in Figure 14, and in section MM of Figure 7.

The Imbricate Zone is not an area in which there is a truly conspicuous drainage anomaly. From the Dez River to the Malbur Basin the zone of sheared folds is transected by six drainage lines; however, all but two of these cross the zone by paths that gravitate toward the saddles between adjacent imbric slabs, though they do not coincide with them exactly. The Malbur Basin is distinguished by a major resurgence of the drainage anomaly, for in this inlier of open folding several Cenomanian anticlines are severed by through-flowing tributaries that ignore open paths between and around the structural barriers.

The Thrust Zone

The Thrust Zone succeeds the simply folded part of the orogen north of the Dez River, and the Imbricate Zone south of this line. The Thrust Zone rises strongly in the northwest, but has a rather intermittent surface expression south of Junaqan, where it is frequently submerged by Quaternary deposits. Whether a nappe or an extruded mass, the radiolarite zone in Kurdistan and Luristan has a negative surface expression, but the Cretaceous limestone thrust immediately to the northeast creates a line of magnificent peaks behind Kermanshah, and less imposing crestlines as far south as Junaqan. Behind the Cretaceous limestone thrust is a final thrust complex of highly altered Paleozoic sedimentary and intrusive igneous rocks, which seldom create imposing mountain ranges. This is largely due to the perishability of the granites, which are very rich in feldspar.

The mountain features of the Thrust Zone are not continuous along the strike, as are those of the Imbricate and Fold zones. Most commonly they form isolated ranges and massifs that terminate in erosional scarps or pitch out into broad plains that crisscross the inner part of the orogen transversely, greatly facilitating movement through this part of the Zagros. The highlands of the Thrust Zone generally have a weathered and subdued appearance. Often their geologic structure is difficult to determine as the result of an obscuring mantle of regolith. Synclinal mountains are common in this zone, as are cuestas and hogbacks, for the thrusts are themselves folded. Occasionally, anticlines are resurrected on particularly resistant horizons. The granitic core exposed west of Hamadan produces rather mild scenery.

In addition to broad transverse plains there are some transverse gorges in the Thrust Zone, though far fewer than in any other geomorphic province of the Zagros Mountains. The walls of these cuts are steep, but often rise out of heavy talus accumulations. The streams passing through them are commonly braided or incised in terraced floodplains. Beyond the Persian Gulf watershed, in the area of endoreic drainage, northeast-flowing streams pass through the final arid ranges of the Zagros in similarly alluviated watergaps.

All of the major westward-flowing drainage lines of the Zagros Mountains have their sources in the igneous and metamorphic zone of the overthrust edifice. Though this area is the structural culmination of the orogenic system, it is inferior in elevation to the Imbricate Zone, and even to large parts of the Simply Folded Zone. Thus drainage that rises in open arid country at elevations of 9,000 to 12,000 feet must almost immediately pass through a line of 14,000-foot peaks on its way to the sea.

In truth, the great ranges of the Imbricate Zone are transected by their own runoff, for the headwaters of the through-flowing systems are most strongly nourished by northeast-flowing torrents fed by snowfields on the 14,000-foot peaks themselves. After following longitudinal valleys for some distance these waters break southwestward through the very ranges that gave them birth, the increment from the more easterly ranges being a very minor component of the discharge in this direction. Thus the anomalous relationship between drainage lines and structural lines is carried into the farthest headwaters of the Zagros streams.

Chapter V

Special Features of Zagros Geomorphology

Certain geomorphic features associated with the lithology, climate, agencies of denudation, and recent tectonic instability of the Zagros region are encountered everywhere in the mountain complex, irrespective of regional variations in patterns and types of landforms. Clearly the most significant among these are the unusually constricted transverse gorges known as *tangs*. Other important features are terraces of several kinds, landslips (including the largest known in the Eastern Hemisphere), solution features, and erosional scarps that appear to have retreated at a very rapid rate. All of these phenomena are pertinent in some way to the problem of drainage evolution in the Zagros region.

THE ZAGROS TANGS

The disharmony between drainage and geological structure in the Zagros Mountains is most strikingly seen in the transverse gorges resulting from the collision of the discordant drainage pattern with the individual barriers in the structural matrix. In the Zagros each gorge is called a *tang*: the Farsi adjective meaning "narrow" or "tight." In the local usage the term signifies only a relative constriction and implies nothing about the absolute magnitude or morphology of the feature in question.

Nineteenth-century European travelers, faced with an ever-present problem of negotiating or bypassing the treacherous gorges, seized on the word as a generic term for the peculiar slotlike defiles which they encountered everywhere in the Zagros. Attention was first called to these features in 1855 by W. K. Loftus, a geologist, who noted that

> The tangs are not situated at the lowest or narrowest portion of the range, but most frequently divide it at its highest point, and expose a perpendicular section of 1,000 feet and upwards.[1]

Loftus went on to state his opinion that

> It is quite out of the question to suppose that the rivers themselves have been in the least degree instrumental in cutting these clefts.... Tangs are due to the tension of the cooling mass at right angles to the axis of the chains in which they occur.[2]

A catastrophic rending of the mountain masses by direct tectonic movements appealed to other observers: a point of view perpetuated in a famous work by Lord Curzon,[3] which has continued to appear in general writings on the region.[4]

The *tangs* are pre-eminently the symptom of drainage discordance in the Fold Zone. It is here, particularly in anticlinal transections, that they reach their most awesome proportions. Some of the most notable of these gorges occur at the Mountain Front, where the runoff of the interior finally cuts out onto the detrital foreland.

To man, the principal significance of the Zagros *tangs* is their disruption of cross-country communications, which, in such strongly grained country, would ordinarily utilize the transverse river valleys. The *tangs*, however, commonly convert rivers into a series of *cul de sacs*, moving either up or down stream. They frequently afford no footing along their banks, often lacking banks altogether. Those of the lesser tributaries are passable by wading, but only in low-water periods. In the brief period of European experience in the area, an unusual number of lives have been lost in somewhat legendary attempts to use rafts and other craft in the gorges. Though paths have been hacked and blasted out of many *tang* walls over the centuries, and causeways built through them, several routes of migration and primitive commerce still cross the Zagros Mountains over

---

[1] W. K. Loftus, "On the Geology of the Turko-Persian Frontier, and of the Districts Adjoining," *Quart. Journ. Geol. Soc., London,* 11 (1855), 282.

[2] *Op. cit.*

[3] G. N. Curzon, *Persia and the Persian Question,* 2 vols., London, 1892.

[4] W. B. Fisher, *The Middle East.* New York: Dutton, 1957, p. 263.

the crests of the ranges, while streams flow along in parallel through a succession of wild gorges and pleasant parklands.

Configuration of the Tangs

Most often, as shown in Figure 22, the walls of anticlinal gorges rise vertically from the watercourse to a height of 100 to 200 feet, above which their upper parts fall back at various inclinations. Thus the *tangs* are characteristically two-storied, and may be described as vertical-in-straight-walled, vertical-in-concave-walled, or vertical-in-convex-walled gorges. Each major *tang* is composed of a number of individual watergaps, one at each resistant outcrop. In the majority of the anticlines of the Mountain Front and Luristan, the Asmari limestone forms the carapace of the fold, and where its flanks fall steeply on either side of its axis the streams cutting through the structure are engorged in precipitous threadlike defiles. Between these ingress and egress slots the softer core of the fold is exposed, and in these materials the gorge may be straight to concave from crest to base, lacking a steeper lower story.

Where the Cenomanian limestones are transected, the great depth of the resistant beds produces gorges two-storied throughout: the stream occupying a deep slot between faceted near-vertical beds that rise upward in a concentric array at a somewhat gentler angle (Figures 23–25). In many instances resistant layers create amazing constrictions in the widths of stream channels (Figures 23 and 25). At these points channel depths must increase very abruptly as an acceleration in stream velocity is not conspicuous. This suggests that the near-vertical lower stories of some *tangs,* such as those in Figures 22 and 25, may actually be old (or even present) bank-full channel cross-sections,[5] with similar vertical *tangs* being produced sub-aqueously as channel cross-sections today, as in the situations depicted in Figures 23, 24, and 25.

On tributaries to through-flowing streams, gorge walls are occasionally near-vertical from crest to base. Such *tangs* show no evidence of cyclic erosion, and their jagged and interlocking opposite walls indeed give a visual impression of having been torn apart.

Where synclinal ranges appear in the fold belt, they too are sundered by profound chasms. Since the harder layer in these situations, the Asmari limestone, caps the summits, the transecting streams are at present entrenched in a softer plinth of Eocene and Upper Cretaceous beds in which evidence of

---

[5]Unfortunately, a high-water period was not witnessed by the writer. The snow accumulation and spring rains in 1962 were both far below the expected amounts, so that the usual spring floods were barely perceptible.

FIGURE 22. Tang-i-Chahar, the Sehzar River's transection of a Cenomanian anticline in the Bakhtiari Mountains.

FIGURE 23. The Sehzar River gorge through Kuh-i-Lu'an, showing constrictions in the river at resistant outcrops. Normally 40 to 100 feet in width, the channel in this gorge twice narrows abruptly to about 8 feet.

FIGURE 24. The Sehzar gorge at Keshwar, a characteristic defile through a Cenomanian anticline.

FIGURE 25. Rejuvenation in a narrow strath, the Lu'an River in an anticlinal transection.

stricted than the ingress gorges through the northeastern limbs. Some of the egress slots are truly threadlike, their perpendicular walls rising nearly a thousand feet and maintaining a separation little greater than the width of the watercourse at their base. Thus it appears that the basal portions of the southwest limbs of the Mountain Front anticlines have been exposed by denudation more recently than the limbs that face the interior of the fold belt. This must be the result of a relative subsidence of the area beyond the Mountain Front in Quaternary time, which depressed the base levels of the streams flowing out to the Khuzistan Lowland, at the same time steepening the major flexure which defines the Mountain Front. Northeast of the Mountain Front the ingress and egress gorges in breached anticlines are similar in configuration.

Regional Variations in Gorge Characteristics

There are no significant local variations in gorge character in the Outer Zagros, with the exception of the fundamental differences associated with structure and lithology noted above. Gorges through anticlines, synclinal mountains, and hogback belts are morphologically distinctive, but have in common the characteristic of extreme youth or strong recent rejuvenation. The streams passing through them are invariably swift and turbulent, while the canyon walls are characterized by angular mechanical weathering under joint and bedding control. Though both erosional and depositional terraces occur on the soft beds of anticlinal basins, on synclinal mountain plinths, and on synclinal valley fills (all sites in which ephemeral point bar deposits presently form), there are no such features within the rock-cut *tangs*.

In the Inner Zagros, however, there are successive and highly significant changes in gorge characteristics. In the Imbricate Zone the near-vertical lower story of the transverse gorges in hard rocks disappears. The gorges in this region, though unmatched in depth and still youthful in physiognomy, are either V-shaped throughout, or cyclic—with a deep V-shaped inner story. These streams appear to have been cutting down at a uniform rate for a considerable period; they show no sign of the very recent strong rejuvenation that distinguishes the dissection of the Fold Zone.

On passing into the zone of overthrusts a second and even more striking change in gorge

cyclic erosion is no better preserved than in the similar cores of Asmari-shelled anticlines.

The scenery of some portions of the Zagros, such as the Luristan Saddle, is composed primarily of hogbacks of all sizes and inclinations. As these features are not massive their transections by streams would more properly be called watergaps than gorges. Here two-story cuts are once more characteristic. The present gaps are cut either into older concave valley floors that are sharply defined, or below straight or convex slopes that fall gently from both sides toward the gap. The relief at these breaches is considerably less than at transections of anticlinal or synclinal mountains, for the near-vertical inner slot is normally under 150 feet in depth, and the upper story of the valley is considerably more open in cross-section (Figure 26).

Along the Mountain Front, the egress gorges through the southwestern limbs of the limestone anticlines are commonly more con-

FIGURE 26. Hogback watergap in the Luristan Saddle region, showing characteristic slot cut below a more open valley cross-section. The Kashgan River at Tang-i-Kalhur.

morphology immediately appears. Although the multi-story character of the *tangs* is often preserved, along with the steep declivity of their walls, the gorges are seen to be in almost all cases heavily alluviated. Passing through them are braided channels or streams bordered by continuous alluvial terraces. Whether by lateral planation, cliff back-wearing, or aggradational filling of the canyons, their walls are widely separated at the base. These walls frequently rise from heavy talus accumulations, and are themselves more strongly weathered than any found on hard rocks in the fold belt. Their surfaces evidence chemical as well as mechanical disintegration, the resistant outcrops being rounded and pitted, in marked contrast to the fresh angular outcrops of the exterior ranges. The foregoing characteristics are maintained throughout the Thrust Zone, and are accentuated toward the Iranian Plateau, where in many instances the accumulation of regolith on the ranges, possibly resulting from their exposure to more humid Plio-Pleistocene climates, makes their structure almost inde-

terminate. A representative example of an alluviated gorge in the Thrust Zone is shown in Figure 27.

The increasingly youthful characteristics of the Zagros gorges in a downstream direction are suggestive of through-flowing drainage that originated on the protaxis of the highland and maintained itself through succeeding orogenic spasms as deformation spread to the southwest. Thus the hypothesis of regional drainage antecedence, favored by the sequence of deformation in the Zagros, also *appears* to be supported by progressive changes in gorge morphology in the successive structural zones of the highland.

Thus far we have discussed the morphology of transverse gorges only in the limestone fold structures. *Tangs* are also produced in the Pliocene conglomerate masses, both in the Interior Detrital Belt and the Mountain Front Detrital Apron. As shown in Figures 13 and 28, the cuts of the trunk streams through the Mountain Front Detrital Apron are as precipitous, constricted, and deep as most of the

FIGURE 27. Alluviated watergap in the Thrust Zone, showing (above) the characteristic valley fill and (below) the advanced weathering of gorge walls in this area.

FIGURE 28. Lower story of the Dez River canyon through the Mountain Front Detrital Apron composed of massive Upper Bakhtiari conglomerate. The river is approximately 40 feet in width.

exit gorges through the Mountain Front anticlines. Forty miles to the northeast in the Interior Detrital Belt the gorges of the same streams through deposits of the same age are more than twice as deep as those of the Mountain Front Apron, but are far more open, often rising by stages separated by broad erosional shelves (Figure 29).

Gorge forms in the Pliocene detrital masses of the Inner and Outer Zagros are even more illustrative of increased stream incision toward the exterior of the highland than are the watergaps through limestone structures. However, these gorges are clearly late or post-Pliocene since they dissect late Pliocene synclinal and piedmont deposits. Therefore the gorges in the clastics were formed *after* the fold structures of the Zagros had been established in essentially their present form. As the entire belt of simple folds and the majority of the drainage anomalies lie *between* these post-Pliocene gorges, the possibility of the transecting streams being Pliocene or earlier ante-

cedent drainage paths is thrown into question. Thus the differences in gorge form from the Inner to the Outer Zagros, while significant, cannot be regarded as conclusive evidence of drainage antecedence, and may, in fact, have a different meaning altogether.

SOLUTION FEATURES

In the predominantly calcareous terranes of the Zagros, solution features are an essential element of the scenery. However, the area offers nothing more in the way of spectacular karst landscapes than do the Central Alps, for example; instead, it exhibits the more delicate and superficial effects of surface and ground water in the presence of soluble materials. The crests of some of the broader domes and thrust slabs are immense fields of jagged lapiés. This is particularly true of Kuh-i-Parau near Kermanshah, and Takht-i-Khan west of Dorud. Solution tubes and small cavern systems are common. Solution along the steeply inclined bedding planes of anticlines frequently pro-

FIGURE 29. The Sehzar River canyon through the Interior Detrital Apron at Tang-i-Bahrein. The river has here cut through the Upper Bakhtiari formation and into the subjacent limestones. The open nature of this gorge through Late Pliocene conglomerates is in marked contrast to the gorge of the same river through identical materials at Tang-i-Yek, beyond the Mountain Front (Figures 13 and 28).

duces gallery effects, in some instances leaving immense plates of limestone almost completely detached from subjacent layers.

Solution features are usual in stream channels, and some watercourses flow through a veritable lattice of limestone. The abundance of freshwater springs makes for pleasant traveling in the mountains, and contributions of clear spring water create striking and frequent color contrasts in the turbid green currents of the principal streams. Although large solution pits can be seen, no sinking streams were observed, and the presence of limestone has not produced an artificial surface aridity in the region.

The distinctive morphology of the *tangs* is itself largely attributable to the dominance of calcareous materials in the Zagros. Limestone appears peculiarly susceptible to vertical trenching by running water, the presence of extensive joint systems and the possibility of their expansion by solution being contributing factors. The low susceptibility of limestone to

mechanical and certain forms of chemical weathering allows precipitous slotlike gorges to be associated with this material in all parts of the world, regardless of climatic or tectonic environments. Thus the spectacular Zagros *tangs* have well-known counterparts in the Dinaric Alps and elsewhere.

Tang morphology in general does not, therefore, present a genuine physiographic problem though it *has* attracted attention to the real enigma of the Zagros landscape—the seemingly arbitrary courses of the drainage lines which determine the pattern and distribution of the *tangs*. Of course, *variations* in the morphology of *tangs* cut through similar materials are part of this enigma.

TERRACES AND BEVELS

Three types of terraces or bevels may be seen throughout the Zagros Highland. The lowest of these are fluvial terraces. They are overlooked by smooth catenary projections which are relics of a climatic regime that no longer exists in this area. Far above the catenary terrace fragments are a final set of erosional flats which appear to be the headwater bowls of ancient drainage systems developed in an early stage of the physiographic history of the Zagros region.

The streams of the Zagros Highland are almost everywhere bordered by fragments of constructional, destructional, and compound terraces. Only in the narrow rock-cut *tangs* which split resistant outcrops are these features wholly absent. The fluvial terraces range in elevation from a few feet to some 200 feet above stream level. Both paired and noncyclic terraces are present. The presence of high terraces on both sides of certain streams indicates that existing valley floors are narrower than earlier ones, implying an acceleration of downward erosion as present time is approached.

The fluvial terraces are both climatic and tectonic effects, with the Pleistocene interlude having been a period in which deposition and strath formation alternated with stream incision. The Holocene has been characterized by stream rejuvenation as seen in the slotlike lower stories of many *tangs* and in the trenching of straths and valley floors formed on weak materials (Figure 30).

Jutting out above the fluvial terraces are still higher features which superficially resemble the fluvial terraces. These are smooth catenary projections which have been dissected by gully erosion, producing mature or flat-topped spurs that terminate in sharp bluffs. These high catenary terraces pass upward conformably into the prevailing slope of the rock wall from which they protrude (Figure 31).

The material composing these high terraces is coarse colluvium often containing boulders whose diameters may be measured in yards. They may or may not be cemented. The catenary terraces appear to be ancient rock slides smoothed into gentle hydraulic profiles by mass-wasting processes whose effects are otherwise seldom visible in this region. Many of these features are veneered with what appears to be a solifluction deposit. Below the catenary terraces gullying and badland erosion is dominant. Voute has described a similar high terrace in the Zagros of Iraq. Above the ancient surface of equilibrium represented by the high terrace Voute sees the effect of a very humid and cold climate, and below it the consequences of the present semi-arid regime.[6]

Still another set of significant surfaces is found far above the high catenary terrace remnants. These are isolated erosional bevels of inclined rock layers, occurring at elevations from 1,500 feet above current valley floors to subsummit levels on 10,000-foot peaks. The bevels are of very limited incidence and seldom exceed a quarter of a square mile in area. They have a slope of 5 to 15 degrees and are usually trenched by parallel or dendritic gullies ending on the brink of a cliff. These high surfaces appear to be very ancient headwater bowls lying against the last culminating crags of the ranges, with their lower portions having been carried away by cliff retreat from longitudinal or transverse valleys. They are

[6]C. Voute, "Climate and Landscape in the Zagros Mountains (Iraq)," *Proceedings,* 21st Internat. Geol. Congr., 1960, Copenhagen, Part 4 (1960), 81–87.

FIGURE 30. Holocene rejuvenation of the Lu'an River. At left, rejuvenation in an erosional strath on relatively weak flysch beds preserved in a syncline between Cenomanian anticlines. At right, rejuvenation in a V-shaped transverse valley exposing a succession of hard and soft rocks.

FIGURE 31. Synclinal reach of the Sehzar River showing a high terrace fragment surfaced with slide debris (arrow).

assumed to be the heads of pediments developed consequent to a cessation of downcutting in the orogen in the late Pliocene or early Pleistocene.

As these highest denudational surfaces are rare and vary considerably in elevation, they can not be utilized to construct any major erosion surface. It is certain that they have been significantly and differentially displaced by Pleistocene and Holocene movements in the form of continued folding and broad warping. These high bevels are especially well developed along the west wall of Tang-i-Bahrein, the gorge of the Sehzar River through the Interior Detrital Belt, whose materials are of late Pliocene age. In this area the bevels terminate in cliffs perhaps 2,000 feet above the level of the present river, with the walls behind them rising another 2,000 feet.

LANDSLIPS

The lithology of the folded region, with a thick incompetent marl series interposed between massive limestone bodies, creates ideal conditions for the initiation of large-scale landsliding wherever the upper limestones be-

come steeply inclined. Rock slides and rock falls are associated with another distinctive phenomena encountered in the Zagros Mountains: the high apparent rate of scarp retreat. Individual slides in the Zagros Highlands are impressive enough in themselves or in their effects on hydrology to have merited descriptions in several scientific journals.[7] Indeed, the great landslip in the Saidmarreh Syncline is the largest known in the Eastern Hemisphere, and perhaps in the world.

Landslips are found in all geomorphic provinces of the mountain belt, though they are probably least developed at present in the innermost part of the Thrust Zone, where declivities are somewhat lower and recent up-

---

[7] H. G. Busk, "The Shimbar Valley Landslip Dam, Bakhtiari Country," *Geol. Mag.,* 63 (1926), 355–359; J. V. Harrison and N. L. Falcon, "Gravity Collapse Structures and Mountain Ranges as Exemplified in S. W. Iran," *Quart. Journ. Geol. Soc., London,* 92 (1936), 91–102; J. V. Harrison and N. L. Falcon, "The Saidmarreh Landslip, S. W. Iran," *Geog. Journ.,* 89 (1937), 42–47; J. V. Harrison and N. L. Falcon, "An Ancient Landslip at Saidmarreh in Southwestern Iran," *Journ. of Geol.,* 46 (1938), 296–309.

lift not as strong as in regions to the south-west. The lithologic sequence and sharpness of the folding in the Bakhtiari Mountain sector have contributed to several instances of gravitational gliding, in which intact Asmari limestone plates overlying marls have slipped downward from steep anticlinal flanks, sometimes becoming secondarily folded, and occasionally breaking loose to ride out over adjacent synclinal deposits.[8]

The undercutting of limestone dip slopes by streams in longitudinal valleys has originated many of the rockslides in the region, including (in the author's opinion) the immense Said-marreh landslip.[9] Sapping of the Asmari limestone cliffs by spring action at the limestone-marl interface would also seem to be important. Seismic events may have triggered some of the larger slides, such as that in the Saidmarreh Valley and the great displays along the Karun River below the immense fault-line scarp of Kuh-i-Lijan, and farther southeast along the Khirsan River below Kuh-i-Dina. In the latter situation J. V. Harrison noted that large rockfalls may be observed almost continually during the wet season.[10]

There are a few small permanent lakes in the Zagros Mountains and evidence of many more in the past. All of the present lakes are confined by slides, as was the greatest water body of the past, the Saidmarreh Valley lake. Perched high in the mountains, small flats bordered by boulder-strewn hummocks are evidence of short-lived features of similar origin. The large lacustrine plains of Inner Luristan are the only evidences of static water bodies apparently not related to valley blockages by landslips.

The Saidmarreh Landslip

The enormous rockslide covering 64 square miles of the Saidmarreh Valley at the Kashgan confluence (Figure 32) has been difficult to explain, as conditions for the development of a detachment of such magnitude are not ideal in this location. Here a gently inclined plate of Asmari limestone nine miles long and more than 1,000 feet thick slipped from the flank of Kabir Kuh to be dashed into fragments in the valley below. Some of the debris was projected 1,500 feet vertically over the crest of an anticline five miles distant, coming to rest another four miles beyond, or nine miles from the base of Kabir Kuh. It has been estimated that five cubic miles or 56 billion long tons of limestone rumbled into the Saidmarreh Valley here, the vertical displacement in the center of gravity of the mass being about 3,000 feet.[11]

Harrison and Falcon surmised that only a single catastrophic movement of "unprecedented momentum and fluid turbulence" could have hurled a sheet of rock blocks over the intervening anticline to the far side of the valley, producing a deposit of wide distribution without any grading in its component parts.[12] One of the blocks resting atop the intervening anticline, almost five miles from its source, has a volume of 30,000 cubic feet.[13]

The lake impounded behind the landslip attained a length of about 50 miles, and was at least 600 feet deep. The present Saidmarreh River cuts through the landslip debris in a canyon 600 feet in depth, passing close to the foot of Kabir Kuh. Presumably the stream demarcates the natural spillway over the debris dam. This indication of an initial depression between the debris mass and the mountain base is itself more suggestive of catastrophic movement than of gradual accretion by separate slides of smaller proportions. The problem of the Saidmarreh landslip is examined in greater detail in Appendix A, where a new explanation of the feature is offered.

SCARP RETREAT

Innumerable examples of fresh-looking drainage systems truncated on all sides by escarpments thousands of feet high give an impression of remarkably rapid cliff retreat throughout the Zagros region. While downstream truncations of intermittent tributary drainage profiles might be expected as a result of rapid incision of well-nourished through-flowing streams in time of rejuvenation, the display of beheading and the bites taken out of the middle courses of some streams by encroaching cliffs are somewhat unusual.

Truncated valley systems are found in several different settings. The outermost ex-

[8]Harrison and Falcon, "Gravity Collapse Structures," *op. cit.*
[9]See Appendix A.
[10]J. V. Harrison, "Kuhgalu: South-West Iran," *Geog. Journ.*, 88 (1936), 20–36.

[11]Harrison and Falcon, "An Ancient Landslip at Said-marreh in Southwestern Iran," *op. cit.*, pp. 300–302.
[12]*Ibid.*, 303.
[13]*Ibid.*, 299.

FIGURE 32. The Saidmarreh landslip. The detachment has removed a nine-mile-long and 1,000-foot-thick sheet of Asmari limestone and much of the Eocene marl beneath. The Saidmarreh River has cut a trench 600 feet in depth through the slide debris. In the foreground, four miles from the base of Kabir Kuh, the intact Asmari limestone anticline of Kuh-i-Kialan was overtopped by a large quantity of the slide debris, some of which may be seen on the crest of the arch at the extreme right. The gorge transecting Kuh-i-Kialan is Tang-i-Fanni. (Photo by Aerofilms and Aero Pictorial Limited.)

amples are seen on the conglomerate cuesta along the Mountain Front. The cuesta backslope in the Dezful Embayment has been maturely dissected by consequent runoff. The cuesta scarp cuts directly through the intricate drainage net and its crest is serrate by virtue of the gully relief it truncates. However, the drainage texture on the backslope indicates that the gully network could not have originated more than two or three miles farther headward. As the conglomerates at one time extended all the way to the Mountain Front, at least ten miles beyond this point, it seems that the gullies must have been inscribed in a surface which was uplifted and tilted in the late Quaternary. They would have been extending headward at the same time that the frontal scarp was retreating from the northeast. The deep gullying of the cuesta backslope would appear to be a consequence of that recent steepening of the Mountain Front flexure that has produced slotted drainage in the southwest limbs of the Mountain Front anticlines.

The Asmari limestone hogbacks and flatirons of the Mountain Front at the head of the Dezful Embayment display another set of headless gullies. The flatirons that are dendritically scored always occur on the flanks of broad domes whose axes have been breached and opened in considerable valleys in the Eocene marls. The gullies now beheaded were formed as the domes were still growing, and were left beheaded by the encroachment of axial basins spreading longitudinally in the domes. Steeper intact anticlines in the Asmari, such as Kialan and some of the outer folds of the Luristan Saddle, are stripped from the arch bend downward, layer by layer, and do not exhibit dendritic dissection along their flanks.

In the tightly folded zones, cliffs retreating from the cores of axially breached anticlines are a major element in the landscape, but these seldom truncate gully systems, for the Cenomanian fold flanks are characteristically flatiron or "splinter" sheets undergoing bedding plane spalling rather than gully dissection. An exception is Kabir Kuh, along which an extremely close array of parallel gullies, possibly controlled by extension jointing, is consuming the anticline from the flanks inward, allowing the preservation of marl badlands atop its crest.

The gently folded basin of Inner Luristan displays many synclinal mountains upheld by the Eocene and Asmari limestones. The lateral members of the pinnate drainage systems found on these table mountains are commonly beheaded by inward-moving scarps. In addition, where through-flowing streams have cut across the synclinal heights, the longitudinal synclinal drainage, though strongly entrenched and convex in its lower profile, has not been able to cut down to accordance with the trunk stream. In becoming incised, the longitudinal drainage has, in turn, left its cliff-beheaded lateral tributaries hanging.

Where the Bakhtiari formation overlies the Fold Zone as an apron fronting the Thrust Zone, cliff retreat has produced some of the most remarkable drainage truncations in the Zagros region. Since the Bakhtiari was deposited in synclines undergoing concurrent deformation, its drainage was synclinal and characteristically of a pinnate pattern. These pinnate systems are now beheaded on all sides, and are perched up to 5,000 feet above surrounding lowlands. The complete preservation of the ancient pinnate systems on the synclinal summits during inversion of relief on such a giant scale suggests that cliff retreat is extremely rapid here, as it is along the Mountain Front conglomerate cuesta.

In the Thrust Zone Detrital Belt the Pliocene conglomerate masses always stand back three or four miles from the lines of the through-streams transecting the Pliocene deposits. Whether this is a result of an extreme rate of scarp recession or evidence of a longer period of recession than that available in the limestone gorges of the fold belt is a significant question. As its answer bears upon the origin

of the through-flowing streams, this question is considered at length in Chapter X.

Cliff retreat in the Imbricate Zone has created two additional sets of incomplete valleys, one beheaded, the other hanging. The recession of the great fault-line scarps, such as Kuh-i-Lijan and Kuh-i-Dina, is at the expense of backslope drainage systems dissecting pedimented surfaces on folded Cenomanian beds. Farther northeast in the Imbricate Zone, and again to the west along the Interior Detrital Belt, longitudinal canyons cutting several thousand feet below strath terraces have left the old but still-functioning tributaries hanging, to become confluent by cascades through tortuously winding gorges. Traces of the loops of old meanders now and then appear on one side or another of the new canyons, together with extinct Yazoo tributaries that approach the canyons at highly acute angles, terminating abruptly on their brinks.

Spring-Line Sapping

It is difficult to say with certainty whether scarp retreat and relief inversion—with the accompanying disruption of structurally controlled drainage systems—is in truth exceptionally rapid in the Zagros, or whether one is beguiled into this belief by a semi-arid climate which has preserved relict upland erosional features that have a much greater antiquity than one would initially guess.

The exceptional jointing in all folded resistant beds, with three intersecting joint sets clearly apparent on aerial photographs of almost any anticlinal structure, would facilitate mechanical disintegration. However, the great outer *tangs* are much deeper than they are broad, and, as their facing walls in many cases form an angle of less than 10 degrees, it seems that downcutting by highly seasonal streams is accomplished with far greater facility than is valley widening. On the other hand, the great *tangs* are cut in durable rocks, whereas the retreating hogbacks and cuestas have a plinth of highly erodable material and are subject to sapping at the limestone-marl contact. Where transverse gorges expose the softer Eocene and Upper Cretaceous beds they flare open, the resistant capping layer being driven back sharply as shown in Figure 33. Adjacent transverse gorges through a single Asmari limestone anticline often vary greatly in breadth, depending upon the proportion of the gorge base cut

FIGURE 33. Synclinal gorge of the Zohreh River showing extreme constriction where cut solely in Asmari lime-stones (left) and abrupt expansion where underlying marls are exposed permitting spring-line sapping at the limestone-marl contact (right). Note that bedding is prominent in the gorge walls subject only to weathering but is indistinct where cliff retreat is controlled by sapping and collapse.

through marls as opposed to limestones—the gorge configurations *in* the limestone layers being identical. Where the marls occupy the center third of a transverse gorge, the cut may be V-shaped throughout. If the marls occupy as much as two-thirds of the gorge base, the cut is transformed into a small axial basin between a pair of steep limestone watergaps.

As the marl formations separating the feature-forming limestones in this region, and also underlying the Upper Bakhtiari conglomerates, are relatively impervious, spring-line solution and sapping may play the dominant part in the retreat of both limestone and conglomerate scarps and in the disruption of high level drainage developments. In many instances the Asmari limestone faces enclosing axial basins are more nearly vertical than those of more youthful-looking gorges which have not yet flared open: a fact indicative of sapping in the first case, and purely mechanical disintegration in the second. This is well shown, for example, in two adjacent transec-

tions of Kuh-i-Kialan, the anticlinal range immediately east of the Saidmarreh Landslip (Figures 17 and 18).

The above factors, as well as the conspicuous absence of obsequent gully features in this area, lead to the conclusion that scarp recession does proceed rapidly in the Zagros Highland, and that the mechanism involved is spring-line sapping of well-jointed limestones and conglomerates, possibly accelerated during a Pleistocene relatively wet period.

This conclusion has some bearing on drainage development, for it suggests that relief inversion in the Fold Zone would be rapid, quickly disrupting consequent stream systems. Thus axial basins in tangent Asmari limestone anticlines could become coalescent at a fairly early stage in the physiographic evolution of the country. This would create strips of weak materials transverse to the fold belt, facilitating stream extension *across* the structural grain during the first cycle of erosion in the region.

Chapter VI

The Hydrography of the Central Zagros

General Hydrographic Characteristics of the Region

The runoff of the Central Zagros mountain arc is carried out to the plains of Khuzistan by five streams that converge on the city of Ahwaz from the northwest, northeast, and southeast. These streams are the Karkheh, Dez, Karun, Jarrahi, and Hendayan rivers.

The streams draining the Central Zagros Region are not great rivers in any sense. It has been estimated that the combined flow of the Karkheh, Dez, Marun, and Zohreh rivers, measured at or near the Mountain Front, is in the neighborhood of 34,000 cubic feet per second.[1] Affluents which come from the highland to enter these streams beyond the Mountain Front add another 3,000 cfs. and ungauged catchments, such as those of the Khairabad, A'ala, Balut, and Zal, contribute at least 5,000 cfs more,[2] so that the total outflow from the central part of the highland must be in excess of 42,000 cfs. The area drained by all of these streams is about 40,000 square miles. In Table I, the Central Zagros drainage basin is

TABLE I

RELATIVE AREA AND RUNOFF OF CENTRAL ZAGROS REGION[a]

Drainage basin	Area (thousands sq. miles)	Average discharge (thousands cfs)
Central Zagros Region	40	±42
Susquehanna (Pa. Appalachians)	28	38
Vistula (Poland)	76	38
Rhone (Western Alps)	37	59

[a] Data on rivers other than those of Zagros from L. B. Leopold, "Rivers," *American Scientist,* 50 (1962), 514–515.

[1] Development and Resources Corp., Khuzistan Development Service, *The Unified Development of the Natural Resources of the Khuzistan Region, A Report to the Plan Organization.* New York: Development and Resources Corp., 1959, p. 40. Figures converted from metric equivalents.

[2] Author's estimate based on water yields of adjacent gauged areas.

contrasted with the basins of some well-known streams having either discharges or catchments of comparable size.

The regime of the Zagros streams is seasonal, with the rate of discharge in the late summer and early autumn falling to about one-fifth of the average annual rate. This ratio varies considerably from stream to stream depending upon the moisture storage possibilities in each catchment. The total runoff from each basin also varies considerably from year to year. At Ahwaz the annual discharge of the Karun River has ranged from 10.5 to 48.8 cubic kilometers, with the average being 21.8 cubic kilometers.[3]

The water yields of the individual drainage basins of the Central Zagros Region are not proportional to the sizes of the basins. As shown in Table II, the largest basin, that of the Karkheh, has less total runoff than basins much inferior in size, while the relatively small catchment of the Bakhtiari River has an extremely high water yield.

High water yields are produced by areas having comparatively heavy precipitation and low moisture losses through evapotranspiration: in other words, areas of greater elevation, and those in which there is a minimum of infiltration, vegetation, and agricultural land use, as well as a low rate of potential evapotranspiration. The catchment of the Bakhtiari River satisfies all of these conditions to a high degree—the Dez, Karun, and Marun watersheds to a lesser extent. The surface configurations of the Karkheh and Zohreh basins do not favor the development of widespread orographic precipitation, as Figure 4 indicates. Moreover, both of these catchments contain considerable areas of flat alluvial plains (Figure 14) in which evapotranspiration losses from the scant natural cover, from irrigated cropland, and from subsurface storage further reduce runoff.

Throughout the majority of the Central

[3] G. B. Cressey, "The Shatt al-Arab Basin," *Middle East Journ.,* 12 (1958), 453.

TABLE II
DISCHARGES OF MAJOR CENTRAL ZAGROS RIVERS[a]

River system	Drainage area (sq. mi.)	Average annual discharge (cfs)	Average minimum annual discharge (cfs)	Ratio average to minimum discharge	Area of catchment required to yield 1 cfs of runoff (sq. mi.)
Saidmarreh-Kashgan-Karkheh	15,060	6,000	880	7/1	2.55
Dez-Bakhtiari	6,600	10,770	1,765	6/1	0.61
Bakhtiari	2,320	6,715	1,060	6/1	0.35
Karun-Khirsan	10,400	12,530	3,175	4/1	0.83
Khirsan	3,500	4,950	880	5.5/1	0.71
Marun	2,220	2,120	177	12/1	1.05
Zohreh[b]	2,700	1,940	353	5.5/1	1.39

[a]Areas and average and minimum discharge data from Development and Resources Corp., *op. cit.*, 40. Area of Marun Basin corrected by planimetering. All readings taken at projected dam sites at or near Mountain Front, except for those pertaining to the Bakhtiari, which is gauged near its confluence with the Dez River, and the Khirsan, whose flow is estimated from the Karun discharge above and below the Khirsan confluence.
[b]Does not include the Khairabad Basin, which is not commanded by the Zohreh gauge site.

Zagros, potential evapotranspiration ranges between 20 and 45 inches, and except in the higher areas balances or exceeds the average local precipitation. A water surplus could only be expected in areas above 7,000 feet in the northern portion of the region, and possibly above 8,000 feet in the extreme southeast. As Figure 4 indicates, these elevations are not regularly attained outside of the Bakhtiari Mountain region in the central portion of the highland.

CONFIGURATIONS OF BASINS AND STREAM NETS

The major watersheds of the Central Zagros Region, and the drainage nets within them, are shown in Figure 34. This map reveals that there are strong differences in the configuration of the watersheds and drainage nets from one area to another, and that these differences must be related to the geological matrix in which the drainage has developed.

In the Zagros there is a gradation from somewhat square or rectangular watersheds in the northwest (including those of the Iraqi Zagros) to basins attenuated along or diagonal to the grain of the country in the southeast of the Central Zagros arc. Beyond the Zohreh Basin there is a return to square basins, with the giant Mand watershed actually being delta-shaped, the reverse of the figure which Horton believed normal to even strongly grained landscapes.[4]

The drainage basins of the Central Zagros are decidedly asymmetric in relation to their functional axes. In the case of the Saidmarreh and Karun-Khirsan axes this is easily understood, for these streams occupy structural gutters into which unusually high folds deflect transverse drainage coming from the northeast. However, the asymmetry of the Dez Basin, with the trunk stream being transverse to structure and lying immediately against the western divide just below Dorud, is an anomaly, for there is no possibility of the divide having shifted toward the deeply engorged Dez at this point. In general, the divides separating the catchments of the various transverse streams in the Central Zagros Region are rather tenuous. Headwaters impinge upon one another in synclinal and homoclinal valleys, and captures accomplished and impending along the trend are rife.

There is a tendency for the drainage basins to be elongated along the strike in the Imbricate Zone. This is seen in both the Dez and Karun watersheds, and in the basin of the Sirwan in Iraq. As a result the catchment of the Dez is mushroom-shaped, while that of the Karun is attenuated in a southeasterly direction. Where the Imbricate Zone is absent, or possibly overrun by thrust sheets, as in the Karkheh Basin, this inner expansion of the drainage basins is not found. Each trunk drainage line in the Imbricate Zone skirts a fault scarp or follows a fault line, with few transverse crossings and no lateral tributaries of consequence. The expansion of drainage basins along the strike in the Imbricate Zone is itself indicative of the relative paucity of trans-

---

[4]R. E. Horton, "Erosional Development of Streams and Their Drainage Basins; Hydrophysical Approach to Quantitative Morphology," *Geol. Soc. Amer. Bull.*, 56 (1945), 342–348, 365–366.

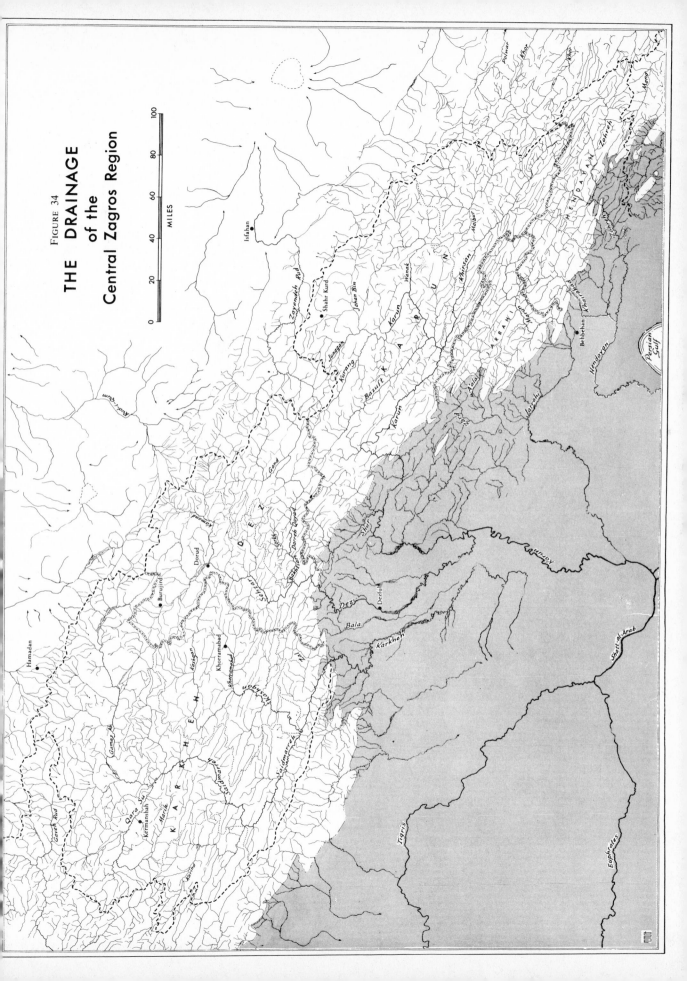

FIGURE 34

THE DRAINAGE
of the
Central Zagros Region

MILES

100
80
60
40
20
0

Isfahan

Zayendeh Rud

Shahr Kurd

Jahan Bin

Junega

Kurang

Bazuft

Karun

Wanak

K A R U N

Khirzan

Majbur

Behbehan Khud

Hindoyan

Persian Gulf

Koh-i-Rud

Gand

D E Z

Sezhfes

Bakhtiari Darreh Royat

J A R R A H I

Aidi

Jarrahi

Maroon

Shur

Dorud

Buyagan

Dez

Deztul

Bala

Karkheh

Karun

Shatt-al-Arab

Hamadan

Burujird

Dorud

Vangan

Khorramabad

Khorramabad

Kashgan

Kaz

Saimareh

Seimarek

K A R K H E H

Gamas Ab

Qara Su

Kermanshah

Marik

Gabrmai

Kuhul

Gaveh Rud

Tigris

Euphrates

Polwar

Khor

Khor

Maroon

M E N D A V A N

Tehreh

verse drainage, and thereby drainage anomalies, in this zone.

A change in the stream pattern is evident in the upper catchments of the Malbur, Wanak, Kamand, and Gamas Ab. Here the tributary array becomes dendritic, with a tendency in the southeastern half of the area toward both deranged and barbed patterns. This hydrographic unconformity marks the appearance of the Thrust Zone in the mountain arc. The most significant aspect of the drainage pattern in the Thrust Zone is the presence here of the oceanic-endoreic drainage divide, which follows ranges considerably lower than those that must be passed by the oceanic drainage in its escape to the southwest, as Figure 4 indicates.

THE EXOREIC-ENDOREIC DIVIDE AND THE EXTENSION OF THE ZAYENDEH RUD

The majority of the divide between oceanic and interior drainage appears stable as it is presently developed. Only north of Kangavar where the water parting lies in a level plain can rapid shifting proceed. In that area the migration of the divide has been northward into the Caspian drainage basin. With the exception of the deep penetration of the Zayendeh Rud, the divide is relatively regular, following the crests of old ridges which accord with the strike of the orogen. Where the divide has been pushed westward into the Imbricate Zone by the Zayendeh Rud penetration, the exoreic and endoreic headwaters encounter one another in trend valleys. Here divide shifting will be inevitable until the penetration is erased. Beyond the Zayendeh Rud penetration there is a progressive diminution in the breadth of the Persian Gulf watershed. The increasing aridity in this southern region has prevented the integration of the interior synclines into the oceanic drainage systems, allowing them to become closed basins of centripital drainage.

Though the drainage of the Thrust Zone links conformably with that of the Imbricate Zone and Outer Zagros in the Karkheh Basin, vagaries of course and apparent elbows of capture are rather common on either side of the Zayendeh Rud penetration, and southward through the Wanak and Malbur basins. While the headwaters of these regions appear dendritic toward the Persian Gulf rather than toward the interior, they are not smoothly articulated to their lower courses. The drainage pattern in the Wanak and Malbur head-

waters suggests that in this region several closed basins of centripetal drainage have been captured by tributaries of the Karun. Similar basins lie northeast of the present divide, in the area of endoreic drainage, some of them being tied together by oddly wandering drainage lines such as the Rud-i-Khor. The exoreic Gand Ab, on the other hand, seems to be the product of one or more captures of longitudinal systems which may have been tributary to the Persian Gulf over lengthy paths to the northwest or southeast. The southern feeder of the Ab-i-Kamand, by contrast, seems to have suffered the loss of a considerable piece of its catchment to an interior system which terminates near Qum on the Persian Plateau.

This notion of divide-shifting in opposing directions from point to point is contrary to the views of Iranian geographers, who have accepted only northeastward expansion of the Persian Gulf drainage systems due to their obvious gradient advantages.[5] Recent maps (1:250,000) and the aerial photographs upon which they are based (1:60,000) indicate that this deductive conclusion is an oversimplification.

The endoreic Zayendeh Rud system disrupts the more or less regular oceanic-interior drainage divide, pushing it sharply westward into low ranges at the eastern foot of Zardeh Kuh (14,921 feet), the highest peak in the Zagros. This east-flowing system incorporates large segments which are dendritic toward the Persian Gulf systems and which actually oppose the dendritic array of the lower part of the Zayendeh Rud (Figure 35).

Geomorphic relationships revealed by aerial photographs are strongly suggestive of a major capture of oceanic drainage by former headwaters of the Zayendeh Rud near the village of Horeh. Variations in the gradient and configuration of the Upper Zayendeh Rud Valley, intersecting pediments, and a valley bottleneck unrelated to lithology at this point, give the impression that two opposing systems were linked here.

The portion of the Zayendeh Rud believed to have been reversed would previously have led directly toward the formerly glaciated imbric slab of Zardeh Kuh. The most recent movements of that mass and the imbrics east

---

[5] The viewpoint of the Iranian geographers was summarized by Prof. A. Mostafi, Geog. Dept., Tehran University in a personal interview, January, 1961.

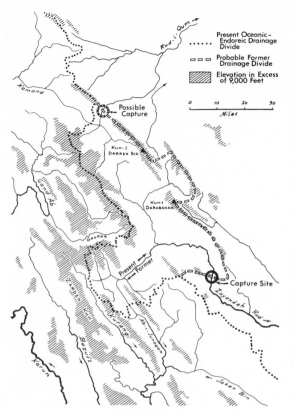

FIGURE 35. The Zayendeh Rud Penetration.

DRAINAGE PATTERNS IN THE FOLD ZONE

Approximately half the Central Zagros Hydrographic Basin is occupied by the Fold Zone. Figure 34 reveals a most interesting situation in this area: the presence of two completely unrelated stream patterns, one overprinted upon the other. In the Fold Zone the trunk streams and their major tributaries form a rectangular or rhombic pattern which is everywhere oblique to the structural grain as well as to the prevailing orientation of tributaries of lower orders, whose own trellis pattern tends to be a good reflection of tectonic lines.

The recognition of two divergently oriented drainage patterns in the same area provokes an immediate question: were the two systems established simultaneously, or did one precede the other, and if so, what was the order of their formation? It is obvious that the low order tributary system reflects the structural and physiographic grain of the country, while the trunk system certainly does not. As the tributary system is, on the whole, unmistakably consequent and subsequent, with obsequent and resequent affluents, it would seem to require no special explanation. But as the vast majority of the trunk stream system is not related to any known elements of structure, lithology, or even broad surface configuration, it is clearly a geographic anomaly.

It is conceivable that the through-flowing systems predate the conformable tributary system. The discordant streams could have been inherited from previous surfaces, in which case they might be antecedent or superimposed—their rhombic pattern still requiring explanation. It is equally possible that the anomalous trunk systems are coeval to or even younger than the consequent-subsequent tributary array, having developed by headward growth. In such a case their angularity would be attributable to longitudinal structural or lithological variations, or even to a fracture set such as that present in the Jura Mountains.[6]

Though it is not apparent from inspection of the drainage pattern, the ostensibly conformable tributary net is itself not always perfectly adjusted to structure; moreover, it receives lateral affluents of a still lower order which are as discordant, on a small scale, as are the great through-flowing drainage lines.

of it may have defeated the old westward drainage in this area, ponding it or increasing the potential energy of the eastward-flowing stream to facilitate the capture. Glacial interference with the oceanic drainage might also have been a factor, though it has not yet been determined whether the Zardeh Kuh glaciers ever reached the valley floor east of the range. Prior to the capture the Upper Zayendeh Rud was presumably tributary to the Karun, entering it by either the Ab-i-Kurang or Ab-i-Junaqan, both of which flow through trend valleys east of the Zardeh Kuh barrier (Figure 35).

In the absence of this diversion the limit of the Persian Gulf watershed in the Zagros Mountains would follow the structural trend almost directly from Hamadan to Qaleh Ekhlas (west of Isfahan) and would lie along the 12,000-foot peaks of Kuh-i-Darreh Bid and Kuh-i-Darabshan, which continue the line of the divide, but now project into the Zayendeh Rud Basin.

[6]See A. Heim, *Geologie der Schweiz,* I. Leipzig (1919), 613–623.

While the physical expression of the drainage anomaly in the Zagros is most striking as seen in the great *tangs*, the *wide distribution* of the discordance between drainage and structure is even more arresting, as well as the variety of the circumstances in which these discordances may be found.

In the following pages the specific nature of the drainage anomaly in the Central Zagros is set forth by describing the courses of the various drainage lines which move southwestward out of the highland. The chapter concludes with a summarization of the peculiar relationships between drainage and structure in the Zagros Mountains.

TRAVERSES OF PRINCIPAL STREAMS

THE KARKHEH BASIN

The 16,000-square mile Karkheh Basin is drained southeastward by three large streams, the Gamas Ab, the Qara Su-Saidmarreh, and the Kashgan. As shown in Figure 36, these streams flow southwestward across the structural grain of the Thrust Zone and Inner Luristan until they are channeled toward the Dezful Embayment by the Saidmarreh Syncline.

The Saidmarreh Headwaters

The Gamas Ab rises on a well-defined trend ridge in the metamorphic region and makes its way westward through gentle undulations in the thrust complex. The main stream and its tributaries from the northeast are engorged in both crystalline and sedimentary formations in several localities, but as geological information on this area is lacking it is impossible to state exactly what types of drainage anomalies are involved. The gorges are heavily alluviated. The Gamas Ab passes through the front of the Cretaceous limestone thrust in a broad transverse lowland overlooked by the cliffs of Bisitun which bear the famous trilingual inscription of Darius (516 B.C.). In the midst of the plain of Kermanshah, excavated in soft radiolarite beds, the Gamas Ab is joined from the west by the Qara Su.

The Marik-Qara Su system is interesting by virtue of its great loop around the Cenomanian anticline of Kuh-i-Charmi. It is situated in subsequent lowlands throughout, moving northwestward on the Upper Cretaceous flysch, then turning 180 degrees to the southeast along the radiolarite outcrop. Its major tributary, the Razavar, issues from the limestone thrust in an abrupt gorge.

The Saidmarreh

With the Gamas Ab-Qara Su confluence the Saidmarreh River is born. Almost immediately the stream deserts its subsequent lowland and swings into the major anticlinal structure to the south, which it severs centrally in a tortuously winding defile cut 5,000 feet below the crest of the range. A contiguous Cenomanian limestone anticline is also sundered without deviation from the line of the initial transection. As Figure 36 indicates, both of these structures pitch out 8 to 10 miles farther east. Subsequently the Saidmarreh splits three synclinal mountains, and the facing hogbacks of an unroofed anticline before running up against Kuh-i-Gavah, a broad intact arch of Asmari limestone. The river turns westward along the strike at this barrier, but does not follow the narrow synclinal valley at its base. Instead, it slits the flank of the previously breached arch, being separated from the structural trough by a curtain of Asmari limestone. After following this unusual course for five miles, the stream turns into the broad fold to the south and slices across its nose in a 2,000-foot canyon. A single mile to the west, in the direction the Saidmarreh was flowing prior to entering the arch, the anticlinal swell pitches out altogether.

For the next thirty miles the southeast-flowing Saidmarreh jogs from syncline to syncline, splitting the intervening anticlines in four spectacular chasms. Two of these sunder the same ridge in opposite directions. The Saidmarreh also transgresses onto the flank of this arch in a loop gorge which leaves a curtain of limestone beds between the watercourse and the open synclinal lowland. These cuts merely extend the course of the stream, which in three cases would intersect its downstream reaches by continuing in the open synclines abandoned in favor of anticlinal transections. Two of the ridges transected pitch out within four miles of the river crossing.

In this section the Saidmarreh receives four small lateral tributaries that produce seven additional anticlinal transections, and one larger affluent, the Cham Rawand (known in its lower portion as the Ab-i-Chanareh), which breaches four unroofed anticlines and one large intact arch. A right bank affluent of the Chanareh splits Kuh-i-Charmin in one of the wildest defiles in the Zagros: a unique near-vertical gash with jagged interlocking walls. The waters of another tributary cut northward across the arch of Kuh-i-Kuljar, then are returned southward through the same mountain by the Saidmarreh a half mile away. From the lowland south of this arch the distances to the Saidmarreh through the tributary gorge and along the south flank of the anticline are identical.

The great barrier of Kabir Kuh prevents the Saidmarreh from encroaching further southward for a distance of 60 miles. In the lacustrine synclinorial lowland known as the Saidmarreh Valley the Saidmarreh River is joined by the Kashgan, whose course across the Fold Zone roughly parallels that of the Saidmarreh.

The Kashgan

The Kashgan rises in open country on the brink of the Sehzar River gorge through the Interior Detrital Belt, flowing northwestward from a divide only 8,000 feet west of but 5,000 feet above the southwest-flowing Dez River. Some 30 miles from its source the Upper Kashgan flows off the front of the limestone thrust in an alluviated gorge about 2,000 feet deep, being joined from the north by a similarly alluviated tributary which cuts a spectacular defile across the grain of the folded thrust.

The course of the Upper Kashgan skirts the Cenomanian anticline of Kuh-i-Safid by following a syncline in the Thrust Zone and then breaking across the fold axis in rough country in the Cretaceous marl series. The stream then swings southeastward in a compound subsequent lowland diagonal to the strike of the folding, passing en route between the noses of a pair of synclinal mountains. At the nose of a Cenomanian arch in the initial stages of denudational resurrection, the Upper Kashgan receives the Ab-i-Khorramabad from the east. The headwaters of this stream breach the nar-

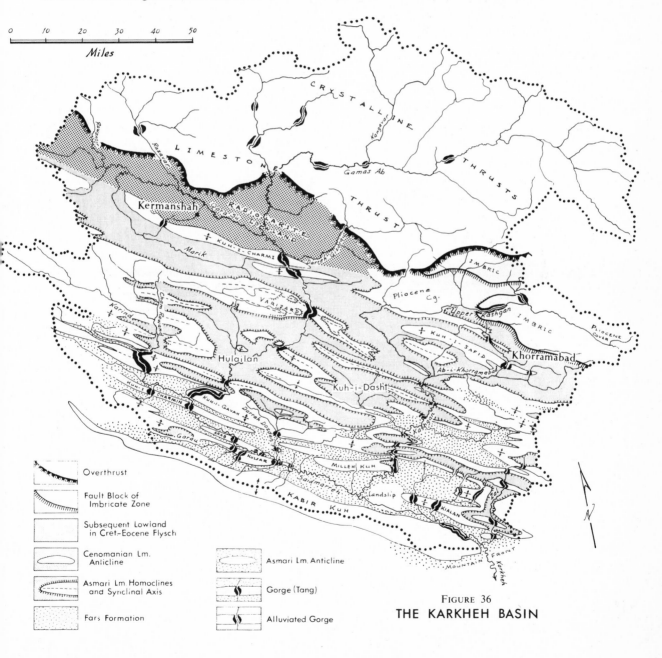

FIGURE 36
THE KARKHEH BASIN

row eastern extremity of Kuh-i-Safid at two points, draining subsequent valleys on both sides of the gaps. These openings, one of them the site of the fortress town of Khorramabad, are bounded by precipitous but widely separated walls.

The Kashgan River crosses the fold belt by transecting a series of six laterally tangent unroofed anticlines. All but two of the watergaps along this stream are homoclinal, the exceptions being cuts through Cenomanian cores which interrupt the floors of the second and fifth axial basins in the series. Five of the six arches are breached more or less centrally, each transection being differently oriented than those adjacent. The outermost fold in the series, Milleh Kuh, pitches out within a half mile of its transection by the Kashgan (Figure 37). This fold, unlike the others in the series, is essentially intact.

The Karkheh

The Kashgan and Saidmarreh rivers are confluent at the edge of the Saidmarreh landslip. The resulting stream, the Karkheh, cuts a ravine 600 feet in depth through the debris, and shortly receives two small tributaries from the northeast that slice through the otherwise perfect Asmari anticline of Kuh-i-Kialan in 1,500-foot gorges (Figure 18). In a final expression of disregard for its geological matrix, the Karkheh then wanders out of the synclinal axis and cuts a threadlike cleft into the limestone nose of Kabir Kuh, just as this 140-mile barrier finally plunges out into the Dezful Embayment. The Karkheh swings southwest around the end of Kabir Kuh, then zigzags southward, its course showing greater regard for the minor structural undulations of the piedmont zone than for the sharp

FIGURE 37. Transection of the plunging nose of Milleh Kuh by the Kashgan River. The Asmari limestone fold carapace is deeply trenched by autogenous drainage, but has been totally removed only in the small axial basin spreading from the Kashgan's watergap at the right of the photo.

All of the watergaps below Khorramabad are narrow defiles. Several involve overlapping spurs whose accordant crests reveal the former valley of this stream to have been a trough some two miles in breadth.

The Kashgan utilizes synclinal paths for distances up to four miles (Figure 38) and appears to have an independent orientation in each axial basin, features unfavorable to the hypotheses of regional drainage antecedence or superposition.

folds of the mountain belt. As it passes beyond the Mountain Front the Karkheh receives the Ab-i-Zal from the north. The Zal rises in an axial basin and cleaves three successive anticlines on its way to the Karkheh.

In summation, both the Saidmarreh and Kashgan first move through a field of unroofed anticlines, transecting the individual arches centrally and ignoring the synclinal paths between them. Encountering essentially intact anticlines farther to the

FIGURE 38. Deflection of the Kashgan River into a synclinal path following an anticlinal transection. Though the fold appears here to be intact, the arched layers presently form a hogback overlooking a spacious subsequent lowland in the core of the anticline.

southwest, the streams are diverted into synclinal paths for varying distances, breaching the adjacent anticlines in short jogs to the southwest, the transections frequently being sited close to the plunging noses of the folds. The courses of the smaller lateral tributaries are as discordant to structure as are those of the through-flowing drainage.

THE DEZ BASIN

The Dez Basin (Figure 39) covers 6,620 square miles, and is drained by two streams which unite in the center of the Fold Zone: the Ab-i-Bakhtiari, sometimes called the Zaliki, and the Ab-i-Dez, known in its mountain section as the Sehzar.[7] Both streams rise in the metamorphic thrust complex bounding the Burujird Plain on the northwest and

lying behind the highlands of the Imbricate Zone farther southeastward. The divide between the Dez catchment and streams which flow into the desert basins of interior Iran fluctuates in elevation between 8,000 and 14,000 feet, and generally lies between 9,000 and 11,000 feet.

The Sehzar River is formed at Dorud by the junction of the drainage of the Burujird Plain and the dendritic system of the Ab-i-Kamand. The eastern head of the latter system appears to have been captured and diverted into the interior by the headwaters of the Rud-i-Qum, resulting in a sharp inset of the oceanic-aretic divide at this point. The Kamand and Burujird come together from opposing directions, and their combined flow immediately turns to split the 6,000-foot limestone wall to the southwest.

The Upper Sehzar

The beginning of the Sehzar canyon, Tang-i-Bahrein, is carved through rocks of the Cretaceous thrust, and is rather open (Figure 29). Four miles below the portal of the chasm the stream cuts below an immense Pliocene valley fill now raised to an elevation of 10,100 feet (Figure 40). The Sehzar gorge through the conglomerate mass continues for

[7]"Sehzar" may be translated as three (seh) yards (zar—roughly a yard), the reputed width of some of the defiles through which the river passes. This is hardly an exaggeration, as shown in Figures 22, 23, 24, and 25. Figure 22 shows the Sehzar below the Bakhtiari confluence where the average discharge is in the neighborhood of 10,000 cubic feet per second. Figures 23, 24, and 25 are views of the Sehzar above this confluence, where the discharge is about 3,000 cfs.

some 21 miles, in which are displayed a series of
hanging flats: the heads of ancient pediments now
perched thousands of feet above the valley floor.

After breaking out of the Pliocene covermass the
Sehzar breaches a fierce hogback of Asmari limestone and receives two left bank tributaries. One of
these, the Rahmat, rises on one imbricate block,
slices through the center of another, then splits a
Cenomanian anticline longitudinally, in its path to
the Sehzar. After receiving the Rahmat, the Sehzar
slices through the nose of the arch cleft axially by
the Rahmat, and then works through rough country
in two unroofed anticlines (Figure 10). The Sehzar
is then deflected westward by the nose of a Cenomanian arch, the first of a swarm of *en echelon*
major anticlines which form the northwestern end
of the Bakhtiari Structural Culmination.

The Sehzar cleaves through this Cenomanian fold
swarm, taking some anticlines directly, others obliquely, and making frequent use of the pinched
synclines between the giant arches. In three instances continuation in open synclinal valleys for a
single mile would have taken the stream around fold
noses. The Sehzar in each case abandons a synclinal
path to breach the adjacent arch in a seemingly
unnecessary transverse gorge (Figure 41). Three
times the Sehzar flows *against* the pitch of synclines
to attack the hemming anticline *centrally,* when a
consequent synclinal path would lead the stream
past the fold nose. All of the gorges are extremely
constricted (Figure 24), that through Kuh-i-Lu'an
being no more than twelve feet wide in three places
(Figures 23, 25). As along the Kashgan, overlapping spurs occasionally define former valley floors

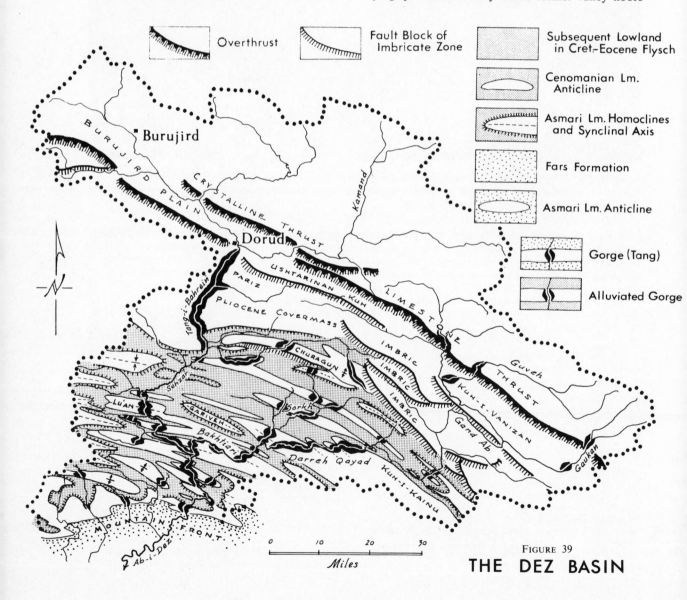

FIGURE 39

THE DEZ BASIN

FIGURE 40. Kuh-i-Pariz, the Pliocene covermass at Tang-i-Bahrein. This accumulation of Upper Bakhtiari conglomerate overlooks the open valley shown in Figure 29 and is identical in age and composition to the material transected in narrow gorges by the Dez (Figure 13) and Karun rivers beyond the Mountain Front.

FIGURE 41. Transection of the nose of a Cenomanian limestone anticline by the Sehzar River. The ridge in the background is another Cenomanian limestone arch, which is breached by the Bakhtiari River a short distance to the left of this view (see Figure 43).

which were much broader than the present. Certain of the synclines have such steeply inclined limbs that they produce longitudinal gorges as precipitous as some of the transverse defiles. Even such unequivocal structural controls are not enough to confine the drainage, which cuts in and out of the near-vertical beds to either side, eventually deserting the structural path entirely in favor of full anticlinal transections.

In its tortuous path through this anticlinal swarm the Sehzar receives tributaries from every syncline. Two of the right bank affluents, the Keshwar and Lu'an, have most interesting courses. The Keshwar twice within a mile breaches the same anticlinal axis in reverse directions, after which its waters are carried across the fold axis a third time in the Sehzar. The course of the Lu'an, down to the smallest meander, is guided by joints and bedding planes. The Lu'an transects two Cenomanian anticlines in most spectacular and intricate defiles, and is almost certainly the result of multiple captures by a headward-extending stream. The gorges of both the Keshwar and Lu'an approach the extreme in constriction (Figures 42 and 25).

FIGURE 42. Vertical gorge of the Keshwar River, illustrative of the intense deformation of the Cenomanian limestones in the Bakhtiari Mountains.

The Bakhtiari

The major affluent of the Sehzar is the Ab-i-Bakhtiari, which joins the Sehzar in the midst of the fold swarm, cutting through eight Cenomanian anticlinal ranges (one of them twice) to arrive at this confluence (Figure 43).

The Ab-i-Bakhtiari rises as the Gand Ab in the crystalline thrust complex and the rugged portion of the Imbricate Zone north of the Zayendeh Rud penetration. The headwater country of the Gand Ab is a maturely dissected plateau of complex structure that is trenched by immense V-shaped canyons whose depths are in excess of 6,000 feet. Trend streams are widely developed and flow along geological contacts that frequently appear to be longitudinal faults (Figure 7, sections FF and GG). The principal feeders of the Gand Ab are the Ab-i-Gaukan and Ab-i-Guveh, which breach both ends of the large imbric of Kuh-i-Vanizan to join the the great loop of the Gand. This loop is the most striking course reversal by a major stream in the Central Zagros. Eliminating minor meandering, the Gand travels twenty-three miles to move from one side of the neck of the loop to the other, only a mile and a half away. Aside from this unusual path there is nothing to suggest a capture here for there is no other outlet from the upper valley of the Gand below 9,000 feet.

Some fifteen miles below its great loop, the Gand Ab enters the Fold Zone, in four miles slicing through two great synclinal hogbacks, a Cenomanian anticline, and a small synclinal mountain. The gorges are all nearly vertical and are cut below older valley floors.

The stream, now the Zaliki or Darreh-Qayad, is subsequently turned northward along the trend by the bulky Cenomanian anticlinorium of Kuh-i-Kainu (Figure 7, sections FF and GG), which towers 7,000 feet above the watercourse. For twelve miles the deeply entrenched stream follows a band of Cretaceous marls rimming this giant barrier on the northeast.

After receiving a tributary that breaches two anticlinal structures to the north, the Darreh Qayad slashes across the northwest-plunging digitations of the Kainu arch, and, ignoring the open subsequent lowland straight ahead, plunges into another major anticlinal complex (Kuh-i-Kisistan), receiving the Rud-i-Sorkh almost on its culmination. The Sorkh splits five Cenomanian ranges to achieve the rendezvous.

The main stream passes out of these gorges as the Ab-i-Bakhtiari, which continues the line of the Sorkh through two sharp folds before changing direction in a steep homoclinal chasm. This path is in turn deserted in moves to the west and south across two more anticlinal ranges, bringing this powerful and enigmatic stream at last into the Sehzar.

FIGURE 43. Confluence of the Sehzar and Bakhtiari rivers. The Sehzar approaches the junction in a tight syncline, while the Bakhtiari splits two adjacent Cenomanian limestone arches to achieve this rendezvous.

The Lower Sehzar

Its discharge almost trebled by the addition of the Ab-i-Bakhtiari, the Sehzar breaches six contiguous Cenomanian anticlines in winding chasms that approach 5,000 feet in depth. Some of the cut "banks" of the stream are truly awesome, one being a perpendicular wall perhaps 2,000 feet in height (Figure 44). The Sehzar finally passes the Mountain Front in threadlike defiles through the limbs of an unroofed Asmari limestone anticline. At the base of one of these 3,000-foot gorges, selenitic stalactites dangle into the branches of palms sheltered beneath the overhanging limestone walls.

Beyond the Mountain Front the stream, known now as the Ab-i-Dez, has one more obstacle to negotiate: the cuesta of Pilocene conglomerate, which presents a 1,500-foot wall toward the northeast. The Dez winds through this mass in a final chasm (Figures 13 and 28) that has recently become the site of a concrete arch dam 647 feet in height.

Accomplishing some 45 transections of major anticlines composed of resistant Cenomanian limestones, the Sehzar and Bakhtiari rivers and their tributaries constitute the greatest drainage anomaly in the Central Zagros. The clearer the contrast between alternative courses, the more often these streams choose the unlikely path; for the more restrictive local structure appears to be, the less influence it seems to exert upon the major drainage features of this region.

THE KARUN BASIN

The Karun Basin (Figure 45) comprises some 11,350 square miles of high mountain country. It differs sharply from the Dez and Karkheh basins in the orientation of its major streams as well as the shape of the catchment as a whole. The drainage map (Figure 34) reveals that the majority of the great streams in this region flow along the trend of the orogen, rather than across it: so that the basin is markedly attenuated along the grain of the country, its sub-basins showing an even stronger development of this characteristic.

A large part of the Karun Basin lies in the Imbricate Zone, in which a consistent expansion of watersheds along the strike has already been noted. Little more than a third of the Karun catchment lies in the Fold Zone, but even here the drainage net seems to indicate an adjustment to structure not charac-

FIGURE 44. Undercut wall in Tang-i-Chahar, presenting a vertical face of at least 1,500 feet.

teristic of the basins to the northwest. An examination of the drainage in relation to the *particulars* of its structural environment will show that such a conclusion is accurate on a broad scale, but not in detail.

The Karun Headwaters

The traditional source of the Karun is the Ab-i-Kurang, which is fed by snow melt and springs issuing from the northeast flank of Zardeh Kuh (14,921 feet). To the east, a tenuous divide on the front of an imbric slice separates the Kurang from the headwaters of the endoreic Zayendeh Rud.

For 47 miles the Kurang follows the strike of the Imbricate Zone in an open valley between the immense bulk of Zardeh Kuh and a subdued fault-line scarp to the east. En route the stream cuts through the middle of a small Cenomanian dome rising from the center of the valley, which might have been avoided by a swing of 2 or 3 miles to either side. Below this cleft the valley opens into a 15-mile terraced alluvial trough, at the end of which it is entered by the Ab-i-Bihishtabad.

The Bihishtabad rises in two branches in the thrust complex northwest and southeast of Junaqan.

In this region 8,000- to 10,000-foot ranges along the trend are isolated by open alluvial plains. The confluence of the headwater branches, however, lies amid vertical beds on the front of the limestone thrust, which is breached in an open alluviated watergap. At the thrust margin the stream cleaves a synclinal mountain, avoidable by a two-mile detour to the north. After receiving the Ab-i-Junaqan the stream cuts through an anticline in a two-story gorge, whose lower portion is a vertical slot, and combines with the Kurang.

Below this confluence the trunk stream, now known as the Karun, makes two loops to the west engorged in a raw canyon that cleaves a maturely dissected mountain landscape in a startling topographic unconformity. This chasm indiscriminately splits both peaks and valley floors of the old relief assemblage, being totally unrelated to any of the erosional forms of the area.

The Karun subsequently receives a left bank tributary draining the axis of the enormous synclinal horst of Kuh-i-Lijan and Kuh-i-Kalar (Figure 7, section KK), and then turns into a fault-line valley below Kuh-i-Lijan. For twenty-six miles the trench becomes progressively deeper and more constricted, until, at the Wanak confluence, the brow of the Lijan scarp stands almost 8,000 feet above the valley floor.

The Lower Wanak, which enters the Karun from the southeast, flows in the continuation of the fault-line valley below the Lijan massif. The pattern of the headwaters of this stream resembles that of the Ab-i-Bakhtiari, with three tributaries converging on a loop oriented similarly to that of the Gand Ab. However, these headwaters flow through broad alluvial plains and open country composed of Upper Cretaceous and Eocene flysch beds: a landscape in the strongest contrast to the wild mountains and stupendous gorges of the Bakhtiari headwaters. The upper half of the Wanak loop is entrenched in a thick slab of Bakhtiari conglomerate, which it eventually leaves to cross the strike along a geological contact which appears to be a transverse fault. Turning northward along the strike, the Wanak, like the Karun, is soon flowing through a gorge 8,000 feet below the crest of Kuh-i-Hazar, the southern continuation of Kuh-i-Lijan.

The Middle Karun

Increased by the Wanak, the Karun turns south of west to carve an asymmetric but straight canyon through a mass of Bakhtiari conglomerate covering the inner margin of the Fold Zone in this region. The Bakhtiari covermass comes to an end in a line of great southwest-facing cliffs. Here the Karun enters the Fold Zone, and its course, as though suddenly released, immediately becomes irregular. The stream first curves to the right along the Bakhtiari cuesta, then cuts back westward in deep winding

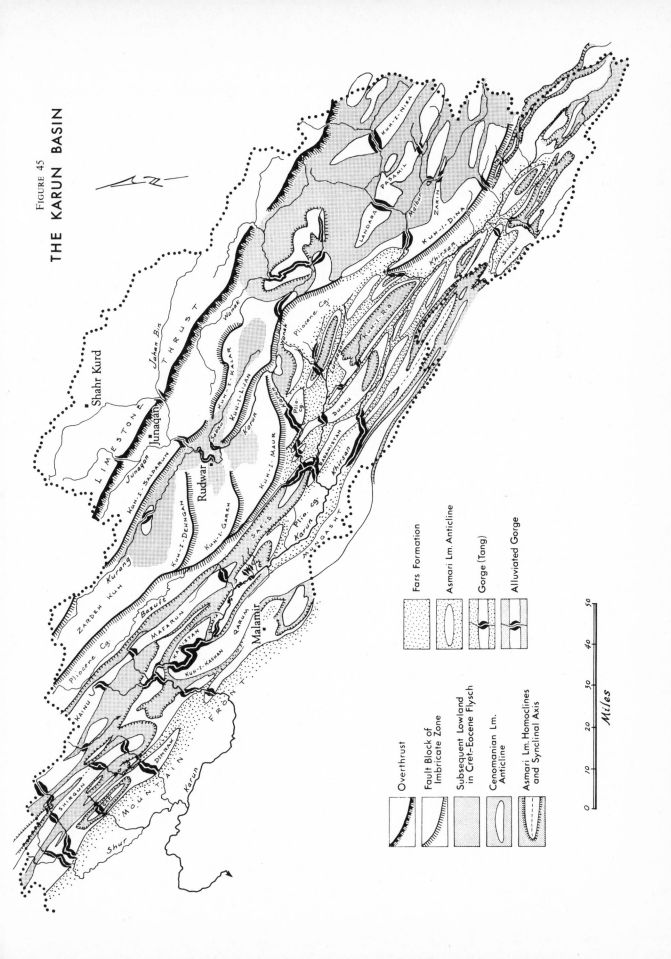

Figure 45

THE KARUN BASIN

Overthrust

Fault Block of Imbricate Zone

Subsequent Lowland in Cret.-Eocene Flysch

Cenomanian Lm. Anticline

Asmari Lm. Homoclines and Synclinal Axis

Fars Formation

Asmari Lm. Anticline

Gorge (Tang)

Alluviated Gorge

Miles
0   10   20   30   40   50

Shahr Kurd

Junaqan

Rudwar

Malamir

LIMESTONE   THRUST

Jahan Bin

Junaqan

Kuh-i-Salparun

Kuh-i-Dehngan

ZARDEH KUH

Kurang

Pliocene Cg.

KAINU

Bazuft

MAFARUN

Kuh-i-Kashan

Qarun

KRISTAN

DINRAK

MOUNTAIN   FRONT

SHIRGUN

Shur

Karun

Kuh-i-Garch

Kuh-i-Kalar

Kuh-i-Lijan

Kuh-i-Maur

Safid

Wonak

Wonak

Pliocene Cg.

Plio.

Pio. Cg.

Karun Cg.

MUNGASHT

Karun

ABDANISTAN

DURAU

Khirsan

Kuh-i-Ra

TUKAB

LANDARA

PASAMIL

KUH-I-NISA

Mabur

ZARIN

KUH-I-DINA

Khirsan

SIVAK

gorges through four anticlinal ranges composed of Asmari limestone.

The Ab-i-Bazuft enters the Karun from the northwest by a subsequent valley along the flank of the third anticline of the above series. The Bazuft is incised 2,000 to 3,000 feet into an 80-mile conglomerate-filled trough between the fault-line scarp of Zardeh Kuh and the great Cenomanian anticline of Kuh-i-Mafarun (12,200 feet). In its lower 9 miles the Bazuft wanders westward out this structural valley onto the weak formations on the side of the third anticline in the group sundered by the Middle Karun.

Between the third and fourth of these anticlines the Karun receives the Ab-i-Lurdagan from the southeast. This stream flows primarily in synclinal valleys, yet crosses the fold belt diagonally. It rises 48 miles to the east in marshy plains, and moves westward through heavily alluviated valleys in the upper two-thirds of its course. Below the village of Lurdagan, the watercourse deserts an open structural valley leading directly to the Karun, and saws through the anticlinal range to the west, returning to a trend path below this watergap. Eight miles farther on the Lurdagan runs against the limestone nose of the third anticline cleft by the Middle Karun, nipping off the nose to join the Karun in the adjacent syncline. A right bank tributary of the Lurdagan, entering at the village of the same name, sunders two Asmari anticlines, one within a quarter mile of its terminus. An affluent of this stream cuts into the upper anticline and follows it axially for two miles before cutting out to link with the main stream. A left bank tributary of the Lurdagan breaches the same anticline twice: where it is unroofed, and again where it is intact.

Below the Lurdagan confluence the Karun splits an Asmari dome which is unroofed to the south, and encounters another slab of the Bakhtiari formation, sharply folded in a syncline. Its gap through the upper rim of this mass is a vertical slot in a concave upper story. Six miles below this cleft the Karun is joined from the southeast by the Ab-i-Khirsan, and swings to the northeast to continue the trend of the latter stream.

The course of the Ab-i-Khirsan is similar to that of the Lurdagan, though the Khirsan is much the greater stream, being the principal tributary of the Karun. The Khirsan rises 135 miles to the southeast in rough and strongly grained country underlain by Eocene limestones and marls. Sixteen miles below its source the Khirsan moves into a syncline filled with Bakhtiari and Fars beds and is channeled into an open alluvial basin at an elevation of about 6,000 feet. The stream continues its line past the stepped front of the giant imbric slab of Kuh-i-Dina (14,450 feet) for some 40 miles, receiving a major right bank tributary, the Ab-i-Malbur, from behind this great mountain near its northern terminus.

The dendritic Malbur system drains an area of isolated Cenomanian anticlines north of the Kuh-i-Dina imbric. Six of these anticlines are transected in open alluviated watergaps, three of which cross the broadest portions of the arches. The main stream cuts across the northern end of the Dina thrust in a wild gorge about 5,000 feet deep.

Below the Malbur confluence the Khirsan remains nicely adjusted to structure in a region of strong folding, following anastomosing pinched synclines past one Asmari limestone anticline after another. Occasionally the stream drifts out of its structural channel to bite into the adjacent domes.

Twenty-one miles above its outlet the Khirsan deserts this consequent path, and, like the Lurdagan, turns to the west to slice through the anticlinal range hemming it on that side. Passing through the axis of this Asmari limestone arch—and another adjacent—in a deep chasm, the Khirsan swings to the right in the shallow syncline beyond, and hews out an eleven-mile trench in its floor: one of the most awesome defiles in the Central Zagros. Along the gorge lip the remnants of old meander loops and acutely entering tributary gullies are hanging thousands of feet above the present stream.

The Lower Karun

The Khirsan exits from its synclinal canyon into a valley floored by Fars sediments, where it enters the Karun. For the next sixty-eight miles the Karun follows the general grain of the country northwestward, and gains no tributaries of consequence.

Though the Karun follows the trend in this reach, it ranges out of its structural channels repeatedly. Twenty-two miles below the Khirsan confluence the Karun jogs eastward, severing the small Asmari anticline previously confining the stream on that side. In the next sixteen miles the Karun breaches this same anticline four more times, jogging back and forth across the structure, which is cleft in five additional places by short lateral tributaries of the trunk stream. At one point the Karun trenches the fold axis for two miles. The anticline dies out less than a mile from its final transection.

The Karun next cleaves a limestone hogback to enter a synclinal gutter which pitches sharply against the stream. This channels the Karun through the rising saddle between two very large Cenomanian domes. An enormous synclinal gorge is the result, the river winding 10,000 feet below the flanking summits.

The Karun leaves this abyss through a slot carved across the northeasternmost of the confining anticlines, also slicing through the Asmari rim of the swell. Receiving a tributary that splits a Cenomanian anticline and a synclinal mountain to the north, the river then swings southwestward, recrossing the Asmari homocline, recrossing the axis of the swell, now a vale on Eocene marls, and cutting through the opposing Asmari plate in a steep chasm joined on the right by the gorge of the Shimbar River. The Ab-i-Shimbar exits to the Karun through a syncline, but so wanders in and out of its axis that it creates spectacular vertical gorges in the steeply inclined Asmari limbs of the trough.

Continuing southwestward, the Karun skirts the nose of a sizeable Upper Fars synclinal mountain, and breaches an Asmari anticline that pitches out three miles to either side. The Mountain Front is passed in this cleft, but beyond it the high face of the Bakhtiari conglomerate cuesta presents a final obstacle to the river. The Karun swings to the west and breaks through this mass in a slightly more spacious canyon than that opened by the Dez in the same cuesta. The river is then channeled northwestward in the foothill badlands where it receives the Ab-i-Shur from the mountains before cutting sharply southward to its junction with the Dez on the Khuzistan Plains between Shushtar and Ahwaz.

The Rud Shur

The Shur flows southeastward along the Mountain Front and collects all of the drainage issuing from the highland between the canyons of the Dez and Karun. Four of the short streams it receives are remarkable in their disregard for the outer fold barriers, which they cleave indiscriminately in direct courses to the southwest. These streams are the Tang-i-Mullah, Tang-i-Balut, Rud-i-Harkash, and Tang-i-Baba Ahmad (Ab-i-Chulbar). The Tang-i-Balut, for example, splits two anticlinal ranges, a major synclinal mountain, and three more anticlines in the twenty-eight miles between its source and the Mountain Front.

The Karun system illustrates two variations of the drainage anomaly. Several portions of the trunk stream and its major tributaries follow the general grain of the folding over great distances, but jog from one syncline to another, producing isolated defiles which separate extended longitudinal reaches. The transected anticlines are Asmari limestone folds of no great amplitude but having considerable longitudinal persistence. The Karun also includes two transverse sections in which a number of tangent Asmari limestone anticlines are cleft in quick succession, with no diversions of the stream into synclinal channels. In the latter cases the folds are breached just before they plunge out into badland areas of Lower Fars beds. Lateral tributaries of the Karun and the Shur accomplish a surprising number of anticlinal transections, both aligned and staggered.

THE SOUTHEASTERN BASINS

The writer has not surveyed the courses of the Marun and Zohreh basins in detail, but topographic maps (1:250,000)[8] and the geological map supplied by British Petroleum Company (1:1,000,000)[9] reveal the same disharmony between drainage and geological structure that characterizes the streams to the northwest.

Whereas the trunk streams of the northwestern basins have a rhombic pattern diagonal to that of their tributaries, the Marun and Zohreh systems (Figure 46) are the epitome of trellis drainage throughout. They include no long reaches diagonal or transverse to the structural trend. The main streams as well as their tributary systems are composed of many short, offset, transverse reaches separated by longer segments along the strike of the folding. These, in the agglomerate, drain their catchments in a direction diagonal to the structural grain without disrupting the characteristic trellis pattern.

The Marun

The Rud-i-Marun and the Ab-i-A′ala combine far beyond the Mountain Front to initiate the Rud-i-Jarrahi. The Marun rises in the rough linear Kuhgalu Country southwest of the Khirsan Basin. Its headwater affluents drain a group of narrow and closely packed Cenomanian anticlines which rise to 10,000 or 11,000 feet, cutting through these ridges and their flanking Asmari hogbacks in a multitude of deep gashes separated by short strike reaches. Discordances between drainage and structure are present in the farthest reaches of these headwaters.

After the large anticline of Kuh-i-Gallal (9,350 feet) is split near its southeast-plunging nose by the northern tributary system, a tributary network enters from the southeast along the strike. An eight-mile path through flysch lowlands then brings the resulting stream, the Marun, to the large anticlinal range of Kuh-i-Nir (11,360 feet), which it severs diagonally after some deflection in course. After breaking through a great Asmari hogback flanking the dome, the Marun receives a tributary from the northwest whose affluents accomplish seven anticlinal transections among the folds of Gallal, Nir, and Kuh-i-Haft Chashmeh.

The Marun then enters a Lower Fars belt, avoiding a massif of Bakhtiari conglomerate, and in a rare demonstration of structural control, utilizes a natural spillway to pass between the plunging ends of the Kuh-i-Safid and Kuh-i-Si anticlines. A large basin of Fars beds and Pliocene conglomerate buttes is crossed directly, beyond which the Marun runs against the side of the Kuh-i-Bingistan anticline and is deflected to the southeast. In direct line with the Marun's approach to this anticline a wind-gap some 3,000 feet deep interrupts its crest, an extremely unusual feature in this country. The Marun passes around the pitching nose of this structure, reaches the axis of the synclinal basin

[8]USAF Aeronautical Approach Charts, 1:250,000, Pub. by USAF Aeronautical Chart and Information Center, Air Photographic and Charting Service, St. Louis, "Ram Hormuz 444 A-II" (1953), "Behbehan 444 A-III" (1953), "Sedeh 444 B-IV" (1955), "Kazerun 444 C-I" (1955).

[9]British Petroleum Company, Ltd., *Geological Maps and Sections of South-West Persia.* London: E. Stanford, 1956.

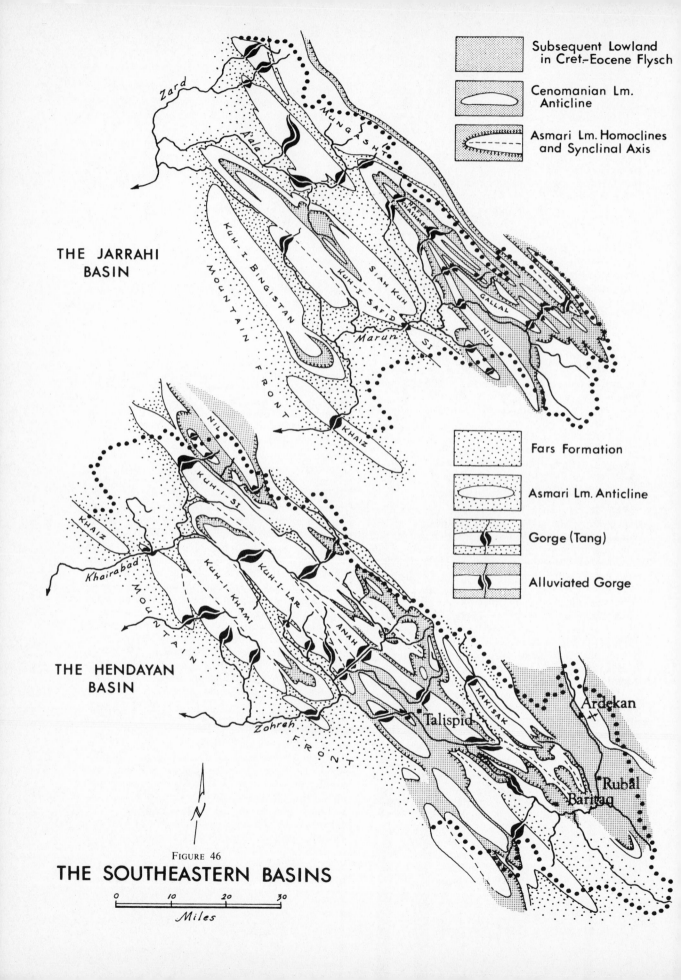

Subsequent Lowland in Cret.-Eocene Flysch

Cenomanian Lm. Anticline

Asmari Lm. Homoclines and Synclinal Axis

THE JARRAHI BASIN

Zard

Aala

MUNGASHT

HAIME

KUH-I-BINGISTAN

SIAH KUH

KUH-I-SAFID

GALLAL

MOUNTAIN FRONT

Marun

SI

NIL

KHAIZ

Fars Formation

Asmari Lm. Anticline

Gorge (Tang)

Alluviated Gorge

NIL

KHAIZ

KUH-I-SI

KUH-I-KHAMI

KUH-I-LAR

ANAH

Khairabad

MOUNTAIN

KAKI SAK

Ardekan

THE HENDAYAN BASIN

Zohreh FRONT

Talispid

Rubal

Barftaq

N

FIGURE 46

THE SOUTHEASTERN BASINS

0   10   20   30

Miles

beyond, then turns southwestward to split the steep Mountain Front anticline of Kuh-i-Khaiz. This range plunges out sharply at either end and stands as a salient of the Mountain Front, surrounded by lowlands on soft formations. The transection of Kuh-i-Khaiz is indeed an anomaly, in view of the close adjustemt to structure displayed by the Marun in the previous forty miles of its course.

The Marun continues westward beyond the Mountain Front, passing over alluvial plains and then entering a syncline in the Bakhtiari formation. The stream swings to the northwest along the axis of this shallow trough until it receives the Ab-i-A'ala.

The Ab-i-A'ala

The A'ala gathers on the faulted Cenomanian anticlinorium of Kuh-i-Mungasht (11,850 feet). Its headwaters rise in steep cirquelike bowls north of the crest of the arch, and flow past its culminating peaks in jagged defiles. A trend fault near the crest of the anticlinorial structure creates a depression which divides the massif lengthwise and receives these transverse defiles. The drainage is led to the southeast, and then turns to continue one of the lateral gorges southwestward, sundering an anticline which pitches out four miles to the east. The stream next turns west to breach a smaller dome, ignoring the passes to either side of it, and follows a Fars syncline out beyond the Mountain Front. In this syncline it receives a series of streams flowing directly off the main dome through the subsidiary folds in front of it.

Beyond the Mountain Front the A'ala receives other streams draining the Mungasht anticlinorium. One of them, the Rud-i-Zard, has two spectacular headwater branches; the northwestern of these flows off the Mungasht flank to split a synclinal mountain and two anticlines, while the other, the Ab-i-Abu'l Abbas, slices through three closely packed anticlines without deviation.

The Rud-i-Zohreh

The Rud-i-Zohreh and the Rud-i-Khairabad unite on the Khuzistan Plains beyond the Mountain Front to form the Rud-i-Hendayan. The Zohreh rises in a loop of mountains reaching elevations between 9,000 and 12,300 feet, whose eastern slopes are drained into the interior basin of Shiraz. To the south, beyond a cross-trend divide varying in elevation from 4,000 to 10,500 feet, is the basin of the Rud-i-Shapur, which enters the Persian Gulf.

The Zohreh headwaters pass through lacustrine basins overlooked by hogbacks and synclinal eminences. The only drainage anomalies are the penetration of one affluent across a narrow Cenomanian fold axis south of Ardekan, and the passage of the northern branch through small axial basins in the vicinity of Rubal. The first real gorge occurs below Baritaq where the Zohreh becomes entrenched in the floor of a syncline that pitches

against the stream (Figure 33). Below this longitudinal gorge a tributary enters from the east, having cut through two Cenomanian anticlines in gorges offset by ten miles. The second gorge is alluviated and follows an oblique shear zone through the sharply displaced anticlinal axis.

Below this confluence the Zohreh lies in a synclinal lacustrine plain, which it deserts at Talispid in a sudden swerve to the west that brings it through two closely jammed anticlines, denuded to their Lower Cretaceous cores. A tributary that links with the Zohreh farther downstream transects the anticline to the east in a direct line with this alluviated gorge, but suddenly veers away from it to follow the syncline abandoned by the Zohreh in favor of the transection.

Below these gorges the Zohreh swings northwestward along the strike and receives an important tributary from the northeast. This stream crosses an Asmari arch, two anticlinal ranges composed of Lower Cretaceous rocks, and a synclinal mountain, all in a straight line; and its extreme headwaters accomplish additional anticlinal transections. After hewing its way through such obstacles the stream is deflected southward into the Zohreh by the plunging Asmari limestone nose of the Kuh-i-Khami anticline.

One small whaleback anticline interposes between this confluence and the Khuzistan lowland. Rather than skirt either of its ends by moving five miles to one side or another, the Zohreh saws directly through the arch, as does the Marun in a similar situation at Kuh-i-Khaiz. The arrangement of the anticlines and the behavior of the streams at the Mountain Front are remarkably alike in these two places: a large fold at each site deflecting drainage southward to exit from the highland through a smaller doubly plunging anticline that could easily have been avoided by the utilization of a structural valley.

Beyond the Mountain Front the Zohreh crosses a broad Lower Fars badland belt in a direction south of west, and, like the Marun, swings to the northwest into a syncline fllled with Bakhtiari conglomerate, which it follows out into the Khuzistan Plain.

The Ab-i-Khairabad

In the conglomerate-filled syncline south of Behbehan the Zohreh is joined by the Ab-i-Khairabad. This stream heads in the anticlinal range of Kuh-i-Nir (11,360 feet) and its lower southeastern continuation, and is composed of two branches that are a series of right angle turns creating remarkable defiles across the grain of the country.

The Khairabad's two tributary systems accomplish four transections of major Cenomanian anticlines, as well as cutting through a large Asmari limestone arch and the Cenomanian cores of unroofed welts. In the lower part of the systems, structural control becomes apparent, the streams

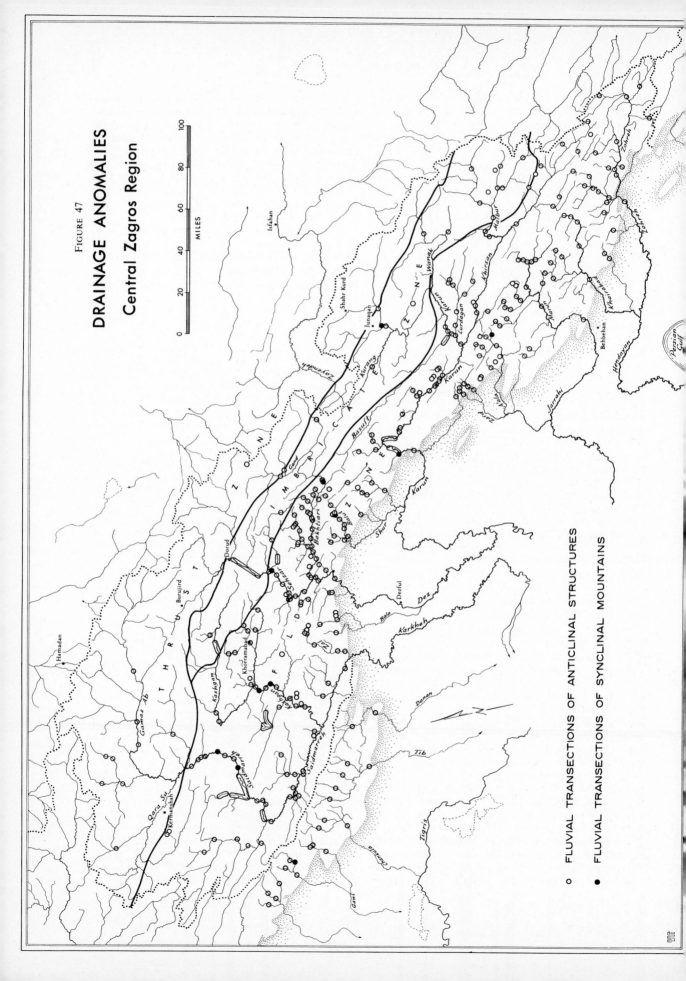

FIGURE 47

DRAINAGE ANOMALIES
Central Zagros Region

FLUVIAL TRANSECTIONS OF ANTICLINAL STRUCTURES

FLUVIAL TRANSECTIONS OF SYNCLINAL MOUNTAINS

being deflected by the plunging noses of Kuh-i-Lar and Kuh-i-Khami, and narrowly missing the structural saddle between the noses of two anticlines on the Mountain Front.

The distribution of transverse gorges in the southeastern basins is more uniform than elsewhere in the Zagros. Minor tributary systems within the trellis drainage net accomplish a greater number of anticlinal transections than do the lesser affluents of the Dez and Karkheh basins, where the great drainage anomalies attach to the courses of the trunk streams themselves. In the southeastern basins there is no distinction between the transection patterns applying to Cenomanian and Asmari limestone arches. Both aligned and offset gorges may be found in all parts of the Marun and Zohreh basins, regardless of local lithology.

THE DRAINAGE ANOMALY

The preceding traverses make it abundantly clear that all of the great drainage ways of the Outer Zagros are disharmonic to geological structure almost throughout, and that a large proportion of the tributary drainage net also opposes the pattern of folding in this region.

Figure 47 shows the distribution of drainage anomalies in the Central Zagros Region. More than 300 major discordances between drainage and geological structure have been discovered in this 40,000-square mile area, the vast majority of them resulting in one or more spectacular transverse gorges, or *tangs*. Though watergaps through individual hogbacks are frequently the most arresting features in a local area, only full transections of anticlinal structures and synclinal mountains are indicated on this map.

Though Figure 47 illustrates the wide distribution of drainage anomalies in the Central Zagros Region, it does not reveal the homogeneous disregard of the drainage pattern for structural barriers of nearly all types. Thus anticlines of both Asmari and Cenomanian limestone may be found transected at any point from one plunging nose to the other; immense hogbacks are split even more often; synclinal mountain ranges are divided almost everywhere but at their transverse axes where they *should* be cut by structurally conformable drainage; imbricate slabs are sundered near their crests and at their termini; and thrust sheets deep in the Inner Zagros as well as cuestas beyond the Mountain Front are crossed both at local culminations and at structural saddles. Moreover, the lines of the transections are oriented at all angles to local structural axes, regardless of the structural type or its lithology.

The drainage anomaly is equally well developed where the folding is intense, and where it is weak; in anticlinoria, in synclinoria, and in plateau-like fold areas; where the flysch is deep, and where it is thin; where the Lower Fars is well developed, and where it is not; where the climate is humid and runoff is high, and where aridity prevails. Scores of *tangs* are aligned with one another, and scores are staggered or isolated. Tributaries cut through mountain ranges to join streams that immediately cut back through the same range in the opposite direction. One stream crosses the same anticline five times, and several cleave a single range twice. Even synclinal drainage creates strange landforms, for it frequently bites into the anticlines to either side, not undercutting them, but flowing *into* them to be separated from the structural trough by curtainlike walls of limestone.

The ubiquity and enigmatic disposition of the Zagros *tangs* as much as their slitlike character allow the modern visitor to develop some sympathy for the folklore relating to their creation. It is hardly less difficult to visualize the mighty Rustam standing astride the mountains and laying about with strokes of his gigantic sword than it is to attribute the *tangs* and stream pattern of this region to one of the classical hypotheses of transverse drainage formation.

Part II

THE ANALYSIS OF THE DRAINAGE ANOMALY

Introduction

The foregoing chapters have portrayed the physiographic characteristics of a region in which there appears to be an unparalleled discord between drainage patterns and their structural matrix. This drainage presents a geomorphic problem because the gross pattern of its primary elements suggests certain modes of formation that are clearly denied by other physiographic evidence, none of the classical hypotheses of transverse stream formation being competent to explain even a majority of the anomalous reaches.

The trunk drainage lines of the Central Zagros flow southward from a protaxial crystalline zone in the overthrust complex of the Inner Zagros, crossing in succession an imbricate zone of faulted anticlines and the simple folds of the Outer Zagros. The Zagros streams thus rise in an area of Upper Cretaceous orogenic movements and pass transversely through progressively younger tectonic zones in gorges which appear to become successively more youthful in configuration. This evidence apparently favoring drainage antecedence is countered by the total watergap pattern, in which vast numbers of anticlinal transections are isolated or widely separated by synclinal or subsequent reaches, a fact also in opposition to the hypothesis of regional stream superposition.

While the *patterns* of the great through-flowing streams are a paradox in relation to their structural environment, many of the most striking examples of both individual *tangs* and continuous gorge systems are found on relatively insignificant tributary streams. Furthermore, the anomalous tributary network as well as the trunk streams of the southeastern basins appear to have developed under different controls than those of the divergently oriented trunk streams of the northwest—the transverse reaches of the former being normal to structure but frequently discontinuous, while those of the latter are diagonal and continuous through swarms of folds.

Throughout the region, and from point to point on the individual drainage lines within it, there is evidence of the concurrent development of transverse drainage of several different types. Certain streams ignore structure completely; some appear to "seek" obstacles to transect; others are deflected by barriers only to breach them at some point near their termini. Many streams cut in and out of anticlines without transecting them completely, and a few cross the same barrier more than once in reverse directions.

Though the disharmony between drainage and structure is variously manifested and is found in all parts of the Zagros and in every structural and lithological situation, there *are* consistencies in the precise nature of the drainage anomaly in certain structural and lithological regions. Hence there are a number of generically distinct drainage anomalies in the Central Zagros, each providing an independent problem of drainage genesis. The analytical portion of this study will show that the general discordance between drainage and structure in the Zagros may be explained in full by its differentiation into several independent drainage anomalies, whose origins may be understood in terms of geomorphic processes presently affecting the varying structural and lithological environments of the Central Zagros.

Local geological relationships indicate that some discordant reaches may be explained by variants of familiar hypotheses of transverse stream formation. Taken singly, however, the origins of many transverse reaches are not at all apparent, nor would hypotheses developed in explanation of them be demonstrable. Fortunately, in the Central Zagros, it is possible to overcome this dilemma by regional comparison. The histories of the transverse streams of the Zagros are made apparent by the presence in this young mountain landscape of models of the progressive stages in the evolution of the drainage. This is the result of regional variations in erosional landscapes developed as a consequence of broad flexuring in the fold surface. Thus synclinorial regions preserve landscapes which exhibit the earliest stages of stream evolution, while highly denuded anticlinoria display the fully developed drainage anomaly, with the whole range of transitional landscapes and fluvial developments being preserved in the areas between these tectonic extremes.

The origins of the most enigmatic transverse reaches are clearly demonstrated by abundant examples of the successive stages leading toward the ultimate drainage anomaly, the earlier phases of development being illustrated in areas of progressively lesser post-tectonic uplift. Accordingly, the origin of all transverse streams and individual anticlinal transections can be resolved in terms of processes actively changing the face of *some part* of the Zagros Highland at present, and no purely hypothetical mechanisms, events, or structures need be deduced in explanation of the discordant stream pattern.

To make use of all evidence bearing on the problem of drainage formation in this area, the following chapters attempt to establish the origin of every stream reach in the 40,000 square miles of the Central Zagros Hydrographic Basin. By such a means principles have been derived from observation of some of the less striking drainage anomalies, whose origins are clear, and these principles have been brought to bear in explanation of the greater drainage discordances that have attracted attention to this region.

The problem of the anomalous transverse drainage of the Zagros Highland is approached in the following chapters by considering in sequence each of the familiar processes of transverse drainage formation and its manifestations, if any, in the problem area.

Transverse consequent and subsequent streams, antecedent streams, superimposed streams, and the various sub-types of each are examined in terms of their structural and lithological requirements and their distinctive morphological effects on fold landscapes. Criteria for the recognition of these streams are thereby established. The Zagros Highland is surveyed to discover areas in which the operation of each of the stream-forming processes would be either facilitated or precluded, and local physiographic indications of the presence or absence of streams of the different types are described. Eventually a residual drainage anomaly is isolated that cannot be explained by the more familiar mechanisms of transverse stream formation.

The residual drainage anomaly is seen to comprise four of the most important through-flowing streams in the problem area. Though these streams drain strongly contrasting landscapes at present, they appear to have been established in similar structural and lithological environments by a single drainage-forming mechanism that has hitherto been little appreciated, but which may be of great significance in all Tertiary mountain belts characterized by echelon folding and strong vertical lithological contrasts.

Chapter VII

Conformable Drainage in the Central Zagros

To isolate the drainage problem in the Central Zagros it is necessary to define that portion of the stream pattern that is controlled by features of geological structure and lithology which could be expected to channel runoff or facilitate the production of valleys by denudation. Clearly, streams conformable to structure and those developed subsequently by extension in easily eroded beds are not a part of the drainage problem. However, the presence of consequent or subsequent reaches on streams otherwise disharmonic to their geological environment is of significance in the determination of the origin of disharmonies between drainage and structure. On a through-flowing stream, important reaches conformable to structure or lithology imply a termination of the effect of the processes which have originated drainage anomalies elsewhere, meaning that succeeding anomalous reaches have developed independently under new controls whose nature must be established anew.

It is to be assumed that the minor tributary drainage of a fold belt of some relief will be longitudinal and almost entirely consequent or subsequent in origin, and will, in the aggregate, comprise the great bulk of the drainage net. These streams are not the concern of this chapter. It is the relationship between the conformable and the unconformable which must interest us, a relationship most often found on or near the trunk streams of the region.

Three questions must be answered in a consideration of the significance of conformable drainage in a fold region. First it must be established whether there are any major streams transverse to the structure of the orogen that have developed under purely structural or lithological controls. Next it must be asked whether any major transverse reaches of otherwise anomalous streams may be so explained. Finally it should be seen whether there exists any relationship between conformable reaches and either transverse or longitudinal zones in the fold belt; that is, whether there is any systematic termination or

distribution of the effects producing drainage anomalies in various portions of the mountain complex.

The geologic map (1:1,000,000) published by the British Petroleum Company[1] indicates the arrangement of both consequent and subsequent paths available to runoff. The consequent paths lead down the flanks of the major warps and through the anastomosing synclines of the fold belt. Outcrop patterns reveal the location of structural domes and depressions, however poorly these features are expressed in the present landscape, large parts of which are in a state of relief inversion.

Areas in which subsequent drainage extension is favored are also well defined by the geologic map. In any local area of the Zagros each geologic unit, though a chronological division, has a recognizable lithology whose erosional characteristics can be determined in the field. In this area of strong lithological contrasts the geologic map becomes almost tantamount to a relief map.

CONSEQUENT TRANSVERSE DRAINAGE— GENERAL FEATURES[2]

Consequent transverse drainage in a fold region makes use of the natural lateral pas-

---

[1] British Petroleum Company, Ltd., *Geological Maps and Sections of South-West Persia.* London: E. Stanford, 1956.

[2] In the following chapters reference will be made to a series of maps drawn on identical drainage bases. This drainage map must be a selection from the complete drainage pattern which has been shown in greater detail in Figure 34. The base map delineates the trunk streams, their major tributaries, and all other tributaries that include significant cross-grained components. The map excludes the great number of streams entirely conformable to structure and lithology which have no significance to the problem in hand. Thus in terms of drainage density the map is prejudiced against certain areas, such as Inner Luristan, where the majority of the drainage never departs significantly from the strike. This must be kept in mind when comparing the distribution of conformable drainage from one area to another. However, the relative proportions of transverse and compound drainage features are accurately portrayed from region to region since all such streams have been included on the map.

sages at the ends of plunging anticlines. It could be called "spillway drainage" for it would follow lines of overflow if lakes were impounded in the original synclinal valleys. Such drainage could be direct only if folds pitch out along definite lines across the structural grain; otherwise it would be quite circuitous, incorporating long synclinal reaches.

It is questionable whether consequent drainage can immediately characterize any but a fold belt that has initially been exposed to denudation as an archipelago of anticlinal islands. If the folding originated in an emergent landscape, antecedent stream patterns would prevent the inception of purely consequent drainage systems. It seems that, with the slow pace known to characterize *initial* deformation,[3] a perennial stream would be able to maintain itself across rising areas, eventually becoming so entrenched that it is held in its course by the very obstacle it combats. Such a stream would at the same time be increased and empowered by new synclinal runoff from areas previously draining parallel to it or dendritically into it farther downstream, and eventually by an increment of new orographic precipitation.

Had the fold belt gradually emerged from the sea as an archipelago, its initial drainage would be consequent, from the smallest tributary to the largest through-flowing stream. The drainage of each anticline would terminate in synclinal marine straits which would isolate the individual structures, allowing the drainage of each to be purely autogenous. The gradual emergence of the area would leave the marine straits expressed in the drainage pattern as synclinal consequent streams fed by the consequent runoff from the anticlinal flanks. The only early drainage discordances would result from headward stream extension, and from local superposition of drainage from floodplains, lakebeds, or landslips. All such drainage would remain "near-consequent" in pattern.

Consequent drainage can also redevelop by the denudational resurrection of the original fold structures. When this occurs the previously dominant drainage, whatever its origin and pattern, may be rearranged to conform to some degree to the convolutions of the progressively exposed feature-forming horizon. In the Franco-Swiss Jura the exposure of a resistant Jurassic limestone series has re-established the old fold pattern in this manner, and in it, in addition to discordant transverse streams usually attributed to superposition, there also are found a number of consequent drainage lines which make extensive use of lateral passages between the noses of pitching anticlines.

Major transverse sags in the structure of a fold belt should be utilized by transverse streams, if consequent drainage is truly characteristic of the fold belt. Though consequent through-flowing drainage is most easily visualized winding through a landscape of anticlinal ranges, it is truly consequent on synclinal axes, both longitudinal and transverse. Accordingly, through-flowing drainage of consequent origin can be recognized even when an area is in a state of relief inversion. With relief inversion a consequent stream pattern would appear to "seek" transections of synclinal mountains, both laterally and axially, with transverse gorges frequently being sited near the greatest breadth of the synclinal range. The adjacent subsequent lowlands, though spacious, should be occupied by lesser streams tributary to the intermittently engorged consequent lines.

In the first relief inversion, originally consequent streams should pass out of each synclinal mountain in a gorge cut below the original spillway into the next structural lowland. Through several cycles of erosion this outlet might become displaced, both as a result of slight disharmonies in folding at depth and through planation in weak formations. Resulting drainage anomalies would characterize such a stream as being of superposed-consequent origin.

When the uppermost sediments folded are highly erodable, drainage disharmonies can develop from originally consequent runoff in the initial cycle of erosion. In soft formations, such as marls, stream planation during downcutting is likely. In response to regional movements and accidents of course, synclinal drainage may, in the earliest phases of folding, wander laterally above areas that upon the ex-

---

[3] Initial local deformation appears to long precede the onset of full orogenic spasms, as shown by stratigraphy in the Zagros and elsewhere, so that rates of local displacements recently discussed by Schumm and others would not apply in the initial phases of tectonic movement. See S. A. Schumm, "The Disparity Between Present Rates of Denudation and Orogeny," U. S. Geol. Survey *Prof. Paper* 454H (1963), 4–7. In addition, Schumm's rates of denudation relate to areal lowering rather than stream incision.

posure of more resistant beds will prove to be fold flanks.

CONSEQUENT DRAINAGE IN THE CENTRAL ZAGROS

Figure 48 shows the extent of that part of the drainage pattern that appears to be a consequence of the detailed tectonic structure of the Central Zagros Region. It also reveals the distribution of the Bakhtiari series laid down in the depressions of the late Tertiary period, during the time of peak erosion in the orogen. The Lower Bakhtiari areas are the earliest certain structural depressions in the emergent orogen, and thus should have been nodes of consequent drainage in late Miocene time.

Relation to Mio-Pliocene Basins

In almost all cases the Bakhtiari beds are found in synclines or in ramp valleys below fault-line scarps. In such positions they are being dissected by present drainage or veneered with Quaternary alluvium, depending upon the most recent movements of the local areas. In either case the majority of the Pliocene basins remain lowlands today, relative to the upwarps around them. Thus many current valleys were either terminal basins or the routes of consequent streams in the late Miocene and early Pliocene.

A quite different set of ancient valley systems is indicated west and south of Khorramabad where fragments of the Bakhtiari formation overlie Cretaceous flysch beds southwest of the Kuh-i-Safid arch. Thus extensive subsequent valleys had already developed in the flysch during the late Pliocene. Like most of the Pliocene structural lowlands, the old subsequent vales continue their drainage-directing function to the present.

Present Consequent Drainage

Figure 48 shows all streams that presently follow synclinal lowlands along the strike and that pass through structural gaps or spillways around and between the ends of pitching anticlines. Anomalous transverse streams that cross pitching synclines without deviation are not indicated as consequent, as the syncline actually did not channel them in any way. On the other hand a few consequent tributaries that drain long homoclinal slopes have been indicated, as they contribute to the appearance of transverse drainage in the orogen and could create significant watergaps through hogbacks buttressing domal structures.

All synclinal drainage has been mapped as consequent though some of this drainage flows against the synclinal pitch. Where this is the case, arrows indicate the plunge of the trough: the true consequent path. Reversal of consequent synclinal streams to integrate the drainage of an undulating synclinal line into a single stream system is facilitated by the soft Fars beds which floor the synclines not subjected to Pliocene alluviation.

The Karkheh Basin

The pattern of consequent drainage varies from area to area. In the Karkheh Basin consequent streams are found to follow the strike over long distances, seldom adopting a diagonal or transverse orientation. Since geological information about the thrust complex drained by the Gamas Ab is lacking, the appearance is that consequent reaches are most significantly developed toward the exterior of the orogen. Beginning with the undulating trough of Kishmanar and extending through the Pusht-i-Kuh salient, a great number of synclines exercise marked control of the drainage pattern of Outer Luristan. Sections AA through DD, Figure 7, reveal that these synclines are not especially sharp, but are deep, broad, and well defined. Relief inversion in Inner Luristan has clearly disrupted the old consequent drainage pattern of that region.

In Inner Luristan there appears to be only one case of a transverse sag utilized by a stream: the passage of the Marik around the end of a Cenomanian arch to join the Qara Su in the radiolarite lowland. Two diagonal streams in the vicinity drain a highly eroded Cenomanian anticlinorium consequently into the Qara Su (Naru: section AA, Figure 7), and a third in the same area may be consequent on the front of the limestone overthrust.

The intact anticlines of Outer Luristan have a strong deflecting effect on the through-flowing drainage of the region. Thus four significant streams are diverted around fold noses, three at the Mountain Front, to reach the lowlands beyond. In their upper reaches, by contrast, all of these streams (the Karkheh, the Rud-i-Tib, the Tarhan, and the Duruzeh Nau [Bala Rud west branch]) are notably discordant to structure. Akin to this spillway drainage in Luristan are the anticlinal nose transections accomplished by the Saidmarreh at Kuh-i-Gavah and Kuh-i-Kuljar, by the Kashgan at Milleh Kuh, and by the Ab-i-Danan at Dalpari. These streams adopt a

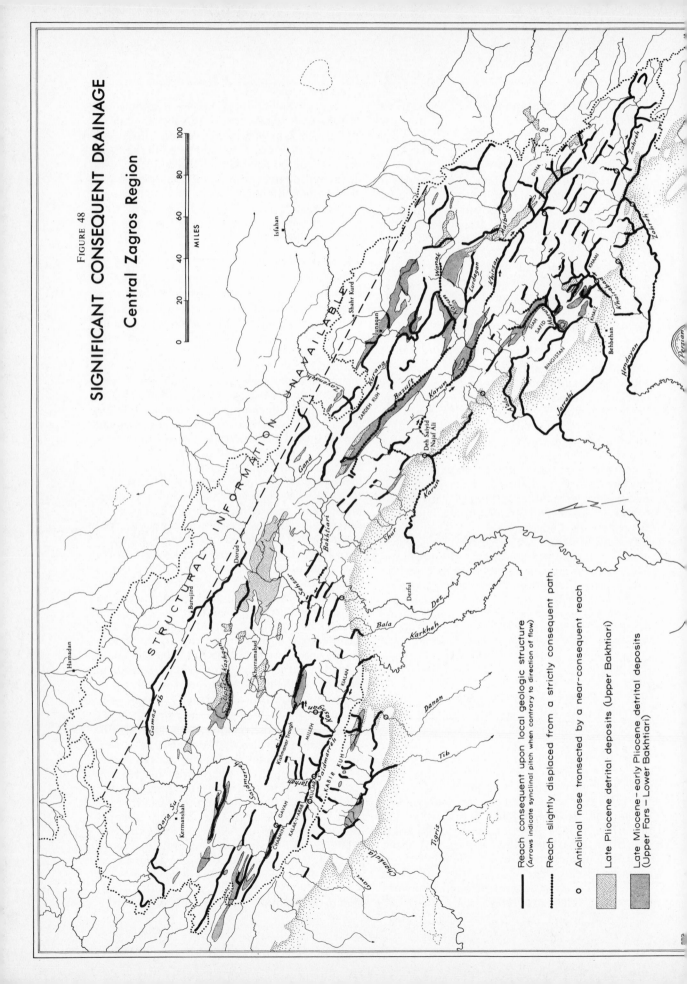

FIGURE 48

SIGNIFICANT CONSEQUENT DRAINAGE

Central Zagros Region

MILES

0   20   40   60   80   100

Reach consequent upon local geologic structure
(Arrows indicate synclinal pitch when contrary to direction of flow)

Reach slightly displaced from a strictly consequent path.

○   Anticlinal nose transected by a near-consequent reach

Late Pliocene detrital deposits (Upper Bakhtiari)

Late Miocene–early Pliocene detrital deposits
(Upper Fars – Lower Bakhtiari)

near-consequent path, but fail to completely circumvent the obstacles before them, in all cases Asmari limestone anticlines. The question is whether they were consequent on the deformed surface of Fars beds, which did not fold in perfect harmony with the underlying limestones, whether they were consequent on partially formed folds and antecedent to the fully developed structures, or whether they are the result of captures by consequent gullies that eventually breached the anticlines. As these near-consequent streams are nevertheless disharmonic to structure, a consideration of the origin of their watergaps must await a later chapter.

The Dez Basin

Despite the increased strength of the folding and the resultant sharp definition of the synclinal troughs in the Bakhtiari Mountains, consequent drainage is rather poorly developed in this area. Every syncline channels some drainage, but significant streams seldom utilize tectonic paths. The great streams of the Dez Basin show a surprising disregard for the deep structural troughs which they repeatly encounter. Only four short reaches on the Sehzar and three on the Ab-i-Bakhtiari utilize synclines and even these are occasionally somewhat offset from a truly consequent path. The negative effect of the strong structures of the Bakhtiari Mountains on the stream pattern is best seen by contrasting the maps of consequent reaches and anticlinal axes in this region (Figures 48 and 6).

There are no *transverse* consequent reaches in the entire Sehzar-Bakhtiari watershed, and no synclinal reaches of great length aside from that of the Burujird Plain, actually a ramp valley marginal to an overthrust. Nowhere in this 6,220-square mile area is a fold nose passed conformably by a drainage line. Though transverse spillways are present in the area they have no effect on its drainage pattern.

The Karun Basin

The various members of the Karun system all show a strong degree of structural control. The Kurang-Karun-Wanak line, the Bazuft Valley, and the Upper Khirsan Valley are all synclines in front of thrust slabs; the Lurdagan is notably synclinal above its enigmatic gorge, and so are the Middle and Lower Khirsan, the Malbur headwaters, the Upper Wanak, and the Sabzu. The transverse reach of the Karun below the Wanak confluence cuts

through an immense Pliocene synclinal fill. Below the entry of the Lurdagan the Karun crosses another Pliocene valley fill, but this time transversely. After receiving the Khirsan, the Karun wanders in and out of synclinal paths until channeled through the rising saddle at Deh Saiyid Najaf Ali. Beyond the Mountain Front it swings into a Pliocene syncline and follows it, not always concordantly, out onto the Khuzistan Plain. Geological information on the headwaters rising in the thrust complex is not available, otherwise the characteristic consequent drainage might be extended into this region as well.

In the Karun system structural control may be seen on streams of all orientations: longitudinal, diagonal, and transverse. In addition, anticlinal nose transections evince near-consequent paths even in the discordant reaches, as along the Middle Karun. On the other hand, some of the discordances are almost beyond belief, as streams otherwise clearly consequent turn away from open structural paths to cleave barriers needlessly, as do the Khirsan and Lurdagan in their strange gorges. The path of the Karun through the saddle at Deh Saiyid Najaf Ali, resulting in a colossal canyon in rocks of maximum resistance, is truly astounding when it is realized that a syncline continues the previous line of the stream past the huge double-humped obstacle.

The consequent stream array of the Karun Basin is a return to the pattern of Outer Luristan, with long synclinal reaches separated by enigmatic transverse cuts. As in Luristan there is one segment of the drainage pattern in which anticlinal transections are more or less aligned: the Karun on either side of the Bazuft confluence resembling the Saidmarreh below the entry of the Gamas Ab. Though the distance between these two areas, measured along the trend, is almost 240 miles, they occupy a similar position in relation to the structural elements of the orogen and can actually be connected by a continuous line along its strike. In both instances the undeflected reaches cross synclinoria between the fault structures of the Inner Zagros and large anticlinoria in the Outer Zagros. The transected anticlines in both areas are composed of Asmari limestone, while the culminations to either side are primarily Cenomanian.

The Marun-Zohreh Basins

Consequent drainage in the Marun and Zohreh basins is widespread and occurs in two contrasting facies. The headwaters of all sys-tems draining these southeastern watersheds incorporate short synclinal reaches separated by transverse discordant segments of some-what less length. Enigmatic transverse reaches are far more widespread than in Luristan, but have somewhat less continuity than those of the Dez-Bakhtiari Basin. As the exterior ranges of the Marun and Zohreh basins are approached, there is a marked increase in structural control of the drainage net. The transverse portions of the lower Ab-i-A'ala, Marun, Khairabad, and Zohreh are *almost* perfectly consequent, utilizing the natural spillways between the noses of overlapping folds or being deflected around the ends of folds as they exit from the mountain complex. In this region drainage lines following dis-cordant paths through the interior of the oro-gen in twelve instances nicely skirt plunging fold noses near the Mountain Front. Near-consequent paths, seen in the transection of anticlinal noses, occur in two additional lo-cales. In the southwestern halves of the Marun and Zohreh basins, an area of 2,600 square miles, there are more than twice as many instances of lateral spillway drainage as in the remaining 37,400 square miles of the Central Zagros watershed.

The Marun and the Khairabad, adjacent streams, are purely consequent throughout the lower halves of their courses as far as the Mountain Front anticlines, and in this dis-tance receive only consequent tributaries. But at the Mountain Front both streams split Asmari limestone anticlines that could easily have been avoided. Farther to the southeast the Zohreh, also briefly consequent, does like-wise. While the Khairabad barely misses a consequent path between two Mountain Front anticlines, the Marun breaks directly through the middle of Kuh-i-Khaiz in a 2,000-foot gorge. This anticline is passed at either end by structural lowlands communicating with the Marun above its watergap, but these natural spillways are cluttered with Lower Fars bad-lands which rise several hundred feet above the present stream.

The Zohreh exits from the highland in a 1,500-foot cleft through the center of a small anticline also passed by a structural lowland which is not utilized by any drainage.

Summary

It has been shown in earlier chapters that major structural culminations and depressions could not explain the general location of the transverse drainage lines of the Zagros orogen. The principal transverse depression, the Luris-tan Saddle, is not utilized by any important stream, and the greatest structural swell, the Bakhtiari Culmination, is crossed by two major streams. Neither the gross nor the minute configuration of the fold surface could originate the present *transverse* drainage pat-tern in a consequent manner. However, in a small area in the south two adjacent trunk streams do show near-complete structural con-trol in the lower half of their courses across the grain of the orogen. Remarkably, both of these streams are discordant to structure in their final moments crossing the Mountain Front. In both cases transverse gorges result from a prolongation of a previously conse-quent path.

Consequent control of the drainage pattern is conspicuous in the Pusht-i-Kuh area and throughout the southeastern half of the Cen-tral Zagros Region. In these areas of anti-clinal mountains, trend streams comprise a greater proportion of the drainage net than in the Dez Basin or Inner Luristan. The vast majority of these streams flow in synclines. Where denudation has removed the majority of the Tertiary sedimentary sequence, conse-quent drainage lines are conspicuously absent. None of the synclinal mountain ranges found in the orogen are crossed centrally by gorges, a fact which seems to indicate that transverse spillway drainage was never characteristic of the highly denuded areas. None of the famous *tangs* of the Central Zagros can be attributed to consequent through-flowing drainage, but a large number are the result of near-consequent streams that transect fold noses.

SUBSEQUENT TRANSVERSE DRAINAGE
GENERAL FEATURES

The second type of conformable drainage is that developed by headward extension along lines of rapid erodability. Before they can ef-fect drainage development, the erodable for-mations must be exposed by denudation under a fluvial regime of consequent, antecedent, or superimposed origin. Thus headward-extend-ing drainage in weak zones is subsequent both to the initial drainage pattern of an area and to the exposure in the area of zones of varying resistance to erosion.

Lithological weaknesses controlling drain-age patterns are of several types. Constitu-tional weaknesses in the rocks themselves, such as a lack of strong induration, friable primary materials, susceptibility to chemical alteration, thin bedding, or bedding fissility, create most subsequent lowlands. The occurrence of secondary surfaces of parting within the rocks—joint sets and faults—can also be important in their durability, as well as in directing the specific lines of stream extension in them.

Headward Extension and Watergap Development

While the extent of the subsequent drainage pattern in plains beveling rocks of varying resistance is easy to define on a geologic map, the role of headward erosion in creating watergaps through mountain ranges is more difficult to determine. Streams extend headward in all types of terrain only by mass-wasting and micro-erosional processes around the peripheries of the hollows they drain. They extend in whatever direction the surface gives way most easily, and if this takes them to the foot of a hard barrier they cannot be expected to "work through it" as long as erosion is accomplished more easily in some other direction. By headward extension alone a stream can tap the other side of such a barrier only when the barrier crumbles away at some point at a rate quite independent of the activity of the drainage lines in front of it.

A headward-extending stream may, however, intercept consequent drainage from the crest of the barrier itself. Even so, to reach through such a ridge to drain the lowlands on the other side of it, this compound stream would require a clifflike gradient advantage over the farther lowland. Its extreme headwaters would still lie in the barrier ridge, where they would be subject to the same limitations as before: they cannot cut backward under their own power; their extension must wait on the slow disintegration of the ridge. If the ridge, in fact, terminates anywhere in the vicinity of such a gash there would seem to be a greater possibility of subsequent extension into the lowland beyond by a route around the end of the obstacle rather than through it.

To escape such difficulties, and to try to account for the exact sites of watergaps, transverse faults have often been invoked in explanation of discordant stream patterns in fold regions. It would appear that erosion in these lines of weakness would present opportunities for stream extension through them, or at least

for the development of subsequent gullies at such points.

Transverse faults are indeed known to be numerous in familiar fold regions such as the Jura and Appalachian Ridge and Valley Province, as they should be in accordance with the physics of compression. However, when A. N. Strahler attempted to determine the true relationship between transverse faults and watergaps in Pennsylvania, where both abound, he found that such lines of weakness, though having a marked physiographic expression, are almost completely ignored by the region's drainage.[4] Streams work through hard rocks within a stone's throw of fractures that notch crestlines and offset ridges as much as a mile.

The fault-control theory is usually the first hypothesis advanced to explain a system of watergaps in fold landscapes. As a hypothesis it often reflects disbelief in the capability of fluvial erosion to produce significant breaches of major geological obstructions, and implies that the gaps and the streams utilizing them are not genetically related to one another. Variations of such ideas are common even in the folklore of regions exhibiting notable watergap phenomena: e.g., the ascription of the Zagros *tangs* to swordblows of the mythological hero Rustam.

Though the fault-control theory can seldom bear close investigation, in exceptional cases it has a certain validity: for instance, in the Jura Mountains and Pre-Alps, where several of the large diagonal faults are followed by transverse valleys. However, these wrench faults are developed on a scale unknown in the Appalachians, and are not related to individual folds; they are diagonal to the fold belt as a whole and a number of them cross and offset the axes of as many as five successive anticlines.[5] Despite the continuity of the valleys produced, not all of them are utilized by streams, and those which do direct runoff are used in different places by different streams. Thus they only incidentally affect regional drainage patterns.

H. D. Thompson set forth a rather convinc-

[4] A. N. Strahler, "Hypotheses of Stream Development in the Folded Appalachians of Pennsylvania," Geol. Soc. Amer. *Bull.*, 56 (1945), 45–88.

[5] A. Heim, *Geologie der Schweiz*, I, Leipzig (1919), 613–623; II (1921), 367–369; summarized in L. U. DeSitter, *Structural Geology*, New York: McGraw-Hill, 1959, pp. 167–171 and Figure 168; also M. P. Billings, *Structural Geology*, New York: Prentice-Hall, 1954, pp. 212–214 and Figure 213.

ing case for subsequent control of the transverse streams of the Central Appalachians.[6] His thesis was that the rivers of Maryland and Virginia, such as the Potomac, James, and Roanoke, have attained their present relationships to structure by headward extension rather than by superposition. In several maps Thompson showed that these rivers either skirt resistant outcrops or cross their narrowest parts, sometimes, however, cutting through the tips of barrier ridges despite the presence of subsequent lowland bypasses. Thompson believed that rock resistance alone is competent to account for the stream pattern of this area, and he discounts faults as factors in the drainage design. To explain the watergaps cutting the noses of plunging barriers he left a choice between local superposition from floodplain deposits and a vaguely stated process by which streams require less energy to take a direct path through an obstacle than to work a longer distance around it. Thompson's streams are, perforce, ephemeral features, as they are related to an outcrop pattern that changes continually as denudation works to progressively deeper levels in the structural matrix.

Indications of Headward-Extending Drainage

A subsequent stream system established by headward extension could have a number of distinguishing characteristics. In a folded region it would have a rectangular or trellis pattern, incorporating lengthy segments along the strike, either homoclinal valleys or basins in the soft cores of unroofed anticlines. Its members should coincide with the outcrop of the most erodable units on the geological map. Unless large-scale transverse faulting is obvious, cuts through successive ridges should be offset, and there should be marked deflections in course between reaches in structural lowlands and passages through structural highs. Cuts through resistant layers should be strongly influenced by joint sets and bedding planes, the lines of weakness facilitating extension in such zones. Gorge direction might reflect the theoretical orientation of shear or extension ruptures as seen on the strain diagram for each individual fold and as reflected in the minor surface sculpture of the fold.

Watergaps might show an absence of rapids, indicating that the presence of fault gouge or other local weaknesses has favored downcutting at such points. Transverse clefts unoccupied by streams or fluvial deposits would indicate that weathering in highly jointed or faulted zones is capable of opening gaps which might elsewhere be utilized by runoff. The presence of watergaps consistently near anticlinal steepenings could mean that jointing is best developed in the most compressed portions of folds, which thereby become the least resistant to transection by local consequent and subsequent gullying. Windgaps would attest to subsequent stream extension resulting in captures of older transverse drainage of consequent, antecedent, or superimposed origin. The details of the stream pattern itself should be indicative of the subsequent headward-extending system, with barbed tributary patterns showing captures of opposing consequent, antecedent, or superimposed systems.

The possibility of subterranean captures must be kept in mind when dealing with drainage evolution in a predominantly calcareous terrain. Though it has never been proved that transverse gorges that cut completely through anticlinal structures have been produced by subterranean capture followed by collapse of passage roofs, such an occurrence is not beyond belief. Subterranean piracy has been suggested in explanation of certain anticlinal watergaps in the Appalachian Ridge and Valley Province, a theory which has never been disproved.[7]

Solution channels and chutes along gorge walls might be indicative of an unroofed subsurface channel, as would a clay coating on smooth vertical to overhanging surfaces. Smooth walls lacking signs of mechanical weathering, which pass upward into freshly exposed joint faces and fracture surfaces, could indicate a recent collapse of a tunnel roof. Dripstone stalactites suspended from the roofs of wall alcoves would certainly favor the cavern collapse hypothesis, as would masses of debris in the stress channel.

SUBSEQUENT DRAINAGE IN THE CENTRAL ZAGROS

The principal formation facilitating gully extension in the Zagros region is the Upper Cre-

---

[6]H. D. Thompson, "Drainage Evolution in the Southern Appalachians," Geol. Soc. Amer. Bull., 50 (1939), 1323–1356.

[7]H. M. Fridley, "Solution and Stream Piracy," Journal of Geology, 47 (1939), 178–188.

taceous flysch, which is developed in varying depth throughout the orogen between the two feature-forming limestone horizons. Where the Cretaceous flysch is not exposed, the Eocene marl-limestone series provides a relatively weak substratum below the massive Asmari limestones, though one nowise as infirm as the underlying Cretaceous marl-silt-sandstone complex. Of limited distribution but having a significant physiographic effect where exposed are the friable radiolarite beds underlying the limestone thrust in the Inner Zagros. The highly erodable Lower Fars marl-evaporite suite lies near the top of the sedimentary column, above the Asmari limestones and below the continental Bakhtiari beds; therefore it could have a disturbing effect on the drainage pattern only where streams have exposed it by cutting through Pliocene basin deposits. More often the Lower Fars lies exposed in synclines underlain by the Asmari limestones, so that its presence does not facilitate any drainage shifts away from the structural paths.

Figure 49 indicates the significant streams of the Central Zagros Region whose courses seem to be controlled by variations in erodability of surface materials. The streams shown are only those whose direction is affected by the orientation of erodable belts. Streams which cross Upper Cretaceous and Eocene outcrops from other formations but do not evidence any control by them, are not indicated.

Also indicated on Figure 49 is the distribution of *nonaligned* watergaps through anticlinal ranges. Antecedent or superimposed drainage should produce gorges more or less aligned and not separated by significant consequent or subsequent reaches along the trend. Headward stream extension, on the other hand, could be expected to result in a more random distribution of transverse gorges separated by synclinal or subsequent reaches.

Continuity of Transverse Reaches

The degree of alignment of transverse gorges with the streams approaching and departing from them is of fundamental importance in determining the origin of the transverse reach. Discordant transverse streams incorporated into a drainage system by headward piracy can be presumed to have originated as consequent gullies on anticlines, as discussed previously. When tapping the far side of the fold these gullies would encounter either a subsequent or synclinal lowland. They could not be expected to extend across such a valley in a direct prolongation of their own anticlinal transection, for the valley would have its own drainage, developed long prior to the encroachment of the transverse gully. Thus transverse drainage developed by headward extension could be expected to *turn sharply out of a longitudinal valley upon entering each anticlinal transection.*

Depending upon the packing of the folds in the vicinity, the drainage proceeding downstream from the anticlinal transection could continue the line of the transection onto a broad structural or subsequent lowland, or could be deflected at once along the strike in a narrower syncline or subsequent valley. Thus it is the behavior of the stream *entering* its gorge which might be evidence of headward extension, and what it does later is of no account in this respect. By contrast, partial proof of drainage antecedence or superposition at any point is seen in anticlinal transections in good alignment with the transecting stream as it enters the lowland *above* the watergap. On one hand the stream has pushed across the obstacle from below, on the other from above, indicating headward extension in the first case, and antecedence or superposition in the second.

It might be objected that subsequent stream captures of antecedent or superimposed systems could also produce streams which *turn to enter* transverse gorges. However, fragmentation of superimposed and antecedent streams would leave windgaps and aligned gorges tributary to different longitudinal streams. As defined, the gorges mapped on Figure 49 are not aligned, this being their distinguishing characteristic and the initial indication of a possibly uncoordinated origin.

The Karkheh Basin

The contrast between the patterns of consequent and subsequent drainage is strong. The stream pattern of Inner Luristan, the area of relief inversion, is overwhelmingly subsequent, developed in the radiolarite beds (the Qara Su), or in the Cretaceous flysch (the Ab-i-Marik, Upper Kashgan, and Ab-i-Khorramabad).

Most important among the subsequent drainage developments of Luristan are nodes toward which tributaries seem to be drawn

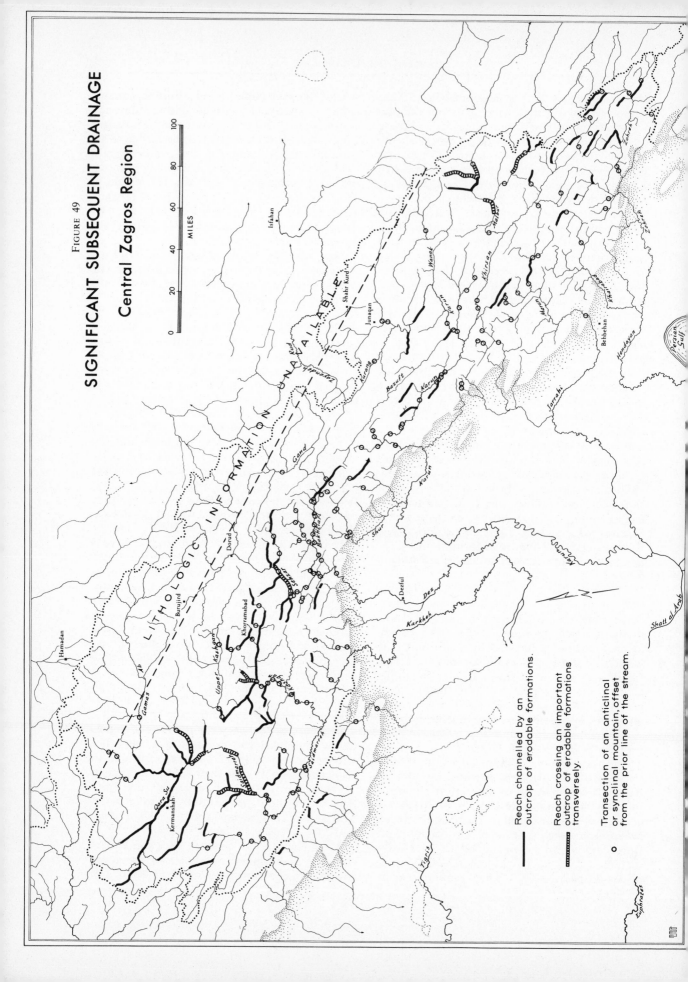

FIGURE 49

SIGNIFICANT SUBSEQUENT DRAINAGE

Central Zagros Region

MILES

100 80 60 40 20 0

LITHOLOGIC INFORMATION NOT AVAILABLE

—— Reach channelled by an outcrop of erodable formations.

••••• Reach crossing an important outcrop of erodable formations transversely.

○ Transection of an anticlinal or synclinal mountain, offset from the prior line of the stream.

Persian Gulf

Hamadan
Kermanshah
Qara Su
Gamas Ab
Burujird
Dorud
Gand
Khorramabad
Upper Kashgan
Isfahan
Shahr Kurd
Junaqan
Yapuslaz
Rud
Kirang
Bazuft
Karun
Shur
Karun
Dez
Dezful
Deh Dasht
Karkheh
Tigris
Euphrates
Shatt al Arab
Vanak
Kaka
Karun
Khirsan
Marun
Behbehan
Jarrahi
Khairabad
Zohreh
Hendeyan
Karun

from several directions, or more accurately, from which subsequent lines have extended. These centripetal drainage areas are found in the plains of Hulailan and Kuh-i-Dasht, the lowland south of Kuh-i-Safid, and the rolling country north of Kuh-i-Charmi. All but the latter, which lies in the radiolarite zone, are developed in the interconnecting vales of unroofed anticlines.

Outer Luristan is an area of intact Asmari and Cenomanian anticlines. Clearly there could be no subsequent drainage in the former and only limited developments in the latter, for the flysch thins rapidly southwestward, becoming inferior in depth even to the Asmari limestone throughout Pusht-i-Kuh (sections AA, BB, and CC, Figure 7). In Luristan as a whole there is an inverse relationship between the distributions of subsequent streams and unaligned gorges, a great number of the latter occurring in Outer Luristan, where subsequent trend reaches are almost totally absent.

Though they are not channeled along the *strike* by erodable belts, it is important to note that the through-flowing streams of Luristan, the Saidmarreh and Kashgan rivers, *cross* the fold belt by flowing from one subsequent basin to another. The Saidmarreh moves through plains formed by the full coalescence of anticlinal basins, while the course of the Kashgan links anticlinal basins tangent only at successive hogback watergaps.

The Dez Basin

In the Dez Basin subsequent streams are nowhere of great importance, though unaligned gorges are common. In this region the Cenomanian limestone structures, including synclinal floors, rise to such elevations that the flysch has been largely removed by denudation, as seen on sections EE, FF, and GG, Figure 7. Though the materials required to initiate rapid drainage extension and to make sites of such extension recognizable are no longer present in this area, their influence must have been felt at an earlier time. In our consideration of the residual or unexplained transverse drainage in a later chapter, the original subsequent drainage of this region will be discussed and shown to be of paramount significance in the origin of the great drainage anomalies in the Bakhtiari Culmination.

The Karun-Marun-Zohreh Basins

With their many consequent streams the southeastern basins show a wide scattering of unaligned gorges and a very limited development of subsequent components in the trunk drainage network. The few subsequent reaches present all lie along the strike of the orogen; there are no lateral or even diagonal subsequent reaches in this area to compare with those of Inner Luristan. The dearth of subsequent drainage in the Karun, Marun, and Zohreh watersheds is attributable to the poor original development of the flysch in this area (sections HH to LL, Figure 7). The formation is frequently exposed, but its outcrops are narrow and fail to affect the courses of the trunk streams crossing this part of the Fold Zone. While the same might be said of the Dez Basin, in this latter area the present apparent absence of subsequent effects is due to the total removal of the soft material, not to original limitations in its thickness.

Summary

The subsequent stream pattern of the Central Zagros Region is largely determined by variations in the original development and present exposure of the Cretaceous flysch formation. In Inner Luristan these beds are both thick and widely exposed and the majority of the stream pattern is subsequent. The extensive exposure of the flysch series in this region is a result of gentle folding and the absence of recent broad uplift of the fold structures. Streams diagonal to the general grain of the orogen, as well as those conforming to the structural trend, are controlled by the outcrop of erodable beds in Luristan. Where the flysch is limited in depth by erosion or nondeposition, subsequent streams are infrequent or unrecognizable. This condition is characteristic of almost three-quarters of that portion of the Central Zagros in which geological information is available.

There is a very poor correlation between the distributions of subsequent reaches and unaligned watergaps. This is largely a result of the relief inversion common in the areas drained by the most important subsequent streams—the anticlines in these areas having a negative rather than positive surface expression. Only 16 of 136 unaligned watergaps in the Central Zagros Region are immediately adjacent to subsequent reaches, 5 of these in the vicinity of Khorramabad and 3 along the northern border of Kuh-i-Kainu. The remainder of the offset gorges tributary to subsequent valleys are widely scattered The poor relationship between the vast majority of unaligned gorges and subsequent reaches does not favor a hypothesis of capture and fragmentation of antecedent or superimposed drainage lines by headward-extending subsequent streams. On the other hand, the strong correspondence between the distribution of unaligned watergaps and *consequent* reaches tends to favor the origin of the gorges as consequent gullies.

CONFORMABLE DRAINAGE AND THE DRAINAGE ANOMALY

Drainage developments consequent upon the individual structures of the orogen and subsequent to the exposure of variations in erodability constitute the largest portion of the Central Zagros drainage pattern. As would be expected, they compose almost the entire tributary network conformable with the the grain of the orogen, as well as significant trend reaches of the through-flowing trunk streams.

Certain portions of the *transverse* drainage pattern are also conformable with the geological matrix, notably the Upper Kashgan, the Upper Chanareh, the Kuh-i-Dasht Basin drainage, the upper Middle Karun, and significant portions of the lower courses of the Marun and Khairabad. In addition, many streams discordant to structure in their upper reaches adopt a consequent or near-consequent path around the last anticlines of the Mountain Front.

Consequent and subsequent reaches occur throughout the Fold Zone both upstream and downstream of major transverse gorges, breaking the drainage anomaly into separate constituents whose specific controls cannot have extended beyond the conformable reaches to either side. This suggests that many individual drainage anomalies had independent origins, which implies, in turn, that the stream systems evolved in piecemeal fashion. This could be the case only if the present drainage pattern was formed by a process of abstraction involving piracy both along and across the strike. The presence of conformable drainage all along the margin of the Thrust Zone and again along the periphery of the Imbricate Zone indicates that the drainage anomalies in each of the major tectonic zones of the highland are also independent phenomena.

Though 136 isolated watergaps temporarily may be assigned to normal gully erosion, some 160 others that are aligned in series, or continue the prior line of the stream through different tectonic environments, require a different explanation. Moreover, the great transverse reaches of the Kashgan, Dez, Bakhtiari, and Middle Karun remain unexplained. If these most important elements of the drainage net did not originate in a consequent or subsequent manner in the present structural and lithological environment, they must have been established by processes of drainage formation peculiar to the present geological environment, by processes operating in a structural and lithologic matrix which has since disappeared as a result of general denudation, or as antecedent or superimposed drainage developments. It will be seen in the ensuing pages that all of these alternatives actually played roles in the development of the transverse drainage of the Zagros Highland.

Chapter VIII

Antecedent Drainage in the Central Zagros

Prior to the realization of the complexity of Cenozoic earth movements and erosional responses, drainage systems transverse to the geological structures of a mountain landscape were frequently explained as being antecedent to those structures.

It is now generally believed that truly antecedent drainage could be preserved only in the youngest Cenozoic mountain systems. Such drainage is thought to have developed on a landscape that was later subjected to diastrophism, with the trunk streams maintaining themselves in their courses throughout the deformation. It would be possible for streams of this type to rise at elevations inferior to those of the ranges later pushing up across their paths. Much of the transverse drainage of such a great range as the Himalayas is still considered by authorities to be antecedent,[1] though the structures crossed are no longer anticlines but piles of immense nappes and flat thrusts.

The theory of drainage antecedence has one very important prerequisite; it requires that the structural elements of the headwater region be more archaic than those transected downstream. The Zagros drainage pattern must be carefully examined in the light of the antecedent drainage hypothesis because the relationship between tectonic evolution and drainage direction in the Zagros epitomizes the requisite conditions for the development of drainage anomalies resulting from the presence of antecedent streams.

As seen in Chapter III, the Zagros Mountain belt has been expanding in a southwesterly direction since the Jurassic. Its runoff heads in what appears to be the protaxial area and is channeled out onto an alluvial foredeep in the same direction. Accordingly, the primary condition for the development of antecedent through-flowing drainage is satisfied in the Zagros region.

The transverse pattern of the major streams is so striking on small-scale maps of the Zagros that those familiar with the youth and history of the highland, including petroleum geologists on the scene, have concluded that the anomalous drainage is antecedent.[2] Their initial hypothesis, based on the general relationship between drainage and structure, is reinforced in their view by the presence here of precipitous meandering gorges in the hardest rocks exposed in the area: a feature popularly taken as evidence of drainage antecedence or superposition.

In this chapter it will be shown that these facts have been misinterpreted, and that in no case does any stream even *possibly* antecedent attain great length across the trend of the Zagros orogen. It will be seen, moreover, that the great trunk streams of the orogen do not incorporate any transverse reaches that could be attributed to drainage antecedence.

Varieties and Indications of Antecedent Drainage

Ideally, antecedent streams head in a very old highland adjacent to a younger orogenic system, or in a protaxial range within the mountain belt, and flow outward through structures that postdate those of the source region. Such a condition is perfectly satisfied in the Himalayas, for example, but not in the Appalachians. In the latter region the drainage rises at the tectonic "front" of the orogenic system, where its folds are gradually passing out into an undeformed foreland, and exits through its protaxis—the crystalline zone. The early realization that, due to this relationship, the present Appalachian streams could not be a lineal descendant of antecedent systems was a great impetus to drainage study in that area.

It might be presumed that unusually high or

---

[1] D. N. Wadia, *The Geology of India*, 3rd ed. London: Macmillan, 1961, pp. 29–30, 435–436.

[2] This idea has been reiterated most recently by H. E. Wright, Jr., "Pleistocene Glaciation in Kurdistan," *Eiszeitalter und Gegenwart*, 12 (1962), 136.

massive structures within an orogen would predate smaller adjacent structures, in which case the former could originate antecedent systems of their own: geologically discordant streams heading in the midst of the orogen. It might also be presumed that such streams would encounter other large structures of a similar early origin and might take a consequent path *around* them, as they do *off* the originating structures. Thus there could be through-flowing streams antecedent to the development of the deformational belt as a whole, streams consequent on the first folding but antecedent to all subsequent deformation, and streams consequent on folds of certain amplitudes and antecedent to all those of a smaller amplitude, assuming the latter formed more recently. On the other hand, it is possible that the highest structures are coeval to the lesser ones and reach their pre-eminence only by rejuvenated folding or broad warping, being unable as a consequence to originate antecedent drainage lines. The presence or absence of direct discordant reaches heading on high structures can thereby shed light on the problem of the relationship between broad warping and local folding.

The surface indications of antecedent drainage are in many ways the reverse of those resulting from consequent and subsequent developments. Most important, antecedent streams should cross the orogen and its individual structures with little deviation. Course inflections should not be attributable to structure or lithology; in fact, there should be no consistent relationships of any kind between an antecedent drainage network and its geological matrix. The watergaps cut by antecedent streams would not transect individual folds in similar angles everywhere, but would be oriented variously to anticlinal axes from one area to another. However, along each individual antecedent reach the watergaps created by the stream could, and perhaps should, have similar geographic orientations, though their orientations to structure might be diverse. Antecedent streams should breach anticlinal barriers at all points, not consistently near plunging noses or at fold culminations.

It is a very important criterion of antecedent streams that their gorges should continue the line of that part of the stream which is not engorged—they should, in other words, be *aligned* or *undeflected* reaches. A deviation of engorged reaches from the general line of the stream implies structural control which is incompatible with the antecedent drainage hypothesis.

Additional evidence in favor of an antecedent origin for a large-scale transverse drainage system would be a progressive change in gorge form, in similar rocks, from the inner to the outer ranges of a highland. If the interior gorges were consistently more open and weathered than those approaching the tectonic front, the natural conclusion would be that the outer gorges are younger and are possibly the product of antecedent streams flowing across a constantly enlarging fold belt.

It might be objected that superposition of drainage from a covermass on the outer folds would produce the same result. Superposition would indeed produce young gorges in the anticlines on the outer edge of the orogen, but it would leave the youngest gorges of all at the interior limit of the hypothetical covermass. Since rejuvenation can only proceed in an upstream direction, the inner margin of such a covermass would be the last part to be transected, resulting in a later superposition of drainage there than at the outer margin of the orogen where the rejuvenation must begin. Were the hypothetical covermass marine, however, a gradual withdrawal of the sea would uncover the orogenic front last, and would result in later stream superposition on the outermost structures. Since the Zagros region has been emergent in its entire post-Miocene history, as proved by a continuous stratigraphic record, the physiographic consequences of a theoretical marine superposition on Pliocene-Pleistocene folds need not concern us.

The concept of antecedent drainage must also include drainage consequent on the initial deformation in an area, but disharmonic to the fully developed folds. Streams of this type would follow paths that have a tendency to be natural spillways, but would not follow these depressions axially. Indeed, they might cut across fold noses and into the lower parts of fold flanks, barely missing a truly consequent path in many instances. Figure 50 illustrates the evolution of a stream consequent upon embryonic folds and fully controlled by them, but antecedent to the folds as they are presently developed. A stream having such an origin could be termed an antecedent orogenic-consequent; it would be difficult to

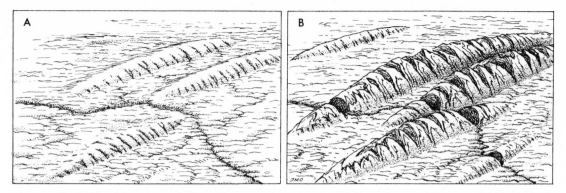

FIGURE 50. Origin of antecedent drainage lines consequent on partially formed or partially exposed folds. A. Drainage consequent on either initial deformation or folds which are not fully exposed due to the presence of an overburden of erodable materials. B. Drainage discordances produced by renewed deformation or full exposure of the fold structures.

distinguish from a consequent stream displaced in down-cutting by planation in soft beds, by disharmonic folding, or by floodplain superposition.

ANTECEDENT DRAINAGE IN THE CENTRAL ZAGROS

All of the foregoing indications of antecedent drainage may be discovered in the Zagros Highland. More than 160 anticlinal transections continue the lines of the streams entering them from preceding lowlands without significant deflection; in many areas strong variations in structure and lithology have no effect on the paths of the streams that encounter them; fold swarms are transected in gorges variously oriented to structural trends; and anticlines are split by through-flowing streams at every point from one plunging tip to the other. Finally, the transverse gorges do appear to be progressively more youthful in each tectonic zone moving southwestward from the protaxis of the highland to the Mountain Front.

Though all of these separate indications of antecedent drainage are present in the Zagros Highland, they are not always present in the proper combinations to *prove* the existence of antecedent streams. Few of the individual indications of antecedent drainage are conclusive unless supported by correlative evidence, for many of the individual traits of antecedent streams can also be associated with other drainage-fixing mechanisms. More important, with the exception of progressive changes in gorge form in a downstream direction, the above indications of drainage antecedence are not strongly characteristic of those trunk streams of the Zagros Highland whose general patterns are most suggestive of drainage antecedence.

Behavior of Trunk Streams at Zonal Contacts

The antecedent drainage hypothesis is most favored in the Zagros region by the origin in the protaxial zone of the drainage that is transverse to the bulk of the highland. If truly antecedent, however, the through-flowing drainage lines coming out of the protaxial zone should pass into the adjacent zone without significant deflection along the zonal contact. Any deflection along the trend at this contact, whether in a consequent or subsequent valley, marks the termination of the effect producing a transverse stream prior to the deflection. If the stream departs once more from a conformable path, it does so under a new set of local controls that may be generically *similar* to those operating upstream from the trend reach, but which are independent of them.

Similarly, if the transverse drainage lines are truly antecedent to the development of any structural zone, their entry into that zone and their passage· across it could not be expected to be in paths conformable with the zone's transverse structure; consistent conformity to structure or lithology would obviate the necessity of invoking the hypothesis of stream antecedence in that zone. Therefore, in evaluating the antecedent drainage hypothesis in any highland, it is necessary to study the behavior of the main drainage lines as they pass out of one structural and historical zone and into another.

In the Zagros Highland there are four zones in which antecedent transverse drainage could have originated: the protaxial zone of crystalline nappes or thrusts, the Cretaceous limestone nappe or thrust, the Imbricate Zone, and the Fold Zone. Streams rising in all but the latter could have been antecedent to one or more entire zones, beginning with the adjacent zone to the southwest. If the drainage of any tectonic zone is not antecedent to the younger structures of the zone immediately adjacent, it cannot be a source of antecedent streams in any other zone, and the drainage entering it from the northeast also cannot be antecedent to any other zone.

The requirement of direct crossings of zonal contacts is fatal to the hypothesis of antecedent drainage in the Zagros Highland. The Thrust Zone, the Imbricate Zone, and the Fold Zone are full of disharmonies between drainage and geological structure, but nowhere does a stream coming from one of these zones create an immediate disharmony in the adjacent structural province. The contacts between the zones are in all cases lines of consequent or subsequent drainage deflection.

The Crystalline-Sedimentary Contact

It would seem likely that the streams consequent upon the final exposure of the protaxis of the Zagros orogen, presently seen in the crystalline ranges southwest of Hamadan, might have been antecedent to the Cenomanian limestone arches of the Mountain Front as it was expressed in Upper Cretaceous time— the Mountain Front later becoming overthrust onto the detrital beds of the Upper Cretaceous foredeep to form the limestone thrust complex. However, such streams, if they ever existed, cannot be found crossing the limestone thrusts today.

Figure 36 indicates that in the Karkheh Basin the present courses of the streams heading in the crystalline zone are quite direct across the crystalline thrusts until the line of the Gamas Ab is reached, where they are deflected along the contact between the Cretaceous limestone and crystalline thrust sheets. Where the runoff of the protaxis (the Gamas Ab) at last breaks through the limestone thrust at Bisitun, it is not certain whether the gap is a recess between two converging thrust arcs or an erosional vale in the most elevated portion of the Cretaceous thrust. The Lower Gamas Ab moves transversely across a broad lowland in which the limestones of the Cretaceous thrust are replaced by older radiolarites and associated basic igneous masses. The transverse reach of the Gamas Ab at Bisitun may be either consequent or subsequent, but in view of its previous deflection along the crystalline-sedimentary contact it could hardly be antecedent. A consequent origin might be favored by the structural control of the Upper Gamas Ab, but fragments of Cenomanian limestone in the Bisitun gap, along with the older radiolarite formations, probably indicate an erosional origin for this transverse vale, which may thus be an unroofed structural culmination.

The headwaters of the Dez River also rise in the crystalline zone. Figure 39 shows that three of the Dez headwater tributaries are deflected along the strike as soon as they reach the limestone thrust, but a fourth crosses the thrust directly at a narrowing in its outcrop— possibly originally a saddle between two plunging anticlinal structures.

The Zayendeh Rud transects the limestone thrust from southwest to northeast, flowing from the Imbricate Zone toward the crystalline thrust. As noted in Chapter VI, this appears to be a drainage reversal with the capture site located in the vicinity of the crystalline-sedimentary contact. Information on the location of this contact in the southeastern half of the Central Zagros region was not available to the writer, so that the behavior of the Zayendeh Rud at this critical line cannot be stated.

The Karun headwaters, which unite east of Junaqan, cross a broad expanse of the limestone thrust on alluvial plains. They appear to rise on the limestone thrust itself, or possibly on the front of the crystalline thrust complex. Due to the unavailability of geological information the effect of structures on the drainage of this interior zone cannot be stated.

The east branch of the Malbur gathers in isolated exposures of the Cretaceous limestone thrust which rise from alluvial basins. The entire Malbur system is developed in folds between the outer imbrics and the thrust margin.

Course deflections thus occur wherever through-flowing streams known to rise in the crystalline zone encounter the rocks of the limestone thrusts. These consequent diversions deny the validity of the hypothesis of antecedent drainage from a crystalline protaxial zone as the originator of the present transverse drainage pattern of the Zagros Highland, despite the ideal disposition of its structural and historical divisions for the development of such drainage.

The deflection of drainage along the contact between the crystalline and Cretaceous limestone thrusts may indicate that upon its first emergence from the Cretaceous sea the anticlinorium originating the limestone thrust complex was a line of islands that were separated from the crystalline protaxial zone by marine straits. Such straits would have received the runoff of the protaxial zone, protecting the late Cretaceous anticlinorium from exogenous drainage and permitting the stream pattern in that area to develop autogenously. When the sea was finally extinguished in Miocene time the hypothetical ancient straits would have remained expressed in the region's hydrography as a series of longitudinal streams receiving consequent runoff from both the protaxis and limestone thrust zones. This trend valley is continuous through the length of the Zagros Highland, but is utilized discontinuously by several different drainage lines coming from the interior. These streams turn out of this structural lowland by paths that might be either consequent (if sited between thrust arcs that were initially islands) or the result of captures by headward-extending valleys in the limestone thrust complex.

The Thrust Zone Contact with the Fold and Imbricate Zones

The limestone thrust southwest of the crystalline zone does not originate any trunk streams in the northern two-thirds of the Central Zagros Region, and is itself transected by the drainage moving southwestward from the protaxis—after its deflection along the thrust margin. This might suggest that headward gullying by consequent drainage originating on the Cenomanian thrust captured the consequent drainage coming from the protaxial zone, and that the streams leaving the Cretaceous limestone thrust were consequent upon the original anticlinorium from which the thrust developed and at the same time antecedent to the formation of the Pliocene Fold Zone, and therefore responsible for the anomalous transverse drainage of that region.

This hypothesis is again defeated by consequent and subsequent drainage deflections at zonal contacts. Except in the Malbur Basin, the lowland along the southwestern margin of the limestone thrust has a strong deflecting effect on all drainage coming out of the Thrust Zone, the effect being similar to that of the lowland along the front of the crystalline thrust. The structures on the far side of this valley, whether anticlines, imbric slabs, or homoclinal belts, all turn the runoff of the Thrust Zone to some extent.

Southwestward beyond the limestone thrust margin all major tributaries in the Karkheh basin are immediately diverted along the strike, as Figure 36 indicates. This cancels the effect of the Cretaceous limestone thrust as the originator of the drainage discordance that soon becomes evident in the Fold Zone. The drainage is deflected in this case by the erodability of the soft radiolarite beds exposed in a broad belt southwest of the Cretaceous thrust. The Rawansir, Qara Su, Gamas Ab, and Darreh Gizarau, coming from the Thrust Zone, are drawn to a drainage node on the radiolarite mass immediately before the center of the nearest Cenomanian anticline ushering in the simply folded belt. This drainage then breaks through the center of the anticline and a second arch tangent to it. The line of the gorge is unrelated to the lines of any of the streams that funnel into it.

Farther to the east, the Upper Kashgan crosses the front of the limestone thrust and then swings along the trend in a structural valley underlain by Fars and Bakhtiari beds. Only after this 24-mile deflection does it slip briefly across the grain of the fold belt, even then utilizing an outcrop of weaker formations between a Cenomanian anticline and a synclinal peak of Asmari limestone. Thus either structural or lithological control seizes the trunk streams of the Karkheh Basin (the Qara Su and its tributaries and the Kashgan) as soon as they escape the Cretaceous thrust.

In the Dez Basin (Figure 39) the limestone thrust is exposed in a band seldom five miles in width between the crystalline thrusts and the Imbricate Zone. The headwaters of the Dez River unite from opposite directions at Dorud to cut across this band, continuing through a canyon in the great slab of Bakhtiari conglomerate which covers the contacts between the thrust margin and the Imbricate and Fold zones. Emerging from the Pliocene conglomerate covermass, the river immediately makes a sharp swing to the south into a subsequent basin in the Fold Zone, which releases it from any previous controls.

Farther to the southeast, two affluents of the

Gand Ab leave the Cretaceous thrust and move without any deviation across the first imbric slab in the zone of sheared anticlines. However, one of the tributaries in question exits from the thrust in a convenient position to encounter only the plunging termini of this initial barrier, and each is immediately deflected along the strike at the next obstacle it encounters: a second imbric in one case, and in the other a lithological barrier rising from an erosional valley. Structural control thus seizes these streams a little beyond the zonal contact, with their initial entry into the new zone in one case being near-consequent even though transverse.

Before crossing the Thrust Zone *from* the Imbricate Zone the endoreic Zayendeh Rud jogs into a homoclinal valley along the front of the limestone thrust for four miles. The Karun headwaters, flowing in the opposite direction (Figure 45), are deflected similarly and for a greater distance at Junaqan, the diverting lowland here being synclinal. The Upper Wanak rises in the Imbricate Zone, moves northeastward toward the Cretaceous thrust at Buldaji, and then parallels the thrust margin for some twenty-five miles before it turns back toward the Outer Zagros. However, the Malbur headwaters move directly away from the outlying thrust fragments at their source and breach the center of the first anticline adjacent to the Thrust Zone.

The consequent and subsequent course deflections described above release nearly all through-flowing drainage lines from the controls which have directed their passage through the Thrust Zone. With the exception of the Malbur all drainage crossing the Imbricate and Fold zones clearly does so under new controls that are determined by the geological characteristics of those zones alone. Thus the present drainage lines passing through the Imbricate and Fold zones could not have originated as antecedent streams that were consequent on the upheaval of any element in the Thrust Zone.

The deflection of drainage along the contact between the Thrust Zone and the Imbricate Zone may, as in the case of the deflections between the crystalline and limestone thrust, have been the result of the emergence of the zone to the southwest as an anticlinorium initially separated from the previously emergent area by marine straits.

The Imbricate Zone Contact with the Fold Zone

It must next be determined whether streams coming out of the Imbricate Zone are once more deflected at the border of the Fold Zone or whether drainage antecedence is favored at last by a lack of structural control at the inner margin of the Fold Zone.

The Saidmarreh and Kashgan rivers enter the Fold Zone directly from the Thrust Zone after the course deflections noted above. The Gand Ab (Figure 39) approaches the Fold Zone obliquely twenty miles southwest of the base of its great loop, then turns 90 degrees to cross a great overturned hogback, an unroofed anticline, and a synclinal mountain. It then swings northwestward into a subsequent valley running along the northeastern flank of the Kainu arch and follows it along the trend for twelve miles before embarking upon its tortuous course across the corrugations of the fold belt. The Gand Ab is thus diverted away from its line across the Imbricate Zone by subsequent valleys even though a continuation of its line across the imbrics would have taken it directly into a syncline in the Fold Zone.

The Upper Karun (Figure 45) flows southeastward along the trend in a fault-line valley between a synclinal horst (Kuh-i-Lijan) and a faulted anticline, and then swings southwestward through a structural saddle betweeen this anticlinal slice and an unfaulted arch to the south of it. The second anticline met by the Karun, fifteen miles farther on, turns the river into a strike path for four miles. Thus the Karun escapes the Imbricate Zone by a consequent path along the trend, and is deflected into variously oriented consequent paths by the first two anticlines it encounters in the Fold Zone. Beyond this point the stream cuts through four Asmari anticlines in rapid succession. Only after entering the Fold Zone concordantly does the Karun adopt a discordant path; this path cannot, therefore, be attributed to antecedent drainage issuing from the Inner Orogen.

The Malbur follows a generally northeastward course across the folds behind the Kuh-i-Dina imbric. It crosses the nose of Kuh-i-Dina in deep gorges, enters a small unroofed anticline in the Fold Zone, and then reverses direction almost completely to move southward into the Khirsan. Thus the stream is channeled away from its previous line across the folded thrust by the first anticline it encounters beyond the zonal contact, the diversion in this instance being subsequent and effected by an anticlinal basin (as on the Gand Ab), rather than consequent, as on the Karun River.

Aside from the Bazuft, a synclinal consequent stream almost throughout, the above are the only streams heading in the Imbricate Zone that later create drainage anomalies in the Fold Zone. None of them crosses the Fold Zone directly from the Imbricate Zone, for each is deflected by the first anticline it encounters in the fold belt. Accordingly, the drainage disharmonies of the Fold Zone can hardly be attributed to any form of antecedent drainage originating in or behind the Imbricate Zone. Though the component parts of the Zagros orogen formed an ideal progression in time and space to initiate antecedent drainage lines which were originally consequent on the upheavals in the interior zones, somehow such drainage is not apparent in the Inner Zagros.

The sections in Figure 7 indicate that, in denudational terms, the Thrust and Imbricate zones evince much greater age than the Fold Zone. Erosional bevels across fault blocks, folds, and beds of all attitudes are striking in the Inner Zagros. Could the original drainage pattern, consequent upon each positive structure as it emerged, and antecedent to those forming later, have been preserved during these planations? It seems that, in view of the time span implied by erosional bevels on hard rocks in the Imbricate Zone, there would be a maximum possibility for the development of subsequent drainage in this zone, and for the disruption of any antecedent pattern not favored by lithological considerations. However, fragmentation of antecedent stream patterns by headward piracy should leave aligned watergaps and windgaps, and, except in areas of relief inversion, the latter are notably infrequent in the Zagros.

In the northeast of the Imbricate Zone there appears to be an extreme development of the Eocene, Oligocene, and Oligo-Miocene (Asmari) formations, and a corresponding absence of the Upper Cretaceous flysch. This suggests that the Imbricate Zone rose as a separate anticlinorium in front of the Thrust Zone, with a sea basin of unusual depth persisting between the two submerged arches

until post-Miocene time. Thus streams issuing from the Thrust Zone as late as the early Pliocene probably encountered a waterbody in front of an emerging Imbricate Zone anticlinorium, which would have protected the latter from all drainage incursions from beyond.

In summation, stream patterns in the interior of the orogen and at the contacts of all the structural belts are such that we are forced to look for some mechanism of drainage diversion here, producing consequent and subsequent streams rather than the direct antecedent or superimposed drainage lines that might have been expected in this region.

Antecedent Drainage Originating Within the Fold Zone

It has been shown that no drainage lines cleave directly through the Fold Zone from the Inner Zagros. Thus drainage from the Inner Zagros does not appear to have transgressed upon the younger structures of the Outer Zagros. The drainage discordances in the Fold Zone are not developed until the through-flowing drainage has already penetrated it concordantly by consequent or subsequent paths. Accordingly, it appears that the anomalous transverse drainage of the Outer Zagros had its inception *within* that zone, being a response to local geologic conditions. It remains to be seen whether antecedent drainage originating within the fold belt could have produced the anticlinal transections so widespread in that area.

In any emergent area having undergone diastrophism it is probable that not all anticlines were formed simultaneously. Certain anticlines must have been expressed in the landscape at a somewhat earlier date than others. In such a case the initial consequent runoff of these anticlines would have been established in courses antecedent to the formation of at least some adjacent folds. Such streams might cut transversely through younger folds upheaved across their paths, but they would be deflected in avoidance of any structure developed in the initial phases of the diastrophism—that is to say, any primary structure coeval to that originating the antecedent stream.

Wide variations in the magnitudes and states of preservation of individual anticlines in the simply folded portion of the Zagros

Highland suggest that some of the folds in this region may be primary structures, all others having been formed somewhat more recently under emergent conditions. This being the case, the development of *locally* antecedent drainage lines would have been favored in the Fold Zone.

Relation to Primary Anticlines

The distribution of transverse gorges created by locally antecedent drainage lines should be related to the arrangement of the most denuded and presumably oldest anticlines of the simply folded belt. It might also be assumed that the primary structures would be the most elevated and perhaps the most complex in the Fold Zone, having undergone repeated compression as later folds were squeezed up about them.

The geognostic map and geological cross-sections (Figures 14 and 7) indicate several anticlines that could be primary structures. The ranges that truly dominate the fold belt are Kabir Kuh, Kuh-i-Kainu and its extension Kuh-i-Mafarun, and Kuh-i-Mungasht; each an immense Cenomanian anticline, the latter trio cresting in the neighborhood of 12,000 feet. Kabir Kuh is 3,000 feet lower and is inferior in height to many shorter anticlines in the fold belt, but clearly dominates southwestern Luristan, rising about 3,000 feet above nearby crests and as much as 6,000 feet above the surrounding valleys. All four ranges are massive barriers, unbreached by transverse drainage except at their plunging termini. In each of these ranges the outcrop of the Cenomanian formations is unusually broad and extends upwards of 80 miles along the strike of the orogen. The amplitudes of these individual folds are also extremely high, as shown on the profiles of the Asmari limestone horizon (Figure 5). Figure 14 shows that either these structures have been stripped of their entire Cenozoic and Upper Cretaceous cover, or they never possessed such a cover. In the first instance, the folds could be presumed to have undergone more severe denudation than adjacent structures owing to their superior height or age;[3] alternatively, these

---

[3] It could be presumed that superior height might be associated with greater age in compressive structures, since folds already formed and subject to jointing and erosion would present less resistance to further compression than the unfolded rocks between them, which resisted compression or were warped downward in the initial deformation, thereafter being subject to sedimentation from the primary folds.

folds would already have pushed above the level of sedimentation when the remainder of the Outer Zagros was still a sea floor, inevitably becoming the first folds emergent in this zone.

The geognostic map (Figure 14), the profiles of the Asmari limestone (Figure 5), and the geological cross-sections (Figure 7) indicate many other anticlines of great amplitude but generally less longitudinal persistence. Outstanding among these are the Anaran-Siah Kuh line at the Mountain Front in Luristan, Kuh-i-Safid north of Khorramabad, the Qandi-Farul-Shirgun line between the lower courses of the Sehzar and Karun, Qarum north of Malamir, Safid and Bingistan north of Behbehan, and Khami and Lar east of the same town. The central portions of these Cenomanian arches are also avoided by through-flowing drainage lines and discordant tributaries, but a few of them are transected in considerable gorges a few miles from their crests. Some of the primary anticlines that have originated antecedent drainage transverse to adjacent folds may not be apparent in the landscape today. This is due to the prevalence of relief inversion in plateau-like fold areas that are characterized by heavy accumulations of the Upper Cretaceous flysch. For example, section DD in Figure 7 reveals that the present surface expression of the Kuh-i-Safid anticline is a poor reflection of the actual magnitude of this structure. A reconstruction of the Asmari limestone carapace of Kuh-i-Safid would show it to be an immense feature by comparison with the anticlines to the southwest, whose surface expressions, due to their intact nature, presently surpass that of the primary fold along the line of the section.

Therefore, in evaluating the possibility of local drainage antecedence in any region, direct anticlinal transections must be related to the distribution of large axial basins, as well as to large mountain ranges. For instance, the former domes now expressed as the Hulailan and Tarhan basins in Luristan appear to have originated drainage antecedent to one or more lesser anticlines southwest of them.

Figure 51 portrays the distribution of watergaps that cause no deflection of the stream passing through them. Also indicated are the anticlines influencing the total stream pattern by originating and deflecting transverse drainage lines. As expected, the great barrier ranges—Mungasht, Kainu-Mafarun, and Kabir Kuh—originate many streams which

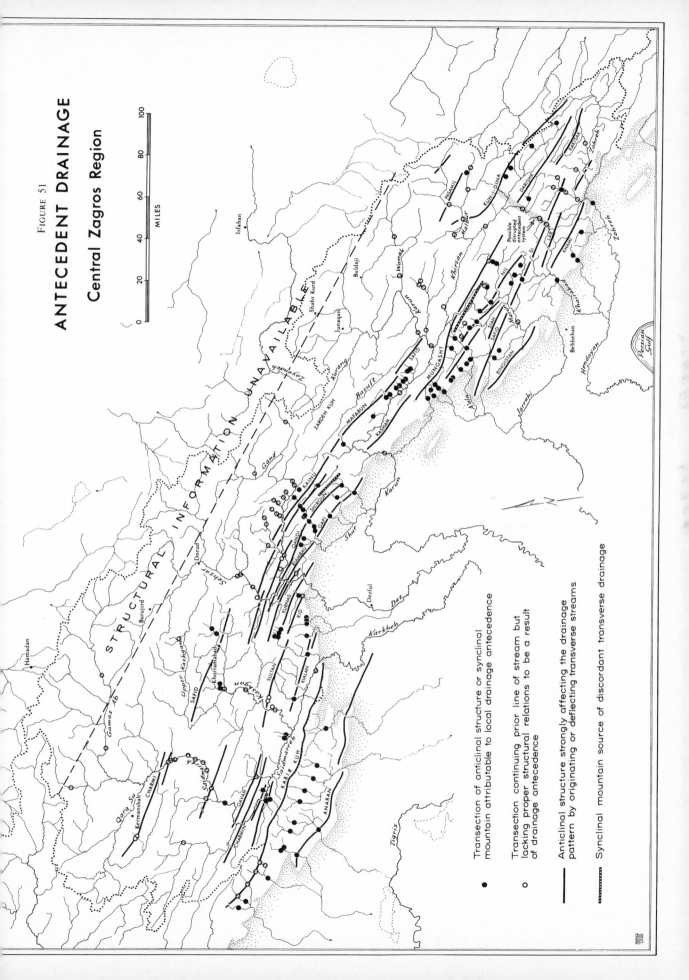

FIGURE 51

ANTECEDENT DRAINAGE

Central Zagros Region

MILES

● Transection of anticlinal structure or synclinal
mountain attributable to local drainage antecedence

○ Transection continuing prior line of stream but
lacking proper structural relations to be a result
of drainage antecedence

Anticlinal structure strongly affecting the drainage
pattern by originating or deflecting transverse streams

Synclinal mountain source of discordant transverse drainage

slice through smaller neighboring anticlines without significant deviation from the general lines of their canyons in the flanks of the great domes. These streams certainly appear to be consequent on primary folds and antecedent to younger flanking structures. At the same time the great ranges deflect all approaching drainage lines and hold the major through-flowing streams to trend courses for significant distances. Accordingly, the notion of the primary nature of the greatest and most denuded Cenomanian anticlines is favored both by their deflecting effect on the stream pattern, and by their nurture of drainage which is transverse to smaller adjacent anticlines. Conversely, the hypothesis of local antecedent drainage is supported by the behavior of the drainage lines rising on the primary anticlines.

Complications in the Hypothesis of Local Drainage Antecedence

Unfortunately, the effect of the dominating ranges explains only a small proportion of a rather complex pattern of stream sources and deflections in the Fold Zone. Several short transverse streams head in rather insignificant folds or on synclinal mountains, and many stream deflections are also caused by relatively minor barriers. Antecedent drainage from Kabir Kuh, the Kainu-Mafarun line, and Mungasht could account for no more than 27 of the 160 aligned watergaps in the Central Zagros Region, while the secondary folds mentioned above might be responsible for 11 additional anticlinal transections by direct antecedent streams.

Though the effect of the Kabir Kuh watershed on the next anticline to the south is unmistakable, it seems to be abetted by the open nature of the folding in Pusht-i-Kuh. The adjacent anticline, whose central portion has virtually disappeared under the erosional onslaught of nine transecting streams heading in Kabir Kuh, is a broad fold of low amplitude, some eight to sixteen miles from the primary fold. The immense Kainu-Mafarun arch, which lies in a tightly folded area, has a less obvious effect as a transverse drainage originator. Though its core is the source of six possibly antecedent streams, each of which splits an anticline tangent to the primary structure, none extends more than five miles across the strike before suffering deflection into a synclinal or subsequent valley. Kuh-i-

Safid, a saddle in the southeastern end of Mafarun, is still covered by Eocene beds, but itself originates five streams transverse to an almost equal arch immediately adjacent.

The latter is but one instance of a recurrent paradox: direct transverse drainage whose source is in a quite minor anticline or even a synclinal mountain. Such streams are hardly in accordance with the hypothesis of local drainage antecedence resulting from the prior formation of certain folds. Some of these local drainage enigmas can be explained as the result of fragmentation of former antecedent drainage lines by piratical streams extending along the strike. The most conspicuous example is found on the east branch of the Ab-i-Khairabad, which rises on a low Asmari limestone swell and flows directly through a major Cenomanian arch, splitting a second Cenomanian anticline after an eight-mile synclinal interlude.

The stream in question is part of the drainage of a straight furrow which crosses three anticlines of the Khairabad Basin, two more west of the Khirsan, another east of the Khirsan, and the huge imbric of Kuh-i-Dina itself. The gap in the Dina crest is nearly 4,000 feet deep and appears to be sited on a transverse fault. The furrow, which is currently utilized by three different streams, is suggestive of an ancient transverse valley whose upper portion has been captured by the Ab-i-Khirsan since the present structures were mapped out, but previous to their full development. At the mid-furrow divide, the ridge separating the Khirsan and Khairabad systems is breached by a broad and deep erosional windgap, an unusual feature in regions of anticlinal mountain ranges.

Similar anomalies that cannot be explained as the disruption of older antecedent systems occur elsewhere in the Outer Zagros. Immediately to the southeast of the Khairabad the north branch of the Zohreh takes a direct course through three anticlinal structures, one a highly denuded Cenomanian arch, though the stream heads in a fold whose Middle Cretaceous core is only beginning to be exposed. Primary ridges cannot be invoked to explain the zigzag gorge patterns of the Sehzar or Bakhtiari rivers, or of the Kashgan and Saidmarreh, whose tributaries unite at obtuse angles on subsequent lowlands and pursue straight discordant courses only below these confluences.

Anticlinal transections accomplished by streams presently heading on synclinal ranges cannot be ruled out as effects of drainage antecedence. Clearly the originally consequent runoff of an Asmari anticline will, upon the breaching of the dome's hard shell, drain its retreating Asmari hogbacks while the relief of the structure is being inverted by denudation. Thus the flank drainage of Asmari synclinal ranges is a matter of progressive stream extension across the axes of adjacent breached anticlines, the extension being facilitated by the soft flysch beds underlying the Asmari shell. Downcutting will in time expose the Cenomanian core of the fold, resulting in the superposition of the initially consequent and later obsequent drainage on the hard rocks below. At the same time, the stream may be antecedent to folds forming in its path farther downstream. These relations are all quite normal as long as the first fold transected by the runoff of the synclinal mountain is a major structure that could have originated antecedent drainage in a downstream direction—in particular, a strongly denuded Cenomanian anticline of greater amplitude than the transected arches beyond it (Figure 52). The transection of the Shirgun arch by the runoff of the synclinal range south of Kainu appears to be an example of such a development—the drainage continuing on to slice through several subsidiary arches without deviation (Figure 45). The northwestern feeders of the Marun River also accomplish a series of anticlinal transections below their synclinal mountain source, the cuts all appearing to have been accomplished by headward-extending antecedent streams.

Streams which head on synclinal ranges and first cross insignificant flexures and *then* greater obstacles beyond would not appear to be antecedent above their crossing of the greatest flexure; nor would those transverse streams that head on less significant anticlines to split greater ones immediately adjacent. In such cases it is more likely that the transection of the greater anticline is accomplished over a considerable period of time by consequent gullies that breach the capping formation and extend headward across the fold axis in the soft beds beneath. From expanding subsequent vales in the flysch formations these streams would in time be superimposed upon the harder Cenomanian formations which eventually resurrect the anticline as a positive feature throughout.

The Antecedent Drainage Pattern

Figure 51 indicates the maximum possible extent of antecedent transverse drainage originating within the Fold Zone. The effect of the hypothetical antecedent drainage is clearly limited to the exterior of the orogen, and generally to transections of obviously youthful Asmari limestone anticlines.

In no case does a possibly antecedent stream in the Fold Zone attain great length; conversely, the great trunk streams of the orogen, whose transverse reaches are still unexplained, do not appear to incorporate any transverse reaches that could be attributed to drainage antecedence, either local or regional. The watergaps of the trunk streams either lack any semblance of alignment or cannot be related to the consequent runoff of any primary anticline.

Antecedent drainage phenomena are best expressed in the regions in which the erodable Cretaceous flysch formation is weakly developed. Whereas consequent streams are dominant where the soft flysch is absent as a result of erosion as well as nondeposition, the antecedent network is limited to areas of originally thin flysch development and minimum erosion. Without more detailed study of interstream areas, it is impossible to state whether antecedent drainage lines originally crossed

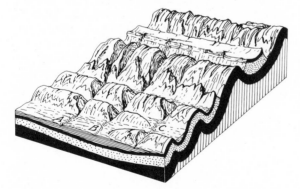

FIGURE 52. Antecedent drainage heading in a syncline. Streams A and B originally consequent on a large arch of Cenomanian limestone and antecedent to two younger anticlines immediately adjacent. The consequent gullies have extended headward through the Cenomanian arch, tapping the runoff of the synclinal range beyond. Stream C is not consequent on the Cenomanian anticline, nor antecedent to the outer folds, for the line of the stream does not continue any significant erosional feature on the Cenomanian arch.

the areas in which subsequent streams are now dominant, for the relief in these areas is largely inverted today. Paired windgaps that appear to be the product of fluvial erosion were observed on the rims of a few synclinal heights in Inner Luristan, and the apparent rapidity of scarp retreat due to sapping by springs may have destroyed many others. However, in the Central Zagros there are no watergap-windgap lines of the type that point to large-scale disruption of past transverse drainage by headward-extending subsequent streams.

The Ab-i-Balut, which rises on Kuh-i-Kainu to split four successive anticlines to the southwest with little deviation, is the best example of an antecedent drainage line in the Central Zagros (Figure 45). However, to the strike deflection preceding its fifth anticlinal transection, this stream is only seventeen miles in length. The east branch of the Rud-i-Gawi which runs off Kabir Kuh to slice directly through two broad swells is only a mile longer. All other transverse streams that could be attributed to drainage antecedence have considerably less persistence across the strike of the folding. Though a multitude of short antecedent streams may have produced, in the aggregate, a considerable number of individual transverse gorges in the Outer Zagros, not one of the *major* streams of the highland could have been antecedent to the structures it now crosses. The drainage anomaly as it is revealed on small-scale maps of the Zagros region cannot be explained as a manifestation of drainage antecedence. The drainage anomaly as it is seen in individual slotlike *tangs* can be attributed in part to local drainage antecedence.

In a number of instances less significant folds than might have been expected appear to have originated direct transverse streams. Similarly, the downstream diversions of some

possibly antecedent transverse lines are accomplished by anticlines not otherwise distinguished from nearby transected folds. These oddities in the pattern of minor transverse drainage are developed in those zones of the fold belt which are characterized by heavy accumulations of the Miocene Lower Fars formation. In the next chapter it will be shown that a second mechanism has produced undeflected transverse gorges on minor streams in the same area in which local drainage antecedence is best developed. This process partakes of both antecedence and superposition, and is functionally related to the presence of the mobile Lower Fars accumulation.

The Residual Drainage Anomaly

More than 90 anticlinal transections can be tentatively attributed to local drainage antecedence, almost 30 per cent of all anticlinal transections in the Central Zagros Region.

Local drainage antecedence has produced most of the anticlinal transections southwest of Kabir Kuh, Kuh-i-Kainu, and Kuh-i-Mungasht. This process also accounts for a sporadic distribution of gorges in the Kuhgalu Fold Plateau area, and isolated *tangs* in the Luristan Basin and around the head of the Dezful Embayment. However, the great through-flowing streams—the Saidmarreh, Kashgan, Dez, and Bakhtiari rivers—remain unexplained by the antecedent drainage hypothesis. Many transverse reaches along the Mountain Front southeast of the Pusht-i-Kuh salient and in the Kuhgalu area also do not appear to be attributable to antecedence alone, as the anticlines on which they rise appear to be similar in magnitude and nearly as youthful as the ones they transect. None of the present transverse streams of the Inner Zagros can be explained as antecedent.

Chapter IX

Superimposed Drainage in the Central Zagros

With increasing awareness of the efficacy of denudation throughout the Cenozoic, current opinion is inclined to disbelieve in the survival of individual drainage lines from the remote times preceding the world-wide Alpine orogeny. Most geomorphologists would prefer to push disharmonic transverse drainage forward in time to an origin on regional erosion surfaces formed in periods of relative tectonic quiescence following the establishment of the main fold structures of the young orogenic belts. The anomalous drainage systems of the Tertiary mountain arcs are regarded as having been "superimposed" from these surfaces. However, the term "superimposed" has been used loosely so that its meaning has become quite ambiguous. Too often discussions of drainage anomalies resemble J. V. Harrison's references to the Zagros problem:

> It seems as if the drainage had been initiated when the country was less folded and tilted southwestward, and as the folds increased in intensity the rivers cut their valley down along the previously determined routes.... The valleys Loftus appears to have had in mind are such as are found along the Karun, where it appears to cross structures haphazard instead of following the trough. As already described I attribute these tangs to superposition of the present drainage on an earlier one.... The behavior of the Karun River at Darkash Warkash, at Ardal, at Wanak, and at many other places, and of the little brooks at Gapi and Riyal can be explained by the supposition that the drainage was initiated when the relief was less and the river system stood about 3,000 feet above the present river level.[1]
>
> The behavior of the rivers in relation to the mountains makes it clear that much of their course was planned on a surface at a level higher than the ranges they now cut through.... Only a few hills ridged its breadth, such as the precursors of Kuh-i-Safid, Kuh-i-Gavah and Kabir Kuh in Luristan and Zardeh Kuh and a few others in Bakhtiari land... The present scenery has resulted from the wearing away of the surface upon which the drainage pattern was initiated, probably during tilting and uplift.[2]

Such statements do not resolve the problem of the *origin* of transverse drainage lines; they merely note that the streams have been rejuvenated in older courses. Yet the term "superposition" is used. Harrison's description of old plains ridged with "the precursors" of the present great folds suggests a belief that the streams were actually consequent on an embryonic fold landscape. If so, they would have been antecedent to the latest and strongest folding and would owe their discordance to present structure to this fact. The streams would thus be antecedent orogenic-consequents dating from the early fold landscape rather than from the pre-fold landscape.

But Harrison also states that "the present scenery has resulted from the wearing away of the surface upon which the drainage was initiated." This phrasing does not imply renewed folding across antecedent stream courses—in which rapid incision would be expected, rather than the wearing away of a surface. Thus Harrison seems to fall into the error of originating drainage in an embryonic fold landscape in a consequent manner and then having it superimposed from some kind of surface onto later structures which his hypothesis offers no time to develop. If the streams were consequent on the primary structures in a time when other structures did not exist, they could not avoid being antecedent to the later structures, obviating all necessity of true superposition across these from an erosion surface or covermass.

In the absence of a marine covermass there must be a stage before that of superposition in which the superimposed systems are established transverse to the fully formed fold belt by some *other* process. Thus every superimposed system is first an antecedent, consequent, subsequent, or compound system, developed in a previous landscape: either the fold landscape itself or a covermass laid over it.

In the Pennsylvania Appalachians there is no trace of the marine cover widely held re-

[1] J. V. Harrison, "The Bakhtiari Country, South-Western Iran," *Geog. Journ.*, 80 (1932), 204–207.
[2] Harrison, "South-West Persia: A Survey of Pish-i-Kuh in Luristan," *Geog. Journ.*, 108 (1946), 70.

sponsible for the superposition of drainage usually thought to have occurred there. In fact, to account for the notable adjustment to geology of the majority of the drainage of the region, the most widely accepted theory of Appalachian drainage supposes a final peneplanation of the area after the removal of the covermass and preceding the rejuvenations which have given us the present landscape.[3] This pushes the hypothetical covermass so far back in time and in the denudation chronology that it is not to be sought in actuality, nor to be questioned because no trace of it has ever been found.

In the Tertiary mountain systems it requires more than a likely arrangement of watergaps to give convincing evidence of superposition. Regardless of the denudational histories of these areas, and whether or not they were fully or partially leveled by erosion—and how many times—their stratigraphic record reveals that they have not suffered marine incursions since their present structures were established. Superposition in the Tertiary mountain systems must therefore proceed from covermasses or erosion surfaces formed by the aggradational or degradational activity of antecedent streams, streams consequent upon the folded surface, or subsequent streams flowing in lines of weakness. In such a situation no stream could be superimposed in its entirety, as would be possible from a marine covermass. Each deposit or surface from which superposition could be accomplished is inseparable from the runoff originating it—a stage in the continuous evolution of a drainage line with a previous history. Drainage problems are not solved by the statement that streams were superimposed from erosion surfaces or alluvial deposits, for these features presuppose earlier transverse streams which must themselves be explained.

VARIETIES OF SUPERIMPOSED DRAINAGE

In the Tertiary mountain systems of the world, episodes of accelerated erosion have alternated with periods of less vigorous denudation. Basins among ranges undergoing rapid demolition have sometimes been so filled with coarse detritus that it has spilled through cols into areas beyond. These basin deposits, unconformable on the folded rocks beneath them, have themselves been warped, uplifted,

and dissected. Thus they become a significant source of superimposed drainage.

Climatic changes that affect hydrology and sediment yields, tectonic events, and temporary elevations of base level occasionally result in aggradation along the drainage lines of a highland. As the lower slopes of valleys become drowned in alluvium, the aggrading stream, or perhaps a distributary channel or an entering tributary, may at some point be floated above resistant spurs. Erosional rejuvenation may later result in the superposition of the drainage onto the buried mountain flanks. Strong tilting of a region in connection with broad warping would facilitate a slight displacement of streams during their rejuvenation; both by the actual migration of a stream toward the lowered part of its flood plain, and by the fact that vertical downcutting in the tilted plain would no longer bring the stream to the previous valley axis. Different types of superposition can also be imagined, which do not involve unconformable covermasses. When resistant layers are separated by great thicknesses of easily eroded materials, streams consequent upon the deformation of the upper horizon may migrate laterally when they expose the weaker subjacent beds. When these beds are transected the stream may encounter underlying resistant horizons discordantly at some points, if not throughout. Similar discordances can result when folding is disharmonic at depth.

Different mechanisms of drainage superposition are unassociated with either erosion surfaces or depositional covermasses. One presumes a greater development in the past of known thrust sheets or recumbent folds.[4] It is assumed that the forward edges of such structures have been consumed by erosion, but that drainage initially consequent on them cut through them to become entrenched in the structures they concealed. Accordingly, the discordant drainage of the erosionally exhumed structures would merely reflect the structural slopes of the vanished exotic slab.

Whether the drainage of such a feature would in fact be consequent upon its *final attitude* has been questioned.[5] It seems more reasonable that consequent drainage would

[3]D. W. Johnson, *Stream Sculpture on the Atlantic Slope.* Columbia University Press, 1931, 142 pp.

[4]H. A. Meyerhoff and E. W. Olmsted, "The Origins of Appalachian Drainage," *Amer. Journ. Sci.,* 232 (1936), 21–41.
[5]A. N. Strahler, "Hypotheses of Stream Development in the Folded Appalachians of Pennsylvania," Geol. Soc. Amer. *Bull.,* 56 (1945), 45–88.

develop on the structure in its initial emergence as an anticline (when it might also have been breached by antecedent streams) and that this drainage would be dissecting the mass continually during its forward movement, so that it would arrive in its final position in an advanced state of denudation. It could hardly then originate new consequent drainage. Though it is not likely that the drainage superimposed from a thrust mass could be consequent upon a reconstruction of its *in situ* geological structure, it seems that drainage of *some* kind must frequently have been superimposed from such a cover. In a very young orogen one would expect to find erosional outliers of such structures. As these would probably be synclinal, their drainage might resemble the consequent pattern described in Chapter VII, one which is recognizable even after relief inversion.

A final mode of stream superposition is inevitable where rocks of varying resistance to erosion are involved in folding. If an anticlinal range is upheld by a resistant formation, so that the drainage divide follows the crest of the structure, gully erosion will attack the arch-bends of the anticline, and will eventually expose less resistant subjacent materials. The consequent (or resequent) gullies will then extend headward across the crest, assisted by the sapping of the resistant layer. The originally linear water-parting will gradually become scalloped, with headward-extending gullies penetrating across the fold's axial plane from both sides. In time this extended consequent drainage will be superimposed upon the crests of harder layers underlying the erodable materials, producing a gorge that transects the anticlinal axis but not the entire structure.

It is not certain how asymmetries in folding would affect this development. Runoff on the steeper limbs would appear to have superior energy to trench the fold envelope and also to produce rapid headward gully extension. However, this runoff might not attain sufficient concentration to entrench as rapidly as the runoff of the more gently inclined limb, on which larger streams would result from expanded possibilities for channel cross-grading.

In the unlikely event that the divide on an asymmetric structure is lowered without shifting one way or the other, the crest of each successive formation, hard and soft, would lie downstream of the head of the drainage of the gentler limb, and would have to be transected

by this drainage. It is realized that this eventuality is too much an abstraction to be relevant to a real situation. However, divide-shifting *toward* the steeper limb as a result of a greater concentration of the runoff on the gentler limb would produce even better possibilities for drainage superposition on the successive crests of the anticlinal strata than would a static divide.

INDICATIONS OF DRAINAGE SUPERPOSITION

Much of the permanent evidence of superimposed drainage is so similar to that of antecedent drainage that in fold systems dating from Paleozoic or Mesozoic time the two could seldom be distinguished. The chief prerequisites for both are a wholesale disregard for the geologic map, alignment of watergaps (or watergaps and windgaps) in series, and a lack of consistency in angles of approach and transection of structural barriers.

In very young fold regions, on the other hand, more conclusive indications of drainage superposition might be preserved. The presence of beveled anticlines in a region indicates a planation postdating the final establishment of the fold structures, the condition most favoring large-scale drainage superposition. If late Tertiary deposits overlie such bevels it is evident that a planation not only occurred, but that any streams associated with it were floated out of their channels, however initially determined, allowing them the maximum opportunity to develop discordant relations in ensuing rejuvenations.

Strongly meandering gorges through anticlinal or synclinal mountains, often said to be evidence of superposition, are at best only a sign of rejuvenation in a mature floodplain or even in rough badlands overlying the resistant beds. Unless such streams have shifted laterally from their original positions on an erosion surface or covermass, their present gorges are merely a continuation of their history as an antecedent, consequent, subsequent, or compound drainage line.

Evidence of recent regional uplift or tilting after significant periods of stability, seen in deep dissection of later Tertiary deposits or erosion surfaces, favors superposition but is not proof of it. The best indication of floodplain superposition would be alluvial terrace fragments preserved at higher elevations than the lips of any anomalous rock gorges. Terrace fragments at an appropriate level in tributary valleys would serve as evidence where declivity of slope or planation by the main stream has not allowed the preservation of high terraces in the trunk valley.

The most certain indication that stream superposition has originated disharmonies between drainage and geological structure is the observation of this process as it occurs: the discovery of a stream entrenched in one lithological environment at the very moment it uncovers another set of geological conditions beneath the first. Somewhat less conclusive evidence of drainage superposition would be a remnant of an unconformable covermass, particularly if it shows grading or facies changes toward the present transverse stream. Unless there is some evidence in the internal composition of the covermass of its genetic relationship to the stream transecting it, it is precarious to assume the superposition of the stream from it. This is an especially critical point in consideration of drainage superposition in the Zagros region, where several types of unconformable covermasses exist, some of which seem to present tempting solutions to local drainage problems.

SUPERIMPOSED DRAINAGE IN THE CENTRAL ZAGROS

Nearly all of the foregoing indications of discordant superposition of drainage may be seen in the Zagros Highland. Local covermasses of Eocene marine formations overlie erosion surfaces in both the Thrust and Imbricate zones; and massive detrital accumulations of Pliocene age fill many synclines, occasionally spilling through structural cols and overlapping onto erosion surfaces. Streams crossing unconformable deposits of both types are discordant to the structures beneath them. Many streams incised below alluvial and bedrock terraces have cut notches into the flanks and across the noses of anticlinal barriers. Erosionally beveled anticlines are widespread in the Imbricate Zone, and are occasionally overlain by Pliocene and Quaternary deposits. The folds in the late Tertiary clastic beds are disharmonic to those of the underlying marine geosynclinal accumulation; and a great depth of highly erodable formations separates the two feature-forming horizons in the stratigraphic succession.

The evidences of drainage superposition are so widespread that the question is not whether the process occurred here, but how important a role it played! The answer appears to be

that, as a process fixing drainage lines across structural barriers, stream superposition has been effective on about the same scale and in the same regions as local drainage antecedence. It will be shown in the following pages that none of the major through-flowing streams of the Central Zagros Region have been superimposed from any type of discordant covermass or erosional bevel; however, a great number of the transverse gorges of the region have resulted from the operation of a unique process that partakes of both drainage antecedence and discordant superposition. This process is made possible by the peculiar behavior under compression of one of the geological formations widely distributed throughout the Outer Zagros.

In the following pages each of the potential superposing media in the Zagros region is examined in terms of its effects on the Zagros drainage pattern.

Marine Covermasses

The first strong deformations in the Zagros geosynclinal tract occured in late Middle and Upper Cretaceous time when the Inner Zagros was folded and thrust southwestward over some of its own detritus. Following this orogenic spasm, the first strongly unconformable deposits were laid down in the northeast of the Zagros geosyncline. The late Upper Cretaceous and Eocene marls and limestones accumulated heavily in synclines formed by the first orogeny, and were also deposited over some Upper Cretaceous erosion surfaces beveling highly deformed beds in the areas of the present Thrust and Imbricate zones. In the area of the present Fold Zone all marine formations through the Miocene were laid down conformably with the exception of local overlaps and attenuation toward the crests of primary anticlines. No post-Eocene beds have been mapped in the Thrust Zone, but synclinal strips in the Imbricate Zone continued to be submerged until early Miocene time.

The Eocene outcrops of the Thrust Zone do not appear to be related to the through-flowing drainage of that region, but in the Imbricate Zone one unconformable Eocene slab at a high level lies near enough to a transverse stream to warrant attention as a possible originator of superimposed drainage.

Between the Sehzar and Bakhtiari rivers a small cap of Eocene marine detrital beds is found overlying an erosional bevel of near-

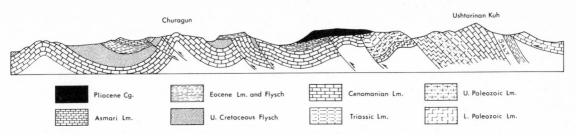

FIGURE 53. Structural and stratigraphic relationships in the vicinity of the Churagun anticline and Tang-i-Bahrein covermass. Length of section: 47 miles; vertical and horizontal scales equal.

vertical Cenomanian limestones in an anticlinal structure that has suffered great fault displacement (Figure 53). The underlying erosion surface appears related to pediments on either side of the crest of Kuh-i-Churagun, a faulted arch immediately to the southwest. The surfaces could be brought into line by opening the syncline between the two anticlines. They could also have been graded toward an erosional valley in the Cretaceous flysch of the syncline, the valley having been little modified from the Eocene to the present due to its protection by the Eocene cap.

A tributary of the Sehzar River crosses the Churagun anticline diagonally from the vicinity of the Eocene slab atop the adjacent imbric. This stream now flows through an alluviated gorge cut 4,000 feet below the pedimented crest of Churagun, and is the single instance in the Central Zagros Region of possible discordant superposition from an unconformable marine cover. The Eocene is occasionally unconformable elsewhere in the Imbricate Zone, but nowhere, to the writer's knowledge, to such a degree as the above; nowhere else could it originate drainage markedly discordant to underlying structures. Even the above case is tenuous, for it is premised on the most general information and must assume an extension of the Eocene cover across Churagun, of which there is no present evidence.

As detailed geological information on the Thrust Zone is unavailable, it is impossible to say whether superposition from a marine cover could have established any of the transverse streams of that region. Whatever the origin of the transverse drainage of the Inner Zagros, the synclinal and subsequent deflections of through-flowing streams at the borders of the Imbricate and Fold zones indicate independent stream controls in the outer regions where the paradox of transverse drainage is most strongly manifested. The structural control implied by stream deflections at all zonal contacts denies *regional* drainage superposition as effectively as it does regional drainage antecedence.

The Lower Fars Formation

The disharmonic folding of the incompetent Lower Fars marl and evaporite succession in the Fold Zone presents excellent opportunities for the discordant superposition of drainage in this region.

The Lower Fars formation was laid down conformably over the Asmari limestone horizon, with some attenuation over the precursors of the primary anticlines. Thus its effect is distributed over the entire southwestern half of the Fold Zone. The significance of the Lower Fars formation to drainage evolution is that its erodability and mobility under compression allowed the mass of clastic formations above the Asmari limestone to maintain a near-planar surface throughout the strong Pliocene folding of the subjacent limestones. Thus consequent streams could develop on the Fars and Bakhtiari surface amid the height of the orogeny in the Outer Zagros, almost independently of the strong folding at depth.

Cross-sections EE to KK, Figure 7, indicate that the Lower Fars beds tend to be greatly attenuated over buried Asmari limestone anticlinal crests, and to thicken enormously in the synclines between them. There is therefore a disproportionately thick Lower Fars cover over any subsidiary anticlines between major arches. There was also a primary attenuation of the Lower Fars beds at the crests of those anticlines that were already beginning to form in the Miocene. However, the thinning of the Lower Fars over the crests of the majority of the anticlines is the result of the erodability of the marl and evaporite formations and of their incompetence under compression. The Lower

Fars mass, in effect, "flows" away from the rising limestone crests and crowds into the synclines between, occasionally becoming extruded in thrusts which overrun the clastic beds laid down atop them in the early stages of the Pliocene orogeny. Such thrusts are shown in sections II and JJ of Figure 7. The inequalities developed in the Lower Fars surface by deformation were smoothed by erosion and the deposition of Pliocene stream deposits, which accumulated heavily in tectonic depressions in the Fars surface. Accordingly, the Miocene-Pliocene landscape in the area of the Lower Fars depositional basin did not reflect the presence of the diastrophism at depth until denudation exposed the structures formed beneath the viscous Lower Fars mass.

Superimposed Antecedent Streams

When the distributions of aligned watergaps (Figure 51) and thick Lower Fars accumulations (Figure 54) are compared, they are found to be related. Where undeflected anticlinal transections appear to be best developed, the intervening synclines are found to be loaded with the Miocene marl-evaporite masses. The significance of this association is clearest in the Saidmarreh Valley. Here streams entering the Saidmarreh from the north are cutting ravines through thick Lower Fars accumulations. In the bottoms of these ravines strips of Asmari limestone are beginning to be exposed: the crests of the anticlines that rise above the surface farther west as Kuh-i-Kuljar and Kalak-i-Arab.[6] In these examples we see the actual mechanism of transverse gorge formation in the low Asmari limestone folds of the Outer Zagros. In the Saidmarreh Valley the streams that are now beginning to accomplish new anticlinal transections are barely five miles in length, and rise on the adjacent flanks of the exhumed Asmari limestone domes of Kuh-i-Charmin and Milleh Kuh (Figure 37). The portions of these folds that originate the runoff are only a few hundred feet higher than those transected by it, and probably were stripped of their own Lower Fars cover during the Pleistocene.

The incipient anticlinal transections in Outer Luristan appear to be the result of both drainage antecedence and superposition from the thick Lower Fars accumulation. The streams are antecedent to the transected structures because they rise on anticlines that were *exhumed* from beneath their near-planar Miocene-Pliocene cover before the transected anticlines were expressed in the landscape, though they were not necessarily *formed* prior to the transected folds. In the presence of a near-planar covering medium a very slight difference in the absolute elevation of the structural crests could produce drainage lines consequent on one structure and antecedent to the *exposure* of another, though the structures were formed simultaneously. The massive Lower Fars synclinal fillings nullify the gross similarity between the coeval folds and emphasize the minor variations in their elevations from point to point. In the absence of the Lower Fars masses in which the streams are deeply imbedded, the runoff of the exposed anticlines would have been turned into synclinal paths upon encountering other anticlines of the same age, regardless of differences in the magnitudes of the structures.

Evidence of the prior exposure of certain young folds is seen in their surface sculpture, which is advanced beyond that of the anticlines transected by their runoff. Figures 37 and 18 contrast two Asmari limestone anticlines of comparable size, one of which is an originator of transverse drainage, and the other a fold transected by several short through-flowing streams. Similarly, as the higher parts of individual arches were exposed prior to saddles and pitching fold extremities, the former are more denuded than the latter, as Figure 55 illustrates.

In the southeastern portion of the Central Zagros it is possible to determine the original level of the Lower Fars formation relative to the crests of the anticlines sundered by anomalous transverse streams. In the vicinity of the Gach Saran oil field, many fragments of the valley fills on the Pliocene surface of the Lower Fars beds have been preserved. As these fills were sandstones and conglomerates, ultimately more resistant to erosion than the Lower Fars masses around them, the areas in which they occur are now in a state of relief inversion. The difference in elevation between the present Lower Fars badlands and the conglomerate synclinal mountains is a measure of the general lowering of the Lower Fars surface by post-Pliocene denudation. Along the Marun River north of Behbehan the

---

[6]Site shown on Aerial Photographs, Geraldine (Shoran) Project No. 158, strip 69: photos 5772–5773; strip 70: photos 5800–5801. Photo publication prohibited.

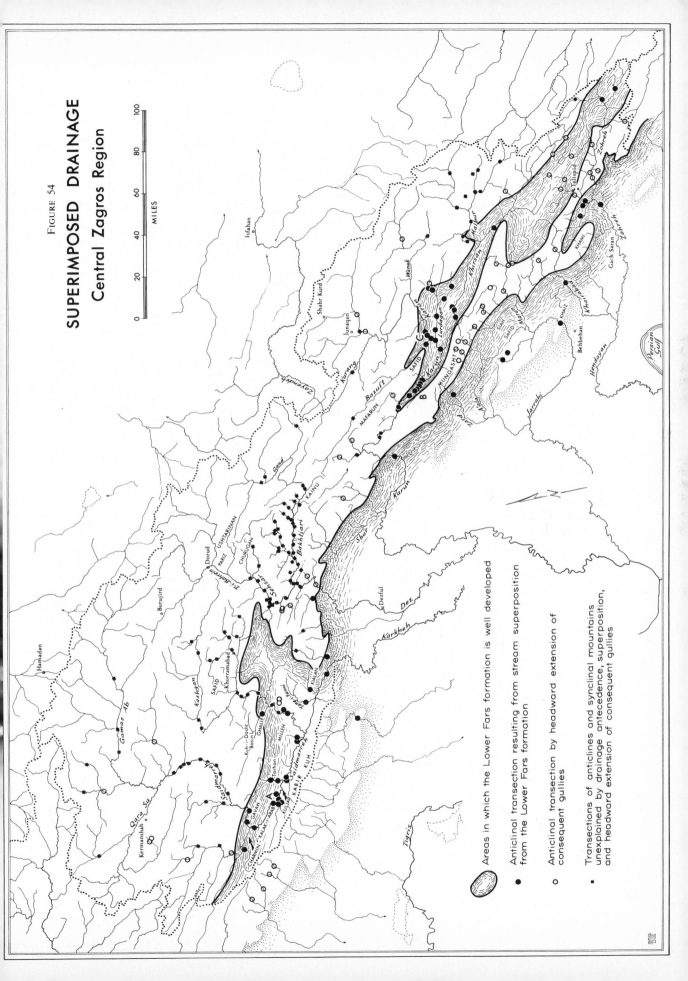

FIGURE 54

SUPERIMPOSED DRAINAGE
Central Zagros Region

MILES

Areas in which the Lower Fars formation is well developed

Anticlinal transection resulting from stream superposition from the Lower Fars formation

Anticlinal transection by headward extension of consequent gullies

Transections of anticlines and synclinal mountains unexplained by drainage antecedence, superposition, and headward extension of consequent gullies

FIGURE 55. Superposition of drainage on a newly exposed anticline in the Frontal Fold Region. At the right the Ab-i-Zal transects the Cenomanian core of the Kialan anticline, which has here been unroofed by both transverse and autogenous drainage. The Zal then cuts a slot through the crest of a subsidiary arch of Asmari limestone that is still largely submerged by the Lower Fars mass. It is probable that both transections were accomplished through super-position of the Zal from the Lower Fars accumulation. In the distance Tang-i-Fanni and Tang-i-Lailum may be seen breaching the intact western extremity of the Kialan anticline. These gorges are also attributable to stream superposi-tion from the Fars beds. (Photo by Aerofilms and Aero Pictorial Limited.)

lowering has exceeded 3,000 feet. More important, the conglomerate buttes marking Pliocene valley floors rise as much as 1,000 feet *above* the intact Asmari limestone anti-clines which are breached by undeflected transverse streams.

As noted in the previous chapter, many transected anticlines in the Lower Fars depositional basins appear little different in age and magnitude from the arches on which the undeflected transecting streams rise. It can now be stated that none of the anticlines transected by such streams stand more than 2,000 feet above the badlands and plains sur-rounding them. Where the noses of higher anticlines are transected by *deflected* streams, the heights of the ranges at the cuts are also less than 2,000 feet above local base levels of denudation—or some 500 to 1,000 feet *below* the surface of the Fars-Bakhtiari accumula-tion in Pliocene time. It is therefore clear that a great number of both direct and deflected transections of Asmari limestone anticlines on the southwestern margin of the Fold Zone were accomplished by drainage superimposed from the Lower Fars surface.

*Transections of Fold Noses by
Deflected Streams*

Undeflected anticlinal transections, such as that shown in Figure 18, are easily explained as the result of superposition from the Lower Fars beds when the marl-evaporite series submerged a greater portion of the Asmari limestone domes. However, in many instances the transecting streams are deflected along the strike prior to sundering fold noses, and the relation of such consequent deflections to transections of this type demands elucidation.

The anticlinal structures whose noses are transected after a deflection of the stream are frequently, in their crestal portions, among the higher in the local area. Owing to the collection in synclines of the viscous Lower Fars masses, the higher whaleback anticlines had too thin a cover of clastic beds to *fix* any consequent drainage superimposed across their axes. If a stream superimposed from the Lower Fars formation encounters the level crest of an anticline, dip shifting down the axis of the fold would not be possible, and the stream would be either incised in the limestone or defeated. It is characteristic in the Zagros that where anticlines have a level crest extending over a distance of many miles their transections do not deviate significantly from the lines of the streams approaching them. Folds of this type are well developed in the Saidmarreh Synclinorium in Outer Luristan, a region of undeflected anticlinal transections.

Drainage superimposed from the Lower Fars beds may also encounter inclined limestones along the axial trace of a plunging anticline. It seems likely that such drainage, if not deeply incised in the superposing medium, would initially shift down the dip of the limestone, undercutting the less resistant beds of the covermass rather than notching the harder beds beneath. The undercut covermass, having a planar surface, would produce a wall of increasing height as the superimposed stream continued to shift down the inclined limestone surface. Initially the down-stripping of the covermass would be facilitated by the gully networks tributary to the borders of the superimposed stream, which would thin the Fars surface before it was undercut. However, the better-nourished superimposed stream would shift into the gully network more rapidly than the latter could reduce the Fars mass. Thus the superimposed reach would come to occupy an asymmetric valley, with the stripped limestone dip slope rising gently on one side of the stream, facing an abrupt wall of the Lower Fars beds on the other. Such valleys may be seen at either end of Kuh-i-Khami east of Gach Saran, at the tip of Siah Kuh northwest of Behbehan, and at the north end of Kuh-i-Asmari, all of these anticlines being smooth whaleback structures.

It seems likely that the constantly increasing depth and compaction of the undercut mass would gradually slow the dip shifting of the superimposed stream, so that each successive point on the limestone surface across which the stream is moving would be subjected to increasing exposure to stream action. If there is an increase in curvature of the crest where the anticline plunges out, extension jointing in the limestone is intensified. Solution and mechanical quarrying would be facilitated by the increasingly slower migration of the stream over the highly jointed areas.

It appears reasonable that at some point the stream would be able to incise the jointed limestones as effectively as it could undercut the Lower Fars cliff. The point at which the drainage is fixed in the limestone might depend on some local incident of its lithology, such as a slightly more open joint or a highly soluble exposure. The notching of fold noses by streams shifting down dip against Lower Fars masses clearly does occur, and is best seen where the stream draining the Kuh-i-Dasht Plain of Luristan turns the end of the Kuh-i-Ghalif anticline prior to entering the Kashgan River.[7] Here the Lower Fars cliff facing the cleanly stripped anticlinal nose is more than 600 feet high. The Fars wall has not yet retreated from the lip of the stream's notch in the limestone, though the cut is already perhaps 75 feet deep. Had the stream been superimposed directly over this point rather than shifting down the dip toward it, masses of the Lower Fars beds would have been left on both sides of the cut.

This example, and those cited in the oil field region, in which the dip shifting of superimposed drainage is still progressing, indicates that it is the depth of entrenchment in the Lower Fars covermass and the inclination of the underlying strata that determine whether a stream superimposed on an anticline will cross it directly or after a course deflection. Where streams are superimposed on plunging

---

[7] *Ibid.*, strip 69: photos 5760–5766.

folds, it seems that they must be entrenched several hundred feet in the superimposing medium before their dip shifting is retarded enough to fix the course of the stream across the limestone fold shell.

Accordingly, the position and alignment of watergaps in the region of intact Asmari limestone anticlines appears to have been controlled by the depth of the Lower Fars formation over the deep folds, which was in turn controlled by variations in the amplitudes and longitudinal profiles of the folds themselves.

Major Areas of Superimposed Antecedent Drainage

Figure 54 reveals that the maximum effect of the Lower Fars formation as a drainage-superposing medium is to be seen in Outer Luristan, Pusht-i-Kuh, and Kuhgalu, where many anticlinal transections have already been tentatively attributed to drainage antecedence. Where the transecting streams originate on Kabir Kuh or Mungasht, true primary folds, drainage antecedence could be expected to be fully competent to create anticlinal transections without the assistance of a superposing and drainage-fixing medium. Elsewhere in Outer Luristan it is a strain on one's credulity to accept the idea that certain ranges originate drainage that was truly antecedent to the *formation* of immediately adjacent structures that are only a few hundred feet inferior in elevation. A combination of antecedent *expression* of the anticline, due to its exhumation by denudation, plus superposition of its runoff from a thick covermass, seems a far more reasonable hypothesis, and one which could also account for the many offset watergaps and anticlinal nose transections in the region, such as those through folds originating transverse drainage themselves, e.g., Kuh-i-Gavah and Milleh Kuh in Outer Luristan.

It is further suggested that the repeated departures of both the Lower Saidmarreh and Lower Karun from their generally synclinal paths in favor of anticlinal transections (Figures 36 and 45, and A and B in Figure 54) are also explained by antecedent exposure of bordering folds and superposition of drainage from Lower Fars masses onto the transected folds. The cuts now utilized by the trunk streams appear to have been created by a series of independent superimposed antecedent streams issuing from the anticlinoria to either side of the synclinoria channeling the two main streams. Thus both the Lower Karun and Lower Saidmarreh would incorporate several separate transverse streams that were deflected along the strike upon encountering individual corrugations in the Kabir Kuh and Mungasht anticlinoria.

The unique structural control of the majority of the Karun system has been emphasized elsewhere. The primary exception is in the middle course of the main stream (C in Figure 54), which slices through four Asmari limestone anticlines between a pair of synclinal mountains composed of Pliocene detritus. The transected anticlines once more rise from a significant Lower Fars accumulation, one of the few found northeast of the higher Cenomanian anticlines. Moreover, all four ranges are sundered near their termini: three of them pitching out a few miles to the northwest of the cuts, and the other—the plunging end of the Kainu-Mafarun-Safid line—disappearing almost immediately to the southwest of its transection by the Karun.

Though the Lower Fars accumulation was not originally thick enough in this area to fix direct transverse streams across the anticlines, it appears to have aided in the production of deflected transections of the anticlinal noses in the manner described above. Structurally, the southeast-pitching Kuh-i-Safid dominates the adjacent folds by a considerable margin. It is likely that this fold, which is locally stripped to its Cenomanian core, originated the consequent drainage which was superimposed from a Lower Fars cover onto the southwesternmost fold of the group. It is conceivable that this range also produced the runoff transverse to the fold tips to the northeast, the drainage having been reversed subsequently. It is more likely, however, that the northeastern anticlines were transected by runoff from the Bakhtiari synclinal mountain immediately adjacent, obviating the necessity of drainage reversal. In either instance the drainage appears to have been superimposed on the fold tips after shifting down the marl-limestone contact until such a wall of the Lower Fars was created that incision proceeded more rapidly than planation. The transection of Kuh-i-Safid itself may have been the result of either consequent gullying or superposition from Lower Fars beds.

In the Bakhtiari Mountains and the northeastern portions of Luristan and Kughalu, the Upper Fars and Bakhtiari detrital beds overlie the Asmari limestones above a very thin substratum of Lower Fars beds. Here there is no disharmonic folding. Accordingly, superposition from an unconformable covermass could not have assisted antecedent drainage in the production of transverse gorges in the interior of the Fold Zone. Where the Lower Fars evaporite series is limited in depth to hundreds rather than thousands of feet, its mobility is not expressed, and it could not be a significant factor in the evolution of transverse drainage.

Streams superimposed from the Fars beds can never attain great length due to the differential thinning of the Lower Fars formation over anticlines of various amplitudes and the frequent appearance and great longitudinal persistence of anticlines having had a thin Lower Fars cover. The maximum thickness of the superposing medium is reached in synclinoria between major anticlines. This favors superposition of drainage on the deeply buried folds of the synclinoria but results in stream deflections at the adjacent major anticlines that had little or no Fars cover. Like the antecedent reaches described in the previous chapter, the transverse streams fixed by superposition from the Lower Fars beds seldom attain a length much in excess of five miles across the strike. The most extended streams of this type are found heading on the southwestern flanks of Kabir Kuh, where their prolongation is favored by the open nature of the folding (section CC, Figure 7). Nowhere does an antecedent or superimposed consequent stream extend as much as twenty miles across the strike of the orogen.

About 50 percent of the more than 300 anticlinal transections in the Central Zagros Region are attributable to either local drainage antecedence or stream superposition from the mobile Lower Fars covermass. Nearly all of the many drainage anomalies in Pusht-i-Kuh and Outer Luristan may be so explained, as well as the great majority of those in the entire region south of the Karun River. It is probable that every watergap through an Asmari limestone anticline is attributable to one of these two mechanisms.

Superposition from the Lower Fars accumulation explains a slight deviation from a consequent course by the Middle Karun, resulting in four anticlinal transections, and ten more individual gorges in the generally longitudinal courses of the Lower Karun and Lower Said-marreh, but, like local drainage antecedence, it does not make the transverse routes of the great through-flowing streams any more comprehensible.

The Pliocene Conglomerate Covermass

The immense depth of the Pliocene detrital accumulation at the contact between the Fold Zone and the Inner Zagros would seem to provide an ideal medium for the discordant superposition of drainage. Unfortunately, the Bakhtiari formation is handicapped as a superposing medium by a characteristically synclinal situation, the formation only occasionally spilling into other structural environments. The drainage of these deposits is normally longitudinal, and its superposition on the synclinal floors creates no anomaly at all. In two locations, however, significant Pliocene accumulations overlie erosion surfaces on highly deformed structures that are at least partially anticlinal, and one of these is at present crossed by the deeply engorged Sehzar River, a transverse stream of major importance whose course has not yet been explained.

The Pliocene cap of lesser importance lies atop a truncated Cenomanian anticline northeast of Khorramabad. This fold was apparently formed in the Cretaceous orogeny, for the Upper Cretaceous flysch pinches out beneath Eocene marine beds at its base. There are no drainage anomalies in a position to be explained by this deposit or an extension of it, nor other evidences of a regional planation in this area.

Tang-i-Bahrein

The most important Pliocene deposit behind the Mountain Front is that lying on either side of the transverse Sehzar River at Tang-i-Bahrein, immediately below Dorud. Over 3,000 feet in depth, this mass (Figures 7, 40, and 53) covers roughly beveled portions of the limestone thrust and the Imbricate Zone, and laps against the Fold Zone. It is the largest area of the heavy Upper Bakhtiari conglomerate within the Central Zagros mountain complex. As a portion of the Sehzar River is cut transversely across formations covered unconformably by the immense conglomerate slab, this river has the appearance of having been superimposed from the surface of the covermass. The question is, therefore, whether or not the covermass is the deposit of a Pliocene river transverse to the structure of the orogen, making the Sehzar the descendent of an ancient antecedent stream. In such a case the deposit should be genetically related to the Sehzar, and the river should have been superimposed from its surface.

Unlike most Pliocene basin deposits, which show rims of the finer Upper Fars and Lower Bakhtiari beds, frequently lacking the heavy conglomerates altogether, the Tang-i-Bahrein covermass is entirely composed of the massive Upper Bakhtiari cobble formation. It overlies an erosional truncation of faulted structures involving Lower Miocene formations. Conditions for the deposition of this mass thus seem to have been initiated only in late Pliocene time, and its bifurcation by the Sehzar River must have been accomplished during the Quaternary.

The only geologic cross-section available through the substratum of the Tang-i-Bahrein covermass has been taken across the southeastern extremity of the Pliocene plate (Figure 53). Here its face is retreating from a synclinal flexure in the underlying beds, while its northeastern margin appears to grade into a dissected erosion surface truncating an anticline broken by a major thrust fault. The geologic map indicates that the southwestern face of the Pliocene detrital mass rests everywhere against Asmari limestone homoclines which dip to the northeast. These homoclines are actually the northeastern limbs of arches crossing the Sehzar River: the sheared anticline of Kuh-i-Churagun to the east, and to the west, the broad unroofed anticline whose Cenomanian core emerges at Khorramabad as Kuh-i-Safid.

The erosion surface which continues the covermass to the northeast truncates faulted structures involving Lower Miocene formations. The faults are thrusts that hike slices of a sheared anticline successively higher northeastward. Two of the three faults are beveled and overlain by the Pliocene conglomerates. The third and greatest fault in terms of displacement is the site of an erosional valley in Lower Paleozoic rocks, beyond which the erosional bevel continues to the foot of the 14,000-foot Cenomanian homocline forming Ushtarinan Kuh.

The movement on all three faults was prior to the development of the erosion surface growing northeastward into the Imbricate Zone. It would appear that the extension of this erosion surface and the deposition of the coarse clastic Bakhtiari beds could have proceeded simultaneously; the first detritus from the erosion of the growing *plis-faille* being deposited in the flanking syncline, overlapping onto the foot of the expanding erosion surface as the shallow syncline became filled, and growing headward thereafter in parallel with the inward expansion of the erosional bevel.

The more or less intact and unfaulted Cenomanian anticline defining the Burujird Plain on the southwest may be the strike continuation of the Tang-i-Bahrein *plis-faille* (Kuh-i-Suffa: section DD, Figure 7).[8]

If the Pliocene detrital mass is a synclinal deposit overlapping onto a mountain-foot pediment, it would not be genetically related to through-flowing Pliocene drainage, such as an ancestral Sehzar River. It can be shown that the Pliocene covermass at Tang-i-Bahrein is not related to transverse drainage of any type.

A peculiarity of the Sehzar as it passes through Tang-i-Bahrein is that the 5,000-foot rise from the river to the line of its watershed on the northwest is accomplished over a mere one and a half miles horizontally. This is not an exceptionally precipitous slope, but it is an exceptional asymmetry in the Sehzar Basin, inasmuch as the various branches of the river rise in the northeast, northwest, and east at a radius of some sixty miles from this point. It is all the more remarkable when it is realized that the adjacent system cannot have extended toward the Sehzar here. On the contrary the deep canyon of the Sehzar so undercuts the adjacent watershed that the divide is clearly being shifted *outward* even though not yet 8,000 feet, horizontally, from the river.

Kuh-i-Pariz, the highest point on the Pliocene covermass (10,029 feet), lies south of the Sehzar River, and appears to mark the axis of a synclinal deformation of the covermass itself. Its narrow concave summit (Figure 40)

---

[8]There is in this area a discrepancy between the geological maps and the cross-sections published by the British Petroleum Company. On the cross-sections the Cretaceous limestone overthrust is limited to the area northeast of Kuh-i-Suffa; the geologic map extends it to include nearly all of the Cenomanian outcrop north of Khorramabad. The writer tends to favor the validity of the cross-sections in this matter due to the presence of radiolarites in the center of the area mapped as the limestone overthrust, in a position that is otherwise synclinal. The radiolarites are elsewhere subjacent to the limestone overthrust. Such a reconstruction would be in accordance with the continuity of the thrust margin in other parts of the orogenic system.

carries a beautifully preserved fragment of an extinct pinnate stream which was directed northward along the strike of the orogen. This system now hangs nearly a mile above the Sehzar and is truncated by cliffs on all sides.

If the relict drainage on the synclinal peak of Kuh-i-Pariz is projected, it will obviously intersect the Sehzar—5,000 feet about its present level. If it is extended further still, across the Sehzar canyon, a more important relationship becomes apparent: the Pariz drainage is seen to prolong the *Upper Kashgan* as the latter drains the western half of the Bakhtiari covermass along the strike in a northwesterly direction.

Rather than a penetration by the Kashgan system into the Dez Basin, the relationships at Tang-i-Bahrein indicate that the asymmetry of the Dez Basin is the result of the headward penetration of the transverse Sehzar into the longitudinal consequent drainage of the Upper Kashgan Basin, resulting in the diversion of a portion of the Kashgan headwaters directly across the grain of the fold belt. It must be assumed that this capture was accomplished prior to the movements that elevated the covermass to such a great altitude. The spacious character of the canyon through the covermass and underlying Cenomanian beds indicates a considerable age and a number of rejuvenations in erosion, some of them probably resulting from further captures, such as that bringing the Burujird Plain and Thrust Zone drainage into the Dez system. The present declivity of the stream profile in this reach is indicated by its lack of point bar deposits even in the low-water period. Aggradational features appear in the summer immediately southwest of the contact between the Thrust and Fold zones, and are regularly developed downstream from this point.

This discovery leaves us with the necessity of explaining the anomalous transverse course of the Sehzar in the Fold Zone below Tang-i-Bahrein. It will be shown in the following chapter that headward extension of the river has, in fact, been the main process forming the Sehzar throughout.

Other Superposition Possibilities

Possibilities of other types of stream superposition are present in the Zagros region, and some of them have had a marked effect on the drainage pattern. The important hypotheses as yet unexplored are superposition of ex-tended consequent streams, superposition from structures formerly covering a greater area, superposition from regional erosion surfaces, and superposition from conformable elements in the geological columns that are so easily eroded that their deformational structures exert no control over the drainage developing within them.

Superposition of Extended Consequent Streams

In the regions of most intense folding, such as the Bakhtiari Culmination, many of the anticlines are asymmetric or overturned. Consequent gullying in the flysch blanket formerly underlying the limestone shells of these structures could rapidly superimpose the drainage of both limbs of the folds across the anticlinal axes in the manner described earlier in this chapter. However, anticlinal transections so produced could not be expected to be accomplished in isolation, as would cuts produced by superposition from the Lower Fars. Any ridge breached by an extended consequent stream would be strongly dissected by other consequent gullies not yet attaining full transection of the fold. Gorges through otherwise intact ridges would be better explained as the result of drainage antecedence or superposition from overlying deposits.

A large number of authentic anticlinal transections have been accomplished by consequent gullying aided by superposition through progressive displacement at the depth of the fold's crestal plane. Frequently such transections are produced by the headward extension of antecedent drainage lines that formerly rose on the denuded Cenomanian arches which they now breach in their uppermost gorges. Thus many streams, particularly in Kuhgalu, gather in a syncline, then turn sharply through a *strongly dissected* Cenomanian anticline, moving thereafter through lesser undissected structures without deviating greatly from a direct line away from the primary fold. This is the general situation illustrated in Figure 52.

Several impending transections of headwater anticlines may be seen in Kuhgalu, a notable one five miles south of Talispid and adjacent to the cut of the Zohreh through the same ridge. In several cases headward extension of this type has captured antecedent drainage lines that have been deflected into synclinal paths by the same primary anticline now breached by the headward-extending gullies. The Zohreh canyon near Talispid appears to be a consequent gully which has captured its present headwaters in this fashion. About fifty gorges of this type are indicated on Figure 54. Very frequently their drainage rises in a syncline on the northeast side of an anticlinorium such as Kuh-i-Mungasht or Mafarun, and turns southwestward across the culmination and down through the anticlines on its farther slope. The northwestern end of Kabir Kuh has been transected fully by several southwest-flowing consequent streams which, having breached its Asmari limestone shell, were extended across its axis in soft flysch beds, eventually becoming entrenched in the Cenomanian substratum.

Superposition from Exotic Structures

A former greater extension of the thrusts in the Zagros area, with drainage being superimposed from the exotic rock layers, is not a feasible explanation for any part of the transverse drainage pattern. In a region in which the major upheavals have occurred at such a recent date, erosional outliers of any former thrust masses would certainly have been preserved. The limestone thrust margin is, on the contrary, remarkably regular in the Zagros orogenic system, and no erosional outliers of this mass may be observed outside of the Malbur Basin. The denudation of the limestone thrust complex in this region has proceeded only to the stage of opening "windows" in the upper thrusts. Though erosion has progressed farther in the crystalline thrusts, their margins have enough continuity to suggest that they never extended beyond their present location.

Erosion-Surface Superposition

Stream superposition from erosion surfaces does not appear to have initiated any of the drainage anomalies in the Zagros region. Anomalies created by transverse drainage are not *explained* by the discovery that a stream has been superimposed from a broad erosional strath rather than a regional peneplane, for the transverse strath is itself a drainage anomaly. Only *regional* erosion surfaces can truly *originate* a major discordance between drainage and structure. Even this would be hard to imagine without a wholesale reorientation of drainage by the deposition of some covermass on the erosion surface.

In the Zagros, local pediments are widespread, beveling rocks of all types, and former erosional straths are present at many levels along the great through-flowing streams of the Bakhtiari Culmination. These straths are as discordant to structure as are the existing streams. The present drainage has been rejuvenated in these discordant surfaces, not superimposed discordantly from them.

There is no evidence of a regional erosion surface in the Outer Zagros, the site of the vast majority of the drainage anomalies of the Central Zagros Region. Nowhere is summit accordance conspicuous. In terms of elevation each anticline, hogback, and synclinal mountain is a law unto itself. Section EE of Figure 7 is misleading in that it appears to show an erosional bevel across Inner Luristan. Structure, lithology, and breadth of outcrop all effect the orography of this area as they do all others in the Outer Zagros, and even synclinal mountains vary in elevation by as much as 3,000 feet in Luristan.

In summation, only local erosion surfaces are present in the area whose drainage is most problematical, and though stream rejuvenation in these surfaces has contributed to the scenic effect of the drainage anomaly in the Zagros region, it has not originated the discordance between stream patterns and structural patterns in the area.

Superposition from Conformable Formations

Though the Upper Cretaceous flysch accumulation is generally conformable with the beds above and below, it facilitates discordant drainage superposition upon its hard Cenomanian substratum. Due to its excessive erodability, the internal structures of the flysch, which more or less accord with the structures above and below, have a minimum control over the development of its drainage. Exposure of the flysch facilitates planation during down-cutting and displacement of stream channels from positions determined by higher structures, which are mirrored by those at depth.

The effect of the Cretaceous flysch is similar to that of the Lower Fars formation in favoring the production of cuts through anticlinal noses, but this time on the *second* highly resistant series in the sedimentary column: the Cenomanian limestones. This means that the superincumbent Asmari limestones transmit a degree of structural orientation to the drainage of the Cretaceous beds that may be modified in the flysch, but may not be completely lost by the time the Cenomanian series is bared. Drainage superimposed from the unconformable Lower Fars beds, on the other hand, lacks any structural orientation related to the deep folds.

Because subsequent drainage in fold belts is generally thought to be sited in longitudinal homoclinal valleys, it might be assumed that the outcrop of the Upper Cretaceous formations could only rarely give rise to transverse subsequent drainage of importance, which could be superimposed discordantly on the deeper Cenomanian structures. However, *anticlinorial* structures in areas of strong flysch development would at some stage in their physiographic histories be expressed as vast subsequent lowlands originating in a series of gradually coalescing anticlinal basins, each initially having its own subsequent drainage. In one great lowland these separate drainage nodes would not retain their identity indefinitely, but would be linked by headward piracies into a single drainage system. Components of such an abstracted system could indeed become disharmonic to the structures beneath, resulting in discordant drainage superposition on these structures.

As this process of autosuperposition does not involve an unconformable covermass, and does require specific conditions of structure and physiographic development, its consideration is deferred to the next chapter, in which it will be shown that superposition of structurally controlled drainage has been of immense significance in the creation of the major drainage anomalies in the Zagros region.

The Residual Drainage Anomaly

The processes of stream superposition from the mobile Lower Fars covermass and headward extension of drainage across primary structures explain virtually all watergaps in Kuhgalu and the Pusht-i-Kuh region that have not already been attributed to drainage antecedence. Some sixty transverse gorges are clearly the result of stream superposition from the Lower Fars mass, and possibly one-third of the more than ninety anticlinal transections already attributed to drainage antecedence were abetted by superposition from this medium. The majority of the transections having such equivocal origins are those created by the runoff of the primary anticlines of Kabir Kuh in the Saidmarreh Basin and Kuh-i-Safid and Kuh-i-Mungasht in the Karun Basin.

Headward extension of consequent gullies appears to have created about fifty transverse gorges, most of them in the Kuhgalu area where the folding has been very tight, producing steep and narrow anticlines susceptible to transection in this manner. Superposition from Eocene marine beds may have produced one drainage anomaly, the transverse reach through the Churagun imbric, but the evidence is inconclusive. This watergap can be more satisfactorily explained as one of the type whose origin is discussed in the following chapter. No major drainage anomalies appear to have been created by superposition of older Pliocene drainage from the surface of the Bakhtiari formation.

The transverse courses of the Saidmarreh, Kashgan, Sehzar, Bakhtiari, and Malbur rivers, and two major tributaries of the Bakhtiari, remain unexplained by the hypotheses of drainage antecedence or superposition from erosion surfaces or unconformable covermasses. Thus the very streams which provoke the hypotheses of drainage antecedence or superposition are almost the only transverse streams in the region which cannot be explained by these mechanisms. The residual drainage anomaly comprises one-third of all the anticlinal transections discovered in the Central Zagros Region, most of them being sited along the great through-flowing streams of Luristan and the Bakhtiari Mountains.

Chapter X

The Residual Drainage Anomaly

The drainage pattern as well as the dispositions of explained and unexplained transverse reaches suggests that the conditions of drainage development in Inner Luristan and the Bakhtiari Country have differed in some way from those in the Pusht-i-Kuh (Outer Luristan) and Kuhgalu. Structurally the areas are not dissimilar; in fact, variations in structure and landscape between the individual watersheds in the northwest are greater than any general contrast between the northwest and the southeast.

Aside from greater aridity in Kuhgalu there is, however, one important difference between the contrasted areas. The depth of erodable Cretaceous-Eocene flysch is inferior to the amplitude of the folding in Kuhgalu and the Pusht-i-Kuh, while it greatly exceeds fold amplitudes in Inner Luristan and the western Bakhtiari Mountains. This means that while the latter regions would at some time be characterized by relief inversion over vast areas, the former would not. This fact is of utmost significance, for the critical factor in the development of the unexplained transverse streams of the northwest is simultaneous relief inversion in adjacent folds, made possible by the presence of a thick layer of easily eroded beds between the upper and lower resistant horizons. It is the presence or absence of this layer of erodable materials that determines the presence or absence of the major through-flowing drainage in the Central Zagros Highland.

GEOMETRY OF THE ANOMALOUS DRAINAGE PATTERN

One of the intriguing aspects of the anomalous drainage pattern of the northwest is the apparent similarity in the directionality and *figures* of its trunk streams. The Saidmarreh, Kashgan, Dez, and also the Karun cross the fold belt in a series of rather linear and more or less parallel reaches that are diagonal to the structural trend whether cut through subsequent lowlands or rocks of maximum resistance. The meandering of the streams within these individual reaches is confined, so that the reaches have a length-to-

amplitude ratio generally in the neighborhood of ten to one. A cursory inspection of the drainage pattern gives the impression that the sequences of reach orientations on the different streams are parallel, producing a number of streams having similar figures.

Henson and others have referred to the apparent directionality of the transverse Zagros drainage pattern as contributory evidence of hidden basement or Mesozoic structural trends in the region.[1] They believe that a number of structural lineaments seen in the foreland of Iraq may be traced into the Zagros orogen, where they are revealed by the pattern of structural culminations and depressions, fold plunges, asymmetries in folding, stream orientations, and so on.

To determine whether the apparent directionality of the northwestern streams is truly significant, the streams were divided into individual reaches of consistent direction, and straight lines were carefully fitted to these reaches by eye. The compass orientations of these lines were then plotted on a circular graph, which is shown in Figure 56. The directionality of the reaches is revealed by the graph to be more random than would at first be imagined. This remains true when the reaches are plotted in relation to the structural trend in their immediate vicinity.

It would require an almost infinite number of tectonic trends to account for such a stream pattern, though interference structures formed by separate movements of different trajectories might be oriented diversely enough that a stream pattern somehow related to them would, in the agglomerate, appear random. In any single drainage basin the orientations of individual transverse reaches do fall into discrete groupings, both in terms of geographic direction and inclination to the local structural trend (Figures 57 and 58). Individual reaches cross local structural trends at angles of 19 to 87 degrees from the east, and 21 to 80 degrees from the northwest. Reaches engorged in hard

---

[1] F. R. S. Henson, "Observations on the Geology and Petroleum Occurrences of the Middle East," 3rd World Petroleum Congr. *Proceedings*, Sec. 1 (1951), 118–140.

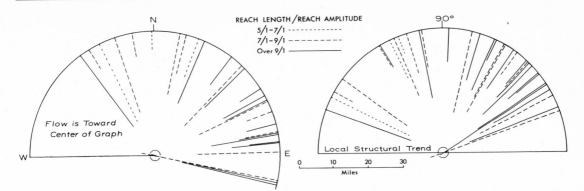

FIGURE 56. Left: Geographic orientations of long transverse reaches in the Dez (Sehzar), Karkheh, and Karun basins. Right: Orientation of long transverse reaches to local structural axes in the Dez (Sehzar), Karkheh, and Karun basins.

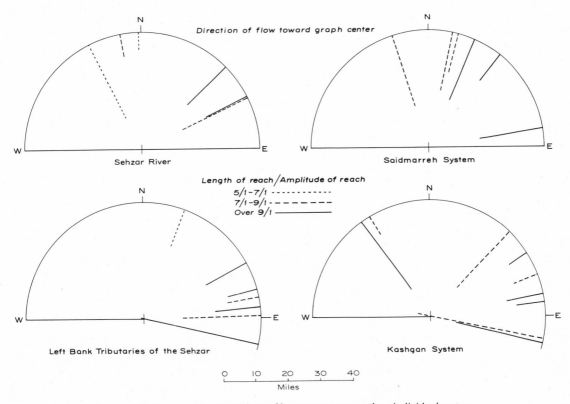

FIGURE 57. Geographic orientations of long transverse reaches, individual systems.

rocks do not differ significantly in geographic or structural orientation from those crossing subsequent lowlands.

The findings indicate that there is no control of the unexplained drainage pattern of the northwest by consistent structural trends discordant to those of the present, unless there is an infinite number of such trends, or unless the trends are sinuous.

Contrary to its visual appearance, the total stream array does not appear to be an antecedent trellis system inherited from older folds which have been refolded in a new direction by Pliocene movements. However, older folds or basement trends may have had a role in the formation of the present streams by their *interference* with the latest folding movements. Echelon folding, locally well developed in the

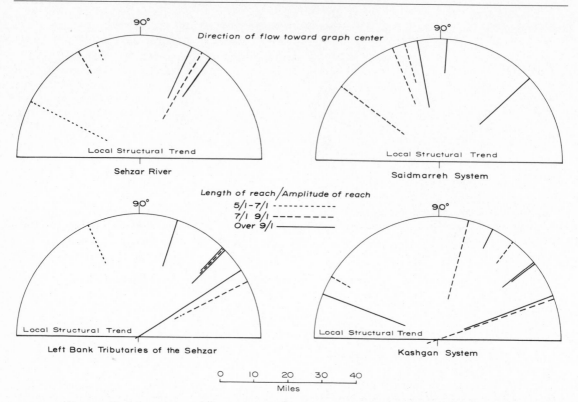

FIGURE 58. Orientations of long transverve reaches to local structural axes, individual systems.

Zagros, is known to be a result of separate deformational phases produced by forces of different trajectories. In the remaining pages it will be shown that the vital factor in the development of the transverse drainage in the northwest of the Central Zagros is erosional modification of transverse structural culminations resulting from echelon folding.

STRUCTURAL RELATIONS OF THE RESIDUAL DRAINAGE ANOMALY

The Kashgan and Saidmarreh rivers frequently cross broad strips of the Cretaceous and Eocene flysch formations in a transverse direction. In addition, they often receive major tributaries in these subsequent lowlands. In the southeast, on the other hand, where the drainage pattern has been completely resolved in terms of genesis, streams seldom encounter extensive outcrops of the flysch. This is due to the meager original thickness of the formation south of the Ab-i-Bakhtiari, and to the limitation on breadth of outcrop imposed by tight folding.

The fluvial reaches crossing the flysch outcrops in the northwest have not hitherto been termed subsequent because they cross individual flysch lowlands transversely and, with the exception of the Upper Kashgan, do not appear to be conspicuously channeled by them. Most of the flysch areas are the cores of anticlines which have been unroofed by erosion; notable among these are the series crossed by the Lower Kashgan River. The route of the Kashgan through a succession of anticlinal structures clearly constitutes a drainage anomaly, despite the present negative physiographic expression of these structures.

The Middle Saidmarreh River crosses an area of full relief inversion, passing through a succession of watergaps through synclinal mountains that are separated by extensive plains. The plains are underlain by the flysch. Though the gorges are cut through the synclinal mountains, the drainage anomaly here concerns the passage of the river through the plains, for structurally they are, once more, basins in unroofed anticlines.

There is no need to reconstruct the original fold surface to realize that the Sehzar and Bakhtiari rivers also cross the fold belt through a series of anticlinal structures, for in the Sehzar-Bakhtiari Basin these elements are most positively expressed in the current landscape. The defiles cut by these two rivers through successive anticlinal swarms constitute the most conspicuous drainage anomaly in the entire Zagros Highland.

The distinctive characteristic of the northwestern streams is, indeed, that they are constantly transecting anticlines: anticlinal mountains, split in spectacular gorges, and anticlinal lowlands, where the drainage anomaly is more subtle. On these streams reaches conformable to structure are limited in both number and

extent. The fact that the well-marked transverse depressions in this part of the Zagros are not utilized by transverse drainage implies that the streams are all sited on the axes or flanks of transverse culminations in structure. This is most clear in the case of the Lower Kashgan, which links a rank of sharply defined anticlinal basins: structures that originally made a transverse ridge separating the Luristan Basin from the Luristan Saddle.

Figure 59 shows the relationship between the major streams of the northwest and present and past subsequent basins in unroofed anti-

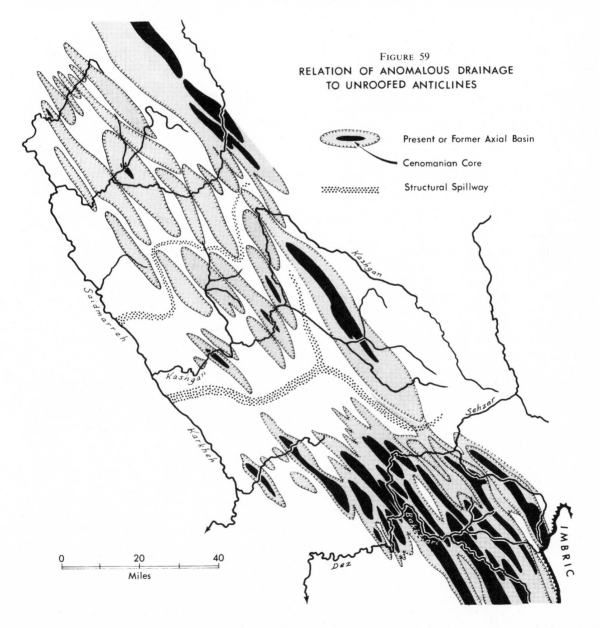

FIGURE 59

RELATION OF ANOMALOUS DRAINAGE
TO UNROOFED ANTICLINES

Present or Former Axial Basin

Cenomanian Core

Structural Spillway

0   20   40
Miles

clinal structures of the region. Where subsequent valleys in adjacent anticlines have merged, obscuring the relationship between structure and the stream pattern, restoration of the former separate basins has been achieved by the use of internal divisions in the Upper Cretaceous or by indicating the exposed Cenomanian fold cores, which occupy the sites of former axial basins. The well-defined transverse synclines of the northwestern regions are also indicated. This map is not to be taken as an actual representation of the landscape at any one time, but as an indication of the individual erosional vales in anticlinal structures that would have had an influence on stream development at various times.

This map is of fundamental significance to the analysis of the Zagros drainage problem, for it indicates that the great transverse streams of the northwest merely string together present and *past* contiguous subsequent basins that have local *en echelon* dispositions. This is true of the Sehzar and Bakhtiari systems as well as the Kashgan and Saidmarreh rivers, despite the immense present differences in the environing landscapes. Projected forward into the future, and downward into the substratum of the present basins, the Kashgan and Saidmarreh will inevitably be engorged in a series of Cenomanian anticlines just as the Sehzar is at present. Projected into the past, the Sehzar and Bakhtiari rivers must formerly have meandered through a series of open anticlinal basins separated by back-to-back hogbacks and synclinal ranges, as do the Kashgan and Saidmarreh rivers today. Both the Kashgan and Saidmarreh are already beginning to uncover Cenomanian cores in their subsequent lowlands, as the Sehzar did long ago; and in a synclinorium at the interior of the Fold Zone the Sehzar is still flowing through open vales in unroofed broad arches, as do the Luristan streams throughout.

ORIGIN OF THE PATTERN OF ANTICLINAL BASINS

Since the correspondence between contiguous axial basins and transverse streams is clear, it must be determined whether the transverse stream pattern is responsible for the subsequent valley pattern, or whether the disposition of contiguous subsequent valleys produced by normal denudation has *determined* the transverse stream pattern.

If the present streams are the primary factor they should disregard local structural lines, cutting through anticlines at all points, regardless of the plunges of individual folds and echelon fold groups. Axial basins should be spreading outward from watergaps at all positions along the fold axes: from the noses, from the crests, from points between.

If, on the contrary, structure and general denudation unconnected with the present stream network control the distribution of the subsequent basins, they should be spreading from anticlinal culminations, and should have a pattern similar to the pattern of fold axes. There should be some evidence of "denudation planes" which limit the elevation at which each formation can survive in a more or less intact state and which determine the distribution of roofed and unroofed anticlines. Axial basins should occur in folds not transected by through-flowing streams. They should be arranged *en echelon* where the fold axes are *en echelon*; and where the fold axes are so disposed the present streams, if subsequent, should cross the fold belt diagonally, "seeking" rather than avoiding structural culminations. As each anticlinal transection would be an autogenous development growing out of the initial consequent dissection of the arch, the lines of transection would be independently oriented from one basin to another.

When the outcrop patterns of the folds are studied, it is seen that large subsequent basins invariably occur where the anticlines attain their greatest local breadths—in their central regions or at local culminations in their structure. Even in the absence of summit accordance the axial basins are distributed exactly as would be the case if a cutting plane had been run over the fold belt, as shown in section CC, Figure 7. The vales form *en echelon* ranks dependent on transverse lines of warping. The transverse stream pattern follows these lines.

By consulting the map of anticlinal axes (Figure 6), it will be seen that the through-flowing streams of the northwest almost never change course in a downstream direction to *avoid* an anticlinal barrier, though they often change direction *in crossing* the structural high. The Saidmarreh leaves the radiolarite zone at the only point where it could possibly encounter four anticlines in a single group (two of them Cenomanian), slanting consistently toward the center of each successive arch to be crossed. It then passes through five more broad anticlinal structures, moving centrally through the greatest of these, and receives a right bank tributary coming across two of the same group without deviation. To the northwest the Cham Rawand crosses four anticlinal vales before suffering deflection at the intact end of a fifth arch. None of these streams alters course to evade the obstacles in its path.

The long terminal reach of the Upper Kashgan moves diagonally through two axial lowlands, being slightly displaced by the emerged Cenomanian core of the second; it then receives the Ab-i-Khorramabad, cuts diagonally across a third unroofed dome, transversely through a fourth, diagonally across a fifth and sixth (each time centrally), and transversely across a seventh at its Fars-blanketed nose. The Lower Kashgan does not change course to avoid any positive structure in its path, though it does undergo a change in direction with each transection.

The Sehzar leaves its Pliocene covermass at Tang-i-Bahrein to cut through the nose of a Cenomanian anticline, two flysch lowlands that it crosses centrally, and another that it encounters near its terminus. It then cleaves seven major anticlinal mountains, with occasional deflections along the strike. In only one case does a change in course allow the river to evade a barrier; more often than not its strike components flow against synclinal pitches to carry it farther toward the *center* of the next fold to be transected. Its final watergap is at a local culmination and could have been avoided by a continuation of its synclinal path into a Pliocene valley beyond the Mountain Front. The Sehzar cuts through the densest fold swarm in the Central Zagros Region, missing only two components of this anticlinorium, both of which are transected by its tributary, the Ab-i-Bakhtiari.

After cutting into the Kainu anticlinorium from a subsequent valley to the northeast, the Ab-i-Bakhtiari is seated in high Cenomanian anticlines almost throughout. It cleaves at least seven of these—its strike deflections, like those of the Sehzar, repeatedly carrying it farther toward the centers and culminations of the anticlines to be transected. The same may be said of its tributary, the Sorkh, which splits four major Cenomanian ranges. Neither stream moves to evade any anticline in its neighborhood.

Viewed in a downstream sense, the through-flowing streams of the northwest thus do not avoid the major barriers in their paths, nor have they made any adjustments that indicate shifts toward easier paths around these obstacles.

Regarded in an upstream direction, the only direction in which a stream can *extend* (in the absence of a prograding shoreline), the through-flowing streams of the northwest appear to *seek out* high structures and to follow transverse structural culminations across the Outer Zagros. Starting at Kuh-i-Gavah on the Saidmarreh, Milleh Kuh on the Kashgan, and at the Mountain Front on the Sehzar, the anomalous streams give the impression of having extended consistently *headward* toward the nearest adjacent anticline of significant amplitude, and to have progressed in this way from one arch to the next across the breadth of the Fold Zone. Unlike the streams thought to be antecedent, the anomalous trunk streams of the northwest frequently have a different orientation from one anticlinal transection to another, crossing some perpendicularly (from northeast to southwest) and others diagonally (from both east to west and north to south). The Kashgan, for example, crosses a series of six tangent anticlinal basins, and in each of them the transverse reach is inclined at an angle of 80 to 100 degrees from the reaches in the adjacent basins. This contributes to the impression that each anticlinal crossing is an independent erosional development, unrelated to the course or controls of the same stream in adjacent structures.

The transverse stream pattern of Luristan is thus subsequent: the result of the linkage of the drainage of separate anticlinal basins by the gradual enlargement and coalescence of these basins through scarp retreat. The broadest portions of the folds are sited on their transverse axes and at their vertical culminations. This is the first portion of the structure to be attacked by denudation and gullying in the gradual emergence of the anticline as a positive landform. As deformation continues this is also the sector of the anticline that will first impinge upon adjacent domes, pinching out the syncline between them, and the area in which the hogback ring will first be consumed by cliff retreat from either side.

Basin coalescence would be favored by significant variations in the altitudes of adjacent synclinal and axial basin floors. Basin coalescence appears to involve "aggressor" basins, tributary to deep synclines and thereby excavated to low levels, whose expansion under-cuts the adjacent higher syncline to which higher level basins are tributary. In the Zagros the characteristic depression of synclinal axes approaching the Mountain Front would favor the coalescence of parallel anticlinal basins and the northeasterly expansion of transverse subsequent lowlands through progressive un-dercutting of successive tiers of axial basins. This process would be especially favored in the anticlinorium of the Bakhtiari Mountains.

Axial basins cannot be fluvially excavated below the level of the syncline to which their drainage is initially tributary. Thus adjacent anticlinal basins lying on either side of a syn-clinal valley to which both are tributary could not become coalescent by scarp recession alone. Their junction could only follow the complete excavation of the hard rocks of the synclinal floor by the synclinal runoff itself.

In some instances fluvial linkage of succes-sive axial basins precedes the physical coales-cence of the subsequent valleys. The Kashgan, as previously noted, passes through reflexive bedding-plane gorges in near-vertical synclinal hogbacks interposed between the contiguous axial basins. These gorges appear to have been initiated by headward extension of obsequent streams, effecting captures of the drainage of adjacent synclinal axes prior to the disappear-ance of the synclinal hogbacks by scarp reces-sion. Headward extension of this type, which utilizes natural partings within a rock body, would be most favored where masses of thin-bedded rocks are very steeply inclined.

In the absence of a reliable structure contour map on some lithological horizon in the Fold Zone, no precise quantitative information on the structural surface is available for correla-tion with stream locations and orientations.[2] However, a glance at the map of fold axes in the northwest (Figure 6) clearly indicates that echelon fold swarms create high zones oblique to the trend of the orogen, and that *all* the anomalous through-flowing streams corres-pond with such zones in both location and general orientation. The stream courses seem attracted to the intermediate structures as they

are revealed by the denudational exposure of their Senonian and Cenomanian cores, avoid-ing primary anticlines and also the youngest folds whose Asmari shells remain essentially intact.

Where anticlines are jammed closely to-gether, as in the Bakhtiari Mountains, they are often transected with little deviation in gorge direction. This would seem to proceed from early lateral coalescence of lenticular axial basins, producing compound subsequent val-leys in which the separate anticlinal structures would not be recognizable. Where the folding is more open, successive anticlinal transections are variously oriented, as along the Lower Kashgan. In these areas the subsequent basins are oval rather than linear, and their coales-cence would involve extensive scarp retreat consuming relatively protracted intervals of time. Thus separate structures involving a succession of hard and soft rocks would pre-serve their individuality under denudation longer in areas of open folds than in those of sharp folding. The stream pattern in regions of open folds clearly supports this, extension having been effected across one unroofed structure at a time, rather than across com-pound anticlinal basins as seems to have been the case in the Bakhtiari Mountains.

Thus the drainage pattern that at first seems quite arbitrary is seen to be totally controlled by structure, though in an inverse fashion. The transverse stream pattern is determined by the pattern of structural highs because a breached positive structure underlain by unre-sistant masses becomes a rapidly expanding negative landform. The development of through-flowing drainage awaits the develop-ment of subsequent basins by normal denuda-tion, so that the same streams that are trans-verse to major Cenomanian structures skirt the lesser structural highs that are not yet un-roofed, as in Outer Luristan, until the Lower Fars depositional basin is encountered and stream superposition on the lower folds be-comes possible.

ORIGIN OF THE CENOMANIAN GORGES OF THE BAKHTIARI MOUNTAINS

The pattern of coalescing anticlinal vales in Luristan is but an early stage in the evolu-tion of the wild landscape traversed by the Sehzar and Bakhtiari rivers. Figure 60 il-lustrates the probable history of this area. The great Cenomanian anticlinorium of the Bakh-

---

[2] J. G. Crichton and C. A. E. O'Brien of the Geological Department of the Iranian Oil Participants have con-structed such maps on the oil-bearing horizon, at a scale of 1:250,000; but due to economic and political consider-ations these maps cannot be released for inspection by the public. The Asmari profiles of Figure 5 are taken from these maps.

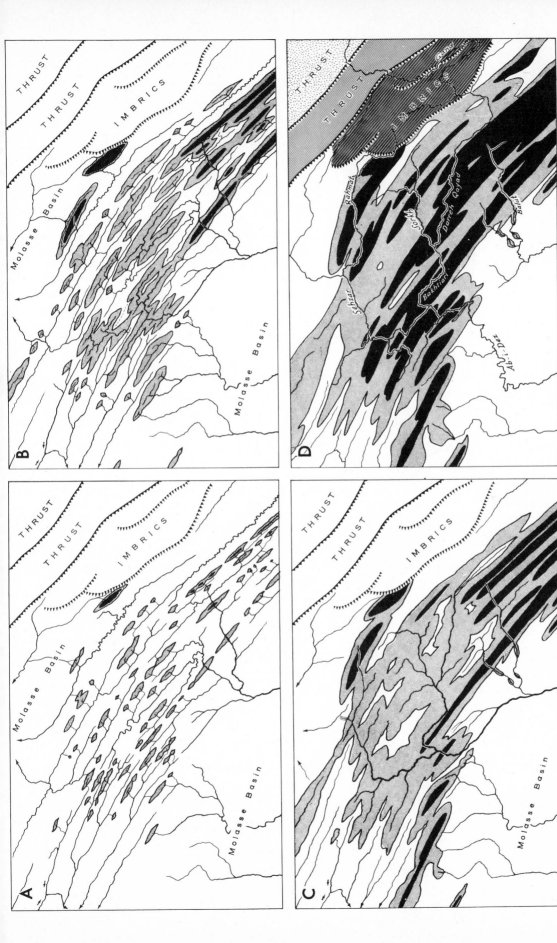

FIGURE 60. Evolution of the Sehzar-Bakhtiari river system. A. Hypothetical consequent drainage of initial stage, showing development of small axial basins by autogenic denudation of anticlinal ridges. B. Expansion and coalescence of axial basins producing compound subsequent valleys. C. Complete inversion of relief producing transverse subsequent drainage from the transverse subsequent valleys shown in C. The Ab-i-Balut appears to be an antecedent stream. The absence of other drainage anomalies in this region is attributable to the poor development of the erodable flysch in this area. South of the present Bakhtiari River the Cenomanian fold cores were exposed shortly after denudation breached the initial Asmari limestone fold envelopes, precluding any extension of subsequent drainage across the strike. D. Exposure of quent lowlands and facilitating drainage extension across the strike, transected on a massive scale as a result of the superposition of Cenomanian fold cores.

tiari Mountains must have been expressed initially as groups of *en echelon* anticlinal ridges of Asmari limestone. These would have been drained consequently down-flank and out through synclinal valleys and around fold noses to the Khuzistan Plains. Antecedent drainage may also have been present. Inevitably, the antecedent streams and consequent lateral gullies on the anticlines cut through the Asmari envelopes to initiate rapidly expanding subsequent vales in the soft flysch beds beneath. Every anticline, in time, became a basin surrounded by an elliptical hogback breached in many places.

Each axial basin would initially have been an independent drainage node with an outlet

the drainage of the separate units became abstracted into through-flowing systems. These systems eventually cut down to the subjacent Cenomanian limestones. Being well nourished, the through-flowing subsequent streams were able to incise the limestones, becoming more and more deeply entrenched in them as the anticlinal structures were being resurrected as mountains by the removal of the flysch overburden. This phase continues at present in the Bakhtiari Mountains.

In the Bakhtiari Mountains the tightness of the folding would have produced a great multitude of linear subsequent basins that would have coalesced most rapidly where the density of the folds was greatest. Figure 61 shows that

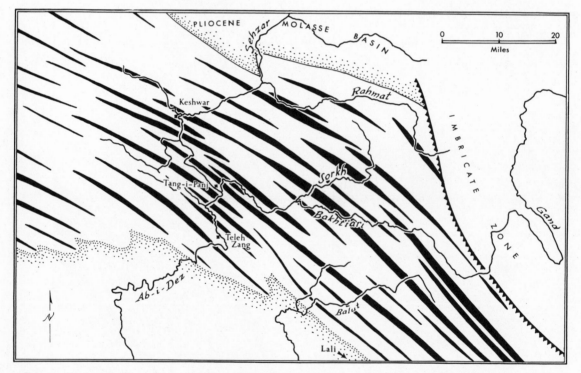

FIGURE 61. Anticlinal axes in the Bakhtiari Mountains, showing the relationship of the major streams to fold density and disposition.

into a synclinal valley. As the hogback rims of the basins continued to retreat, the beheaded and lithogically disadvantaged synclinal drainage was progressively undercut and captured by obsequent streams feeding into the growing subsequent valleys. As these basins coalesced, forming beaded outcrops of erodable materials transverse to the fold belt,

three dense swarms of *en echelon* folds are present here. The axis of one group extends almost due north from Teleh Zang to Keshwar; another runs east through Tang-i-Panj; and the third extends northeast from the Mountain Front behind Lali oil field. The thickness of the Upper Cretaceous flysch was in excess of 5,000 feet in the first two areas

(Figure 62) and the Sehzar and Bakhtiari rivers follow those zones.[3] The flysch declines in thickness to less than 2,000 feet south of the Bakhtiari River (Figure 63, and between sections EE and GG, Figure 7). The third fold swarm, lying in this area of flysch attenuation, is not crossed by any stream that could not be attributed to drainage antecedence.

The transverse subsequent stream pattern resulting from the coalescence of anticlinal basins was "fixed" by the deep entrenchment of the drainage in the flysch when the hard Cenomanian rocks below were first exposed. It is noteworthy that where the Saidmarreh and Kashgan rivers are beginning to expose Cenomanian cores in their axial basins they are not deflected but continue across the

harder rock as they did before its exposure. On these streams only one case of drainage displacement by hard outcrops occurs, that near the confluence of the Upper Kashgan and the Ab-i-Khorramabad. The terminal reach of the Upper Kashgan was superimposed along the length of a Cenomanian anticlinal axis, and has slipped to the north down the dip of the more resistant beds.

Through-flowing streams are not attracted to all Cenomanian anticlines in the mountain complex. These streams scrupulously avoid the primary anticlines in the Fold Zone: Kabir Kuh, Kainu, Mungasht, and Mafarun. Through-flowing drainage coming from the northeast is deflected into synclinal or longitudinal subsequent valleys by all of these massive ranges. The deflection of transverse streams by the great ranges in the Central Zagros is additional evidence of the influence of the flysch in drainage evolution, for all of these ranges lie in areas of marked primary attenuation of the flysch accumulation. Kabir

[3] All references to the estimated thickness of the flysch are based upon isopach maps in P. E. Kent, F. C. Slinger, and A. N. Thomas, "Stratigraphical Exploration Surveys in South-West Persia," *Proceedings*, 3rd World Petroleum Congress, The Hague, Sect. I (1951), 141–161.

FIGURE 62. The depth of the flysch in the Bakhtiari Mountains, looking northwest from above the Bakhtiari River. The local relief is about 5,000 feet. The full thickness of the Upper Cretaceous-Eocene flysch can be seen between the Asmari limestone, capping the synclinal range, Kuh-i-Gariveh, at right, and the Cenomanian limestone peaks in the center of the photo. The depth of the flysch is slightly in excess of the amplitude of the folding in this region. (Photo by Aerofilms and Aero Pictorial Limited.)

FIGURE 63. Northeast flank of Kuh-i-Mafarun showing the thin development of the erodable flysch horizon south and east of the Bakhtiari River. Asmari and Eocene limestones form the curving hogback, and Cenomanian limestones compose the fold core at the right. The resistant fold cores were exposed in this area before adjacent axial basins merged through scarp retreat. Thus through-flowing transverse subsequent streams were unable to develop here. (Photo by Aerofilms and Aero Pictorial Limited.)

Kuh rises to the southwest of the major flysch depositional basin in Luristan and the Bakhtiari Country, and Kainu, Mafarun, and Mungasht lie to the southeast of the main flysch accumulation, which thins drastically toward Kuhgalu. The flysch cover over all of these primary anticlines has been estimated to have been less than 1,000 feet thick. The flysch is likewise poorly developed throughout the Imbricate Zone, an area in which there is a corresponding absence of conspicuous drainage anomalies.

Where the thickness of the Upper Cretac-

eous flysch formation became less considerable than that of the overlying Eocene and Asmari formations, axial basins with well-established subsequent drainage systems could not develop. The Cenomanian cores of such structures were bared too rapidly, dividing the subsequent axial drainage before it could become well established, and shifting it into homoclinal lowlands shortly after the Asmari envelopes were breached. This is the case throughout the Kuhgalu area in the southeast. The high seasonality of runoff and the smaller volumes of the streams in the southeastern region also may have contributed to the general defeat of drainage superimposed on Cenomanian beds from their thin flysch cover. Where the flysch did not form a deep blanket over the harder beds, its dissection was too shallow to retard down-dip stream migration at the limestone-marl contact, allowing drainage adjustments to lithology similar to those described in connection with superposition from the Lower Fars formation.

For axial basins of similar size to evolve (prior to the exposure of Cenomanian fold cores), intensively folded areas would require a thicker flysch blanket than more gently deformed regions. Clearly, for basin coalescence to occur prior to the emergence of fold cores, the thickness of the erodable stratum must exceed the amplitude of the folding. As a corollary, transverse subsequent drainage can develop in a fold belt only where local fold amplitudes are inferior to the depth of erodable materials (Figure 64). In the intensely folded Bakhtiari Mountains, upwards of 5,000 feet of the flysch was required to produce transverse subsequent drainage.

A nicely preserved example of stream defeat by the early exposure of a Cenomanian fold core in the region of thin flysch development is seen in the large windgap near the southeastern end of the Kuh-i-Bingistan anticline. The Marun River formerly crossed this arch in a direct line with its course through the synclinal lowland to the northeast. After cutting down to the hard Cenomanian layers, the Marun could not entrench itself rapidly enough to escape capture by a stream extending through the Lower Fars synclinal badlands east of Kuh-i-Bingistan.

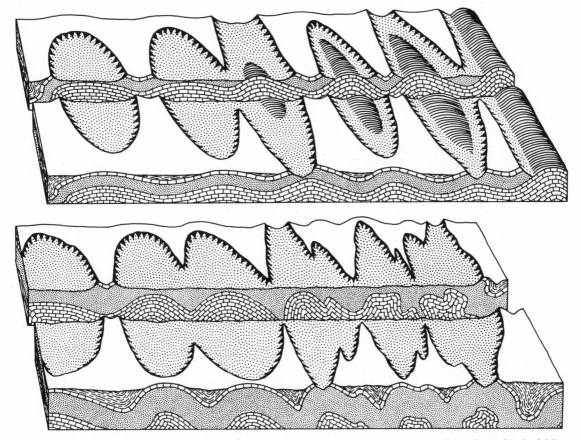

FIGURE 64. Basin coalescence related to strength of folding and depth of erodable materials. Top: Gentle folding but a thin layer of erodable materials interposed between resistant formations produces exposure of fold cores prior to basin coalescence. The development of capacious transverse subsequent lowlands is precluded. Bottom: Although fold amplitudes are greater, the presence of a compensatory depth of erodable materials allows the development of extensive transverse subsequent lowlands prior to the exposure of the second resistant horizon.

This example indicates that complete inversion of relief, with the synclines standing high *above* the flysch valley floors, is a prerequisite for the fixing of superimposed subsequent drainage of any permanence.

The Malbur Basin

The discussion to this point has concerned the great through-flowing streams of the northwest, certainly the best-known drainage paradox in the Central Zagros Region. There is another area of anticlinal watergaps in which the relationship between structure, lithology, and drainage supports the conclusions reached above regarding the origin of the transverse streams of the northwest. The corroborating evidence comes from the basin of the Ab-i-Malbur in the extreme southeast of the Central Zagros mountain complex.

The Malbur Basin lies between the Kuh-i-Dina imbric and the front of the Cretaceous overthrust. The Ab-i-Malbur and its tributaries effect at least seven transections of Cenomanian limestone arches. This is a small number in relation to the area of the basin, and compared to the figure in the Sehzar-Bakhtiari watershed; however, the Malbur Basin is an area of far more open folding than the Bakhtiari Country. Indeed, there are only nine major anticlines in the entire basin.

The watergap pattern in the Malbur Basin is one of offset transections, with the cuts being variously oriented. As in the northwest, the drainage makes no attempt to evade the anticlinal structures, and actually seems attracted to them, its trend reaches frequently leading to central transections rather than toward fold termini.

The Malbur Basin is not only similar to the northwestern region in its pattern of sundered Cenomanian arches; it is also an area in which the Cretaceous flysch, after a near disappearance for 130 miles along the trend, again attains a depth of about 5,000 feet (section MM in Figure 7). Here heavy accumulations of the flysch are limited to the gently folded area between the Kuh-i-Dina imbric and the thrust margin, that is, *to the Malbur Basin,* giving the impression that the Kuh-i-Dina lineament in Upper Cretaceous time was a submarine ridge that barred detrital sedimentation from the outer part of the geosyncline. The imbric line of Zardeh Kuh, Kuh-i-Dehngan, and Kuh-i-Gareh, farther northwest, may have performed a similar function, but the area between these imbrics and the thrust margin has been so upheaved and denuded in Cenozoic time that only limited occurrences of the Upper Cretaceous detrital beds are preserved there.

The association of a heavy flysch blanket and an inverse relation of drainage to structure in both the Malbur Basin and the northwestern watersheds can hardly be coincidental. Absence of the flysch in regions of similar structure results in a distinctively different drainage pattern, in which transverse streams avoid the higher anticlines rather than focusing on them. Accordingly, the anticlinal transections of the Malbur Basin are best explained, like those of the northwest, as the result of the superposition of transverse subsequent drainage upon the Cenomanian beds that presently resurrect anticlinal mountains in areas of former relief inversion.

The inverse relation of drainage to structure in a second and widely separated region of heavy flysch accumulations certainly reinforces the hypothesis offered in explanation of transverse drainage formation in the northwestern region. This solution to the problem of transverse drainage is especially favored as it is based upon relationships between drainage, structure, and lithology that are consistent wherever a through-flowing stream crosses a flysch depositional basin. In all areas characterized by strong development of the flysch, the drainage is transverse and strongly discordant, appearing to seek out transections of Cenomanian arches. There are no exceptions that require explanation, and no invisible structures or processes are invoked. The youth of the orogenic system and the presence of regional variations in the depth of erosion in similar structures allow the axial drainage development, integration, and superposition to be observed at every stage. The initial breaching of anticlines and the extension of subsequent drainage across sharply defined anticlinal basins may be seen throughout Luristan; three stages in the linkage of anticlinal basins are displayed by the Tarhan and Kuh-i-Dasht areas of Luristan, the Kashgan River, and the Saidmarreh River. The first exposure of Cenomanian cores in basin floors and examples of the initial superposition and fixing of subsequent streams across the hard cores are found along the Kashgan and Saidmarreh rivers; the complete resurrection of the anticlinal mountain ranges by the emergence of the cores is seen in the Bakhtiari Country; and the seemingly paradoxical dissection of this landscape by through-flowing drainage super-imposed upon it from the conformable cover-mass of soft valley-forming formations is epitomized by the Sehzar and Bakhtiari rivers.

SIGNIFICANCE OF GORGE MORPHOLOGY

At this point it is appropriate to ask how the variations in the morphology of transverse gorges across the breadth of the orogen can be reconciled with the above mode of drainage evolution. In particular, the spacious gorge through Pliocene materials at Tang-i-Bahrein demands explanation in view of the constric-tion of the defiles through the Middle Cretac-eous and Oligo-Miocene limestone anticlinal structures farther downstream.

As noted in Chapter V, a comparison of the innermost debris-smothered transverse valleys and the rock-cut trenches through the younger frontal folds is strongly suggestive of through-flowing antecedent streams. It has been shown, however, that one of the greatest of these streams, the Sehzar, did not link the Fold Zone and the Inner Zagros until late or post-Pliocene time, when its headward transec-tion of the great Pliocene covermass at Tang-i-Bahrein was accomplished. Tang-i-Bahrein is a capture site whose morphology, oddly enough, is clearly indicative of greater antiqu-ity than that of the *tangs* splitting the Ceno-manian fold swarm farther downstream. This undeniable fact could easily lead to a misin-terpretation of the origin of the Sehzar. Fortunately, it can be explained most simply, for Tang-i-Bahrein is the historical parallel not of the present Cenomanian gorges but of the *initial* Asmari limestone and Cretaceous flysch valleys that enclosed the Sehzar in its formative stages. The walls of the initial gul-lies that penetrated to the flysch have now been pushed back to form the hogback rim west of the Bakhtiari Culmination, as well as Asmari limestone hogbacks and synclinal peaks within the Cenomanian highland. The deep Cenomanian structures in which the river is presently engorged appear to have been ex-posed by denudation as a result of broad doming *after* the capture at Tang-i-Bahrein was completed. Thus, the *line* of the river is older in the region now occupied by Ceno-manian arches, but its *gorges* through the

rocks presently exposed in the Fold Zone are younger than its gorge at Tang-i-Bahrein.

Tang-i-Yek, the canyon of the Dez (Sehzar) River through the Mountain Front Detrital Glacis, is far more youthful than Tang-i-Bahrein, though both are capture points cut through the same formation: the late Pliocene Bakhtiari beds (Figures 28 and 29). Tang-i-Yek is itself a two-story canyon consisting of a vertical slot in the floor of a slightly more open concave-walled gorge. As such, it is con-sistent in form with the Cenomanian gorges farther upstream.

The clear change in gorge character from the Inner Zagros to the Fold Zone is therefore not a sign of the more recent establishment of the present streams in the latter area. It is an indication, first, of the more recent auto-superposition of streams on the Cenomanian fold *cores* of that region; and second, of the greater mobility of the outer area in Quater-nary time, resulting in a rejuvenation of stream downcutting in the Fold Zone that continues at present.

Differential Warping and Tang Morphology

Dunnington assumed that the original de-formation of the Zagros folded belt was ac-complished by its relative subsidence rather than a general upward displacement; the sub-sidence in the deeper basins measuring as much as 20,000 feet, as estimated from the thickness of the Pliocene detrital beds.[4] This accords with Falcon's view that the present elevations of the structures of the outer part of the orogen are attributable to broad flexur-ing, with the individual anticlines being formed prior to the major structural waves such as the Bakhtiari Culmination.[5]

In Luristan differential broad warping has not yet developed (sections BB and CC, Fig-ure 7) and stream downcutting since the Plio-cene can be measured in tens to a few hun-dreds of feet. This is best seen in the lowland crossed by the Upper Kashgan and Khor-ramabad rivers. Here the Cretaceous flysch is directly overlain by Pliocene detrital beds,

---

[4]H. V. Dunnington, "Generation, Migration, Accumu-lation, and Dissipation of Oil in Northern Iraq," in *Habitat of Oil*, Publ. by Amer. Assoc. Petrol. Geols., Tulsa (1958), 1219.

[5]N. L. Falcon, "Evidence for Large Scale Flexuring in the Southwest Persian Mountain Zone," Iranian Oil Expl. Prod. Co., *Geol. Dept. Report* 797 (1950), 3.

with the present streams incised no more than 150 feet into the Pliocene and Cretaceous ensemble (Figure 65). In the Bakhtiari Mountain region, on the other hand, Pliocene valley fills, both at Tang-i-Bahrein (Figure 40) and on the Gariveh synclinal peak in the Fold Zone (Figure 21), are perched more than 5,000 feet above present valley floors. All Pliocene beds found in the Bakhtiari Culmination are

cene deposits that must have been present in the former axial basins.

Thus strong local doming in the Quaternary appears to be responsible for the youth of the Cenomanian gorges of the Bakhtiari Mountains and for the differences between the landscapes of Luristan and the Bakhtiari Highland, whose trunk streams nevertheless retain similar relationships to the individual

FIGURE 65. Post-Pliocene stream incision in the Luristan Basin. The Ab-i-Khorromabad is dissecting Pliocene beds, with the crest of Kuh-i-Safid in the background. Post-Pliocene stream incision in Inner Luristan is to be measured in tens to a few hundreds of feet; by contrast, post-Pliocene incision in the Bakhtiari Mountains is as much as 5,000 feet. Differential post-Pliocene uplift explains the striking contrast in the landscapes and physiographic expression of the drainage anomoly in the two regions.

synclinal; none are preserved overlying the flysch as in the Kashgan Basin; and all are trenched to depths in excess of 2,000 feet.

These circumstances indicate that the transverse drainage of the Bakhtiari Culmination was probably linked during the Pliocene on a fold plateau, the landscape being similar to that of present-day Luristan. Subsequent broad doming in the Bakhtiari Mountains caused intensive stream rejuvenation, superimposing the new transverse drainage lines onto the Cenomanian beds below the flysch, resurrecting the anticlinal mountain systems, and resulting in the total removal of the Plio-

corrugations of their broad structural environment, whether at present a plateau of folds or an anticlinorium.

Solution Piracy

Though all parts of the drainage anomaly in the Fold Zone of the Central Zagros appear to have been traced to their origin in the foregoing pages, some details of the geomorphic evolution of the streams of the region remain a puzzle. The chief indications of this are the strange discordant canyon of the Karun at Rudwar in the Imbricate Zone, and morphological contrasts within the gorges of the

Sehzar through Kuh-i-Langar on the Mountain Front. The morphology of these sites suggests the possibility that solution in calcareous rocks played a part in the linkage of some transverse reaches of the through-flowing streams, whose evoluation has hitherto been stated only in the most general terms.

Virtually all valleys and gorges in the Zagros Highland are multi-stored: near-vertical at the base, flaring at one or more clearly defined horizons, and cut into a structural surface or below a denudational landscape that is graded toward the lips of the gorge. At Rudwar, however, the Karun River flows through a raw canyon interrupting a maturely dissected highland whose ridges and valleys bear not the slightest relation to the line of the gorge.[6] This surface relief is carved in Pliocene detrital formations overlying Eocene limestones which in turn cover impermeable

red beds. The Karun gorge transects the older relief features indiscriminately; and slopes, valleys, and divides interrupted by the slot are resumed on the other side of it without a change in their inclination or characteristics. There is no slope "turn-over" at the gorge lip. It appears that the Karun never flowed over the surface of this region. Accordingly, subterranean captures followed by collapse seem to be the only explanation of the phenomenon.

The role of solution in producing the details of the Zagros drainage pattern is difficult to ascertain. Though the geomorphic relations of no other fluvial reaches demand such an origin, subterranean piracy may have facilitated the initial connection of the separate drainage systems of various anticlinal basins before the actual coalescence of the basins.

A possible example of the effect of solution on drainage development is seen where the Sehzar exits from the fold belt by a pair of gorges through the facing hogbacks of the breached Asmari anticline of Kuh-i-Langar. The differences in the two gorges through the

---

[6]Best seen on aerial photographs, Geraldine (Shoran) Project 158, strip 88: photos 10198 and 10199; and strip 89: photos 10288 and 10289.

FIGURE 66. Homoclinal gorge of the Sehzar River, Tang-i-Seh. The stream is shifting down dip on massive limestones as it edges into the unroofed Kuh-i-Langar anticline. The stream eventually works through this (upstream) homocline, and then breaches the facing hogback directly (Figure 69).

same formation are most striking and are, perhaps, significant.

The gorge through which the stream enters the anticline is cut into the flank of the structure along bedding planes (Figure 66) and exhibits many features which could be attributed to solution. Alcoves in the limestone walls are remarkably smooth, clayey, and reminiscent of cavern passages (Figure 67). Solution tubes are common, and occasionally stalactites, four or five feet long and several inches in diameter, dangle into the fronds of palm glades from smoothly curving overhangs (Figure 68). The water-worn sections are presently being eaten away by rough angular surfaces resulting from mechanical weathering.[7]

The behavior of the Sehzar as it enters this Mountain Front anticline by a tortuous path along bedding planes is in sharp contrast to its direct exit from the structure in a stupendous and all but vertical gorge cut transversely through the massive Asmari limestone rim (Figure 69).

These relations seem to be indicative of headward extension of the drainage of the axial basin into the syncline to the north prior to the destruction of the basin rim by conjunction with the retreating rim of the adjacent basin. This has effected the diversion of the Sehzar away from its former synclinal path, and into a new transverse path across the Mountain Front anticline. In such a case the outlet gorge would be the descendent of the original consequent gully that first exposed the weak formations beneath the Asmari shell. It shows none of the possible signs of solution which are so striking in the upper canyon. As there are no consequent gullies draining the crest northeastward, we may assume that this arch was exhumed from beneath a Lower Fars covering by runoff coming from the northeast.

The Sehzar gorges through Kuh-i-Langar, along with the reflexive bedding-plane gorges of the Kashgan, indicate that captures of adjacent axial basins may be made by extended consequent drainage lines prior to the

FIGURE 67. A smooth alcove in the gorge wall at Tang-i-Seh, with characteristic rough surfaces above and below; part of a pothole, or possibly a solution effect in the massive Asmari limestone.

physical coalescence of the basins, the extension possibly being facilitated by solution along bedding planes in the Asmari limestone.

THE RESIDUAL DRAINAGE ANOMALY

In Figure 70 the drainage pattern of the Central Zagros Region is depicted in terms of its origin from point to point. This map reveals that the residual drainage anomaly in the Fold Zone is explained in its entirety by the process of superposition of linked drainage of coalescent axial basins. Some 90 anticlinal transections, 30 percent of the total in the Central Zagros Region, appear to have originated in this manner. The process has dominated the evolution of drainage in Luristan, the Bakhtiari Mountains, and the Malbur Basin—every area in which the Upper Cre-

---

[7] However, pothole drilling plays a conspicuous role in channel deepening and could likewise have accounted for the smooth alcoves, some of which are now hundreds of feet above the water. In such a case, the mud coating on the gorge walls could be explained as a wash derived from fragments of the Lower Fars beds still found on the dome flanks.

FIGURE 68. Dripstone stalactites along the gorge wall, Tang-i-Seh. Several features associated with solution suggest that subterranean captures played a role in the extension of the Sehzar through the northern homocline of Kuh-i-Langar.

FIGURE 69. Tang-i-Do, the Sehzar's exit from the Fold Zone. Left: The portal of Tang-i-Do seen from the subsequent basin in the center of the Langar anticline. Right: The Sehzar in its passage through Tang-i-Do.

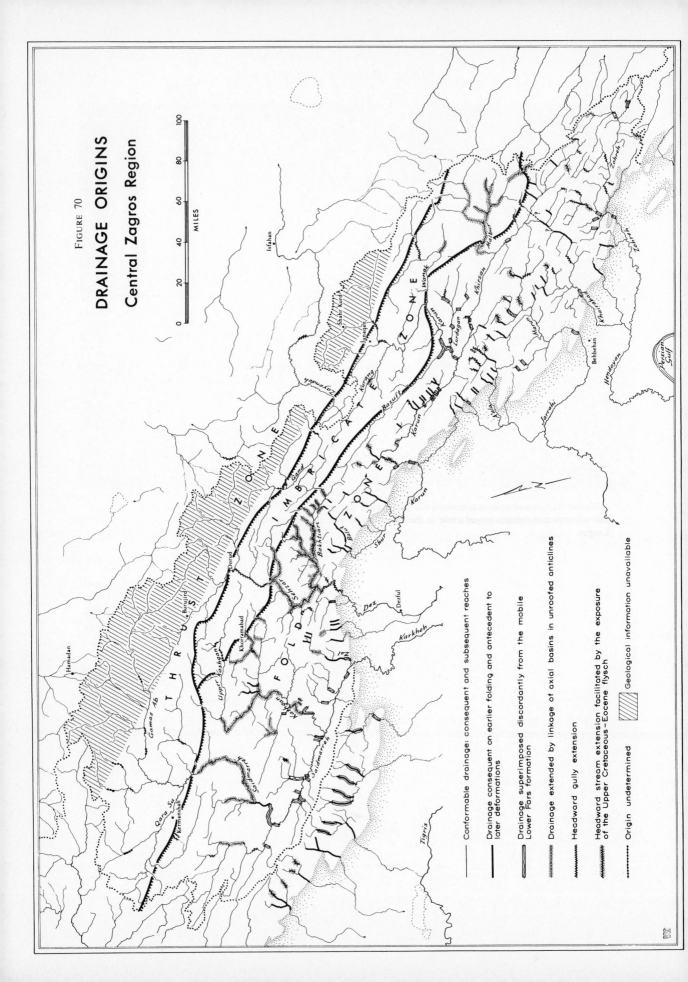

FIGURE 70

DRAINAGE ORIGINS
Central Zagros Region

MILES

0   20   40   60   80   100

Legend:

—— Conformable drainage: consequent and subsequent reaches

—— Drainage consequent on earlier folding and antecedent to later deformations

Drainage superimposed discordantly from the mobile Lower Fars formation

Drainage extended by linkage of axial basins in unroofed anticlines

Headward gully extension

Headward stream extension facilitated by the exposure of the Upper Cretaceous–Eocene flysch

Origin undetermined

Geological information unavailable

Persian Gulf

taceous flysch originally attained great depth. The drainage anomaly in the Inner Zagros, however, remains unexplained.

The drainage anomaly in the Imbricate and Thrust zones is insignificant when compared to that in the Fold Zone, comprising only 20 discordant transverse reaches, as opposed to some 300 in the latter region. Nevertheless, an attempt to decipher the origin of these 20 disharmonic reaches would involve solutions far more conjectural than any advanced in the investigation of the greater drainage anomaly in the Fold Zone. Complex faulting and erosional planations have destroyed the possibility of reconstructing the conditions under which the drainage of the older portion of the highland was formed. The drainage history of this region is as obscure as is that of most of the Cenozoic and older mountain systems of the world whose transverse streams have been deduced, in the absence of evidence to the contrary, to be antecedent, superimposed, or the result of headward extension under unspecified controls.

Geological information on the crystalline and metamorphic zone of the Zagros Highland is as yet too fragmentary for meaningful statements to be made concerning the relation of drainage to structure in that area. The limestone overthrust appears to be transected both at transverse saddles and at unroofed culminations, but here again there is no structural information south of the region crossed by the Dez River. In the Imbricate Zone there is a considerable degree of structural and lithological control of the through-flowing streams, which are characterized by many trend reaches and frequent use of transverse saddles between the noses of sheared anticlines.

Of the twenty clear cases of discordance between structure and drainage in the Inner Zagros (exclusive of the Malbur Basin), six can be tentatively explained on the basis of the evidence at hand. Five transverse cuts appear to be the result of headward gullying, for the gorges are clearly offset from the lines of the streams entering and exiting from them. One other gorge has been developed by superposition of axial basin drainage. This watergap is on a tributary of the Wanak, but lies in the flysch basin otherwise drained by the Malbur system, which has developed many similar watergaps, as noted above.

The remaining watergaps in the Inner Zagros are fairly well aligned with the streams entering them, but owing to the lack of geological information on this region an attempt to explain these anomalies would have no validity. Even if geological information on the entire orogenic system were available, the complex faulting and strong denudation of the Inner Zagros might defeat any attempted explanation of the history of these rivers.

The fact that the origin of the majority of the watergaps in the older structures of the Zagros cannot be conclusively demonstrated emphasizes the unique field of investigation that is present, by contrast, in the younger Fold Zone, where large numbers of drainage anomalies bear consistent relationships of one type or another to structure and lithology, enabling them to be grouped generically and explained genetically in terms of processes modifying the landscape at present.

Chapter XI

The Lesson of the Zagros

PRINCIPAL FINDINGS OF THE STUDY

The foregoing study of the origin of the Zagros streams affirms a fact too long ignored —that ordinary processes of denudation will produce drainage lines transverse to a fold belt, given certain rather ubiquitous conditions of structure and lithology. Though the pattern of through-flowing streams in the Zagros is highly suggestive of regional drainage antecedence or superposition, there is abundant evidence that it has an entirely different origin.

The general discordance between drainage and structure in the Central Zagros has been shown to be an aggregate of independent drainage anomalies of several distinct genera. Each of these is comprised of scores of individual discordances between structure and drainage that bear a consistent relationship to certain elements in the region's geological environment. The regularity of these relationships and the presence of regional variations in the erosional landscapes as a result of differential broad warping of the fold surface in post-Pliocene time allow the different stages in the evolution of each type of drainage anomaly to be observed in the existing landscape. Therefore every step in the origin of the entire discordance between drainage and structure in this region is "documented" in the landscape as it is developed at present.

The classical hypotheses of transverse stream formation, as originally advanced and as generally accepted by geomorphologists, meet little success in explaining the anomalous relationship between drainage and the geologic fundament in the Zagros. These hypotheses are defeated in the Zagros region by the absence of favorable conditions for the operation of the processes that they postulate, by conclusive evidence against the operation of these processes, and by the presence of alternative solutions involving other processes that are visibly modifying the Zagros landscape at present.

Nevertheless, every drainage anomaly in the region can be classified as some *variant* of one or another of the types associated with those hypotheses most commonly invoked in discussions of transverse drainage development.

Transverse consequent drainage is rare in the Zagros. In areas of relief inversion the transverse streams are not in the positions they should occupy if modified from a transverse consequent pattern. However, many engorged reaches in the youngest ranges are near-consequent, transecting anticlines near their noses after deflection along their flanks; and all drainage adopts a consequent path around the greatest anticlines in the fold belt, though portions of these paths are discordant to neighboring arches of less magnitude.

The hypothesis of *regional stream superposition* from an unconformable covermass or erosion surface is defeated by the absence of any evidence of regional covermasses or erosion surfaces in the younger portion of the mountain belt, where the majority of the discordances between drainage and structure occur. However, local superposition of drainage has occurred from originally conformable elements in the sedimentary column, one of which (the Lower Fars) folded disharmonically, while the other (the Upper Cretaceous flysch) released any drainage encountering it from all structural control. Indeed, drainage superimposed from the mobile covermass and from transverse subsequent valleys dating from a period of relief inversion has produced half the transverse gorges in the Central Zagros Region.

The hypothesis of *regional drainage antecedence* is denied in the Zagros by stream deflections at the contacts of each structural and historical zone in the orogenic system. As structural or lithological control seizes all through-flowing streams prior to the development of drainage anomalies in each successive zone of the highland, it appears that the drainage of each tectonic division is an independent and autogenous development. Nevertheless, a form of drainage antecedence is widely manifested in the region—short streams consequent on older folds being antecedent to immediately adjacent younger arches—and, in the agglomerate, the number of transverse gorges created by many such drainage lines comprises almost a third of the total in the problem area, even though no trunk stream had such an origin.

Headward stream extension in zones of lithological weakness, a hypothesis set forth most explicitly by H. D. Thompson with regard to the Appalachian problem, actually inaugurated the conditions leading to the most apparent drainage anomalies in the Zagros Highland. The major transverse streams in the fold belt were established by the integration of the drainage of contiguous axial basins into through-flowing systems that were later superimposed on hard rocks that now resurrect anticlinal mountains. The ultimate effect of such a process has been to establish drainage lines across the broadest parts of the resistant outcrops, rather than across their narrowings as Thompson's theory stipulated, but this is the effect of autosuperposition after the drainage has formed. The *initial* streams *did* link the points at which resistant outcrops were most tenuous: the points of tangency of the axial basins.

The important difference between Thompson's hypothesis and the present case is that the through-flowing streams of the Zagros are essentially the product of the headward extension of consequent gullies on an initial deformational surface, whereas the Appalachian streams were thought by Thompson to have extended headward at the expense of fully integrated drainage systems on an uplifted erosion surface· initially exposing rocks of varying erodability. Stream extension in the northwestern Zagros was not along pre-existent weak outcrops, but was, in effect, the mere expansion of consequent gullies into axial basins whose growth was controlled by scarp retreat in all directions. It was the headward growth, transverse to the weak rock outcrops, of these consequent gullies (in the form of axial basins and their obsequent tributaries) which created, simultaneously, transverse zones of weak rocks and transverse through-flowing drainage lines.

THE WIDER IMPLICATIONS OF THE STUDY

Analysis of the drainage pattern of the Central Zagros casts doubt upon the generic and genetic unity of the transverse drainage that frequently characterizes fold belts, particularly where the anomalous drainage has been attributed to regional drainage antecedence or superposition. This study indicates that the transverse gorge systems characteristic of many fold mountain belts are probably the effect of a number of different geomorphic processes rather than of a single mechanism operating on a regional scale.

In the post-Cambrian mountain belts of the world the majority of the transverse drainage lines usually considered to be antecedent or superimposed in their entirety are not straight, but are characterized by separate variously oriented reaches similar to those of the trunk streams of the Zagros region, which are of compound origin. The orientation of each more or less linear reach on any stream is determined by present or past geomorphic controls: the direction of a structural or topographic slope that may no longer exist, or variations in the erodability of the geological fundament. Major changes in the controls locally determining the orientation of a stream produce major deflections in the stream's course. Where streams transverse to fold belts are characterized by abrupt inflections of course, some doubt may be held as to the unity of their development, the more so if they have been considered to be antecedent or superimposed streams whose development has been unrelated to the present structural matrix. When major course changes of supposedly antecedent or superimposed streams can be related in any way to elements of the structural environment to which the streams are otherwise discordant, the allogenous nature of the drainage should be seriously questioned, and the possibility of its origin under local structural and lithological controls should be considered.

The Zagros drainage pattern offers the valuable lesson that transverse drainage which is spectacularly discordant to geological structure can be an *inevitable consequence* of normal stream development in a certain structural-lithological environment. It remains to be said that this particular environment is a common one in those orogenic systems that display transverse gorge systems almost universally attributed to regional drainage antecedence or superposition.

The lithological sequence critical to the development of this type of drainage is found throughout the mountain zones developed from the Tethyan geosynclinal belt, and also in Mesozoic and Paleozoic highlands. From the Alps to the Himalayas the prevalent limestone succession of the Mesozoic is succeeded by an immense accumulation of flysch beds developed by a late Cretaceous orogenic paroxism, with a return to the deposition of limestones prior to the Cenozoic orogeny. Though facies developments in the various sectors of the geosyncline are not perfectly synchronous in time, they are consistent with regard to sequence. The presence of the erodable flysch in great depth means that wherever transverse warping or echelon folding creates higher zones extending *across* a highland, these zones will, in the initial cycle of erosion, be converted into beaded subsequent lowlands conducive to the formation of through-flowing drainage also extending across the highland.

The structural prerequisite to the development of transverse subsequent drainage is met by the formation of *en echelon* anticline groupings. Echelon folding is frequently the result of the interference of earlier structural trends with later ones superimposed over them—a characteristic seen throughout the Tethyan system, in both fold and thrust structures.[1] In the Alps the flysch was best developed in the regions of the Helvetides, Prealpes, and Southern Alps, all of which are transected at present by through-flowing drainage from crystalline axial ranges in the same manner as is the belt of Pliocene folds in the Zagros. These are the exact areas of the Alps thought to be characterized by antecedent drainage.

The most spectacular evidence in support of the broader application of the process creating the through-flowing streams of the Zagros comes from the Himalayas. The Himalayan nappe complexes are affected by transverse deformation, and they likewise incorporate immense masses of the Cretaceous flysch. Moreover, at least one of the greatest through-flowing streams of the Himalayan region is known to follow the axis of a transverse ridge in the nappe complex. It has been recognized recently that the massif of Mount Everest itself has been carved out of a deep transverse syncline, with the Arun River, immediately to the east, having cut perhaps 50,000 feet below the crest of a transverse anticline in the nappe edifice.[2] The present fragmentary knowledge of the longitudinal structure of the Himalayas does not permit a statement of the relation of the other transverse streams of this highland to transverse structural lines.

Preliminary investigation of deformational zones of all ages from Paleozoic to Cenozoic indicates that pitching anticlines and echelon structures are a normal development in fold zones. Immense accumulations of flysch deposits are also so widespread throughout the post-Cambrian orogenic systems of the world that tectonic theory postulates flysch deposition as one of a general sequence of events in the evolution of an orthogeosyncline. Thus it appears that conditions favorable to the development of autogenous transverse drainage are at least as widespread as conditions favorable to regional drainage antecedence or superposition—the difference being that in the younger orogens the presence of autogenous transverse drainage of the type seen in the Zagros may be verified by studies of the relation between transverse structural lines and transverse drainage lines. Once relief inversion has occurred, as a result of thick flysch accumulations beneath a limestone veneer, through-flowing drainage developed by normal erosion should *follow* (rather than avoid) anticlinal groupings, whether they are expressed as mountains or valleys. It is this very circumstance that has too often provoked the undemonstrable hypotheses of regional drainage antecedence or superposition.

It is realized, of course, that disharmonies in folding and nappe structures would cause superimposed subsequent streams to be displaced, relative to structural axes, during downcutting. Thus transverse drainage initiated in this manner might not be recognizable in the older or more complex tectonic systems. This by no means rules out the possibility that the enigmatic drainage of such areas had its inception in transverse subsequent lowlands. If lithological variations continue to appear at depth, readjustments of the drainage should occur, bringing it to the new transverse structural culminations as soon as less resistant materials are exposed in the structural highs.

---

[1] DeSitter has stated that "interference of the Hercynian direction with the Alpine trend created an EW zoning in the Alps (Western, Central, and Eastern Alps), and caused the very strong axial plunges which can be seen even in relatively small units." L. U. DeSitter, *Structural Geology.* New York: McGraw-Hill, 1959, p. 388.

[2] P. Bordet and M. Latrielle, "La Geologie de L'Himalaya de L'Arun," Soc. Geol. de France, *Bulletin,* Ser. 6 T.5 (1955), 529–542.

Though transverse subsequent streams are the product of normal denudation in a normal structural and lithological environment, their formation inevitably leads to a more consistent discordance between structure and drainage than that produced by any other mechanism of drainage development. Having been formed during relief inversion, their courses in young orogenic systems will have an inverse relation to structure almost throughout. Indeed, the most certain indication of the presence of such drainage is a stream which accomplishes miracles of gorge cutting in seeking out what appears to be, from a tectonic point of view, the "least likely path."

Appendix

The Saidmarreh Landslip

The major problem connected with the Saidmarreh landslip is that the Asmari hogback on either side of the detachment is not steeply inclined. It lies against the gentle Cretaceous arch at an angle of only 20 degrees. On the same mountain, talus cones in gullies appear to be stable at an angle of 30 degrees.[1] Harrison and Falcon pointed out that the underlying Eocene marl in which the detachment took place is not liable to form a "slurry" even when soaked. To explain an immense slip in such an unlikely situation, Harrison and Falcon were forced to adopt a combination of a local inward "knee-bend" or underfold at the base of the Asmari hogback—to leave it somewhat unsupported—with an unusual wetting of the substratum and a violent earthquake to detach the mass.[2] As Harrison and Falcon admitted, there is absolutely no evidence of such an underfold in the Asmari hogback to either side of the detachment. Normally an underfold of this type would be associated with more intensive folding, or with a very strong development of the incompetent flysch horizon, facilitating disharmonic folding. The flysch is, in fact, quite thin in the Kabir Kuh area, as section CC of Figure 7 indicates. Two possible interpretations of Harrison and Falcon's hypothetical "knee-bend" are given in Figure 71.

The writer feels that Harrison and Falcon overlooked a more rational explanation of the Saidmarreh landslip. This explanation involves the drainage anomaly which is the subject of the present research.

It is suggested here that the detachment of the gently inclined Asmari beds occurred because they were unsupported when a seismic shock jolted this area, not as a result of underfolding, but due to *undercutting* of the mountain flank by the Saidmarreh River.

Between its great gorge through Kuh-i-Charmin and its cut through the landslip, the Saidmarreh River four times deserts synclinal

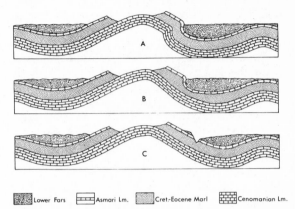

Lower Fars | Asmari Lm. | Cret.-Eocene Marl | Cenomanian Lm.

FIGURE 71. Hypotheses to explain a seemingly necessary lack of support producing the Saidmarreh landslip. A and B: two possible interpretations of Harrison's and Falcon's hypothetical "knee-bend" in the Asmari limestone. C: the author's hypothesis, involving transection of the detached hogback by stream superposition from the Lower Fars formation.

channels to cut *into or through* adjacent anticlines to both north and south. Beyond the landslip the stream once more wanders away from the synclinal axis to bite into the pitching nose of Kabir Kuh itself. All of these anomalies are the result of superposition of drainage from the Lower Fars beds which formerly submerged the lower portions of the transected anticlines.

Before it enters its gorge through the landslide debris, the Saidmarreh curves from the center of the synclinal lowland directly toward Kabir Kuh and the landslip scar. The Saidmarreh also emerges from the landslip very near to the foot of the hogbacks rimming Kabir Kuh. The present course of the river across a lacustrine plain and through a landslide a thousand feet thick may not be an accurate reflection of its course 10,000 years ago, before the slide fell onto its old alluvial terraces, but this course is an indication of the probable solution to the problem.

A mechanism capable of pushing the Saidmarreh River against the flank of Kabir Kuh at this point is indicated if the line of the Kashgan River is considered in relation to the

[1] J. V. Harrison and N. L. Falcon, "An Ancient Landslip at Saidmarreh in Southwestern Iran," *Journ. of Geol.,* 46 (1938), 303.

[2] *Ibid.,* 304.

site of the detachment. Prior to reaching the open Saidmarreh Plain, where it follows a path around the perimeter of the landslip, the engorged portion of the Kashgan is directed exactly toward the landslip scar. In the late Pleistocene, when the Saidmarreh was building the alluvial plain (now terraced) upon which the landslip rests, the Kashgan was undoubtedly pushing a large alluvial fan into the Saidmarreh Valley. A fan built directly out from the last watergap cut by the Kashgan would have the effect of deflecting the Saidmarreh against the exact spot at which the detachment occurred. It is also possible that the rejuvenations that caused the dissection of the floodplain into terrace sets also effected the superposition of the Saidmarreh on the fold flank, to transect the Asmari layer by downcutting.

It is clear that the soft Lower Fars formation once submerged a far greater portion of the Kabir Kuh flank than it does at present. The Saidmarreh may have been deflected toward the Kabir Kuh anticline by the Kashgan fan early in the Pleistocene when the Lower Fars surface encountered the fold structure at a higher level, and closer to its axis. Rejuvenated downcutting would then superimpose the stream onto the arch from the Lower Fars beds, causing the transection of the Asmari plate by incision.

As an explanation of the Saidmarreh landslip, the hypothesis of fluvial undercutting or transection of the detached mass does not invoke an unlikely local structural accident otherwise associated with folds of a different type, but depends only upon a regional hydrographic peculiarity that is seen five times along the same stream, both above and below the site in question. How the Saidmarreh came to be displaced from its normal structural path in *all* of these instances is a part of the larger question of the origin of the discordance between drainage and structure in the orogen as a whole, which, it is hoped, has been resolved in the preceding pages.

Bibliography

Abdalian, E., "Le Tremblement de Terre de Toroud en Iran," *Nature,* Paris, 81 (1935).

Allison, A., and F. C. P. Slinger, "The Dezful Embayment Mountain Front Survey 1947–1948," Iranian Oil Exploration and Production Company, *Exploration Department Report* 723, Tehran (1948).

Bobek, H., "Beiträge zur Klimaokologischen Gliederung Irans," *Erdkunde,* 6 (1952), 65–84.

Bockh, H. de, G. M. Lees, and F. D. S. Richardson, "Stratigraphy and Tectonics of the Iranian Ranges," in *The Structure of Asia,* ed. by J. W. Gregory, London: Methuen, 1928, pp. 58–176.

Boesch, H. H., "Das Klima des Nahen Ostens," *Vierteljahresschr. d. Naturforsch. Ges.,* Zurich, 86 (1941), 8–61.

Boileau, V. H., A. K. Dashti, and L. G. Milliward, "Report on the Dezful Embayment Survey 1937–1938," Iranian Oil Expl. Prod. Co., *Geol. Dept. Report* 584 (1938).

Bordet, P., and M. Latrielle, "La Geologie de L'Himalaya de L'Arun," *Soc. Geol. de France Bulletin,* Ser. 6, T. 5 (1955), 529–542.

Braidwood, R. J., *et al., Studies in Ancient Oriental Civilizations,* Chicago University Oriental Inst. Publ. 31, 1960.

British Petroleum Company, Ltd., *Geological Maps and Sections of South-West Persia,* London: E. Stanford, 1956.

————, "Oil and Gas in Southwest Iran," *Proceedings,* Internat. Geol. Congr. Mexico, 1956, 2 (1956), 33–70.

Busk, H. G., "The Shimbar Valley Landslip Dam, Bakhtiari Country," *Geol. Mag.,* 63 (1926), 355–359.

Cooper, M. C., *Grass,* New York: G. P. Putnam, 1925.

Crichton, J. G., "Hypothetical Reconstruction of Folded Asmari Surface in Bakhtiari-Kuhgalu Country," Iranian Oil Expl. Prod. Co., *Geol. Dept. Report* (1947).

Curzon, G., *Persia and the Persian Question,* 2 vols., London, 1892.

Davies, L. M., "Note on Three Himalayan Rivers," *Geol. Mag.,* 77 (1940), 410–412.

Davis, W. M., "The Rivers and Valleys of Pennsylvania," in *Geographical Essays,* New York: Ginn and Co., 1909, republished Dover Publ., 1954, pp. 413–484.

Desio, A., "Sull Esistenza di Piccoli Phraccia Neela Persia Occidental," *Estratto del Bolletino del Camitato Glaciologico Italiana,* 14 (1934).

————, "Appunti Geographia Geologia Sulla Catena Della Zardeh Kuh in Persia," *Memoir Geologiche Geog. Rafichi di Giotto Dianelli,* 14 (1934).

————, "Sull Esistenza di Piccoli Ghiacciai in Persia e Sull Traccie di Espansioni Glacioli Quaternaire," *Congr. Internat. Geog. Warzawa C. R.,* 2 (1936).

Dickson, B., "Journeys in Kurdistan," *Geog. Journ.,* 35 (1910), 357–379.

Dunnington, H. V., "Generation, Migration, Accumulation and Dissipation of Oil in Northern Iraq," in *Habitat of Oil,* publ. by American Assoc. Petrol. Geologists, Tulsa (1958), 1194–1251.

Dunstan, H. E., "Some Structural and Stratigraphic Aspects of the Oil Fields of the Middle East," 18th Internat. Geol. Congr. London: Part C (1948).

Edmond, C. J., "Louristan," *Geog. Journ.* (1922), 335–350, 437–453.

Falcon, N. L., "The Bakhtiari Mountains of Southwest Persia," *Alpine Journal,* 46 (1934), 351–359.

————, "The Evidence for a Former Glaciation in the South-West Persian Mountain Belt," *Geog. Journ.,* 107 (1946), 78–79.

————, "Note on the Geology of the Western Side of the Dezful Embayment," Iranian Oil Expl. Prod. Co., *Geol. Dept. Report* 712 (1948).

————, "Evidence for Large Scale Flexuring in the Southwest Persian Mountain Zone," Iranian Oil Expl. Prod. Co., *Geol. Dept. Report* 797 (1950).

Foerste, F. A., "The Drainage of the Bernese Jura," *Proceedings of the Boston Society of Nat. History,* 25 (1892).

Fridley, H. M., "Solution and Stream Piracy," *Journ. of Geol.,* 47 (1939), 178–188.

Furon, R., "Sur la Structure du Plateau Iranien. Evolution des Zones Geophysicales, Axes Tectoniques," *Proceedings,* 17th Internat. Geol. Congr. Moscow, 1936 (1938).

————, "La Geologie du Plateau Iranien," *Mem. Musee Nat. d'Hist. Naturelle* 7, Paris (1941).

Gansser, A., "New Aspects of the Geology in Central Iran," *Proceedings,* 4th World Petrol. Congr., Rome, Sect. 1/A/5, Paper 2 (1955), 5.

Germaine-Jones, D. T., "Seismic Survey Over Asymmetric Structures in S. W. Persia," *Proceedings,* 3rd World Petrol. Congr., The Hague, Sect. 1 (1951), 546–563.

Goguel, J., *Tectonics,* translated by H. E. Thalmann, San Francisco: Freeman, 1962.

Gray, K. W., "A Tectonic Window in SW Iran," *Quart. Journ. Geol. Soc. London,* 105 (1949), 189–223.

Hagen, T., "Uber Gebirgsbildung und Talsysteme im Nepal Himalaya," *Geog. Helvetica,* 9 (1954), 325–331.

————, *Mount Everest,* London: Oxford, 1963.

Handel-Mazetti, "Zur Geographie von Kurdistan," *Petermanns Mitt.,* 63 (1912), 133–137.

Harrison, J. V., "The Bakhtiari Country, South-Western Persia," *Geog. Journ.*, 80 (1932), 193–210.

———, "Kuhgalu: South-West Iran," *Geog. Journ.*, 88 (1936), 20–36.

———, "The History of the River System of Southern Iran," (Abstract) *Proceedings,* 17th Internat. Geol. Congr. Moscow, 1936 (1938).

———, "Some Routes in Southern Iran," *Geog. Journ.*, 99 (1942), 113–129.

———, "South-West Persia: A Survey of Pish-i-Kuh in Luristan," *Geog. Journ.*, 108 (1946), 55–70.

———, and N. L. Falcon, "Gravity Collapse Structures and Mountain Ranges as Exemplified in S. W. Iran," *Quart. Journ. Geol. Soc. London*, 92 (1936), 91–102.

———, ———, "The Saidmarreh Landslip, S. W. Iran," *Geog. Journ.*, 89 (1937), 42–47.

———, ———, "An Ancient Landslip at Saidmarreh in Southwestern Iran," *Journ. Geol.*, 46 (1938), 296–309.

Heim, A., *Geologie der Schweiz*, Leipzig, 1919, 1921, 2 vols.

———, "The Himalayan Border Compared with the Alps," *Rec.*, Geol. Surv. India (1937).

Henson, F. R. S., "Observations on the Geology and Petroleum Occurrences of the Middle East," *Proceedings,* 3rd World Petrol. Congr., The Hague, Sect. 1 (1951), 118–140.

Ion, D. C., S. Elder, and A. E. Pedder, "The Agha Jari Oilfield of Southwest Persia," *Proceedings,* 3rd World Petrol. Congr., The Hague, Sect. 1 (1951), 162–186.

Kent, P. E., F. C. Slinger, and A. N. Thomas, "Stratigraphical Exploration Surveys in South-West Persia," *Proceedings,* 3rd World Petrol. Congr., The Hague, Sect. 1 (1951), 141–161.

Lees, G. M., "The Geology of the Oilfield Belt of Iran and Iraq," in *Science of Petroleum,* 1 (1938), 40–148.

———, "Foreland Folding," *Quart. Journ. Geol. Soc. London*, 108 (1952), 1–34.

———, "Persia," *Science of Petroleum,* 6 (1953), 73–82.

———, "Recent Earth Movements in the Middle East," *Geol. Rundschau,* 43 (1955), 221–226.

———and F. D. S. Richardson, "The Geology of the Oilfield Belt of S. W. Iran and Iraq," *Geol. Mag.,* 77 (1940), 227–251.

Loftus, W. K., "On the Geology of the Turko-Persian Frontier, and of the Districts Adjoining," *Quart. Journ. Geol. Soc. London*, 11 (1855), 247–344.

Margarie, E. de, *Le Jura*, Paris, 1922.

Martonne, E. de, "Tectonique et Evolution des Valleés Alpines," *Annales de Geog.*, 45 (1936), 337–348.

Meyerhoff, H. A., and E. W. Olmsted, "The Origins of Appalachian Drainage," *Amer. Journ. Sci.,* 32 (1936), 21–42.

Misch, P., "Diastrophism in the Himalaya Mountains," *Earth Science Digest,* 5 (1950), 19–22.

———, "Late Cenozoic Diastrophism in the Himalayan System," (Abstract) *Bulletin,* Geol. Soc. Amer., 61 (1950), 1487.

Mitchell, R. C., "The Tectonic Foundation and Character of S. W. Asia," *Egyptian Journ. Geol.,* 3 (1959), 1–70.

Morgan, J. de, *Mission Scientifique en Perse—Etudes Geographiques,* 2 (1895), —*Etudes Geologiques,* 1, 3 (1905), Paris: Ernest Leroux.

Nickell, F. A., "Reconnaissance of the Karun River Basin and the Diz River Gorge Near Dizful," *The Khuzistan Region of Southwest Iran,* Geological Report No. 1, New York: Development and Resources Corp., 1957.

O'Brien, C. A. E., "Compilation Contour Map of the Asmari Limestone," Iranian Oil Expl. Prod. Co., *Geol. Dept. Report* (1949).

———, "Tectonic Problems of the Oilfield Belt of South-West Iran," *Proceedings,* 18th Internat. Geol. Congr. 1948, Pt. 6, Sect. E (1950), 45–58.

———, "Salt Diapirism in South Persia," *Geol. en Mijnbouw,* (1957), 357–376.

———, and J. Law, "A Detailed Stratigraphic Survey of the Geology of South West Luristan," Iranian Oil Expl. Prod. Co., *Geol. Dept. Report* 725 (1948).

Pabot, H., *Native Vegetation and Its Ecology in the Khuzistan River Basins,* Ahwaz, Iran: Khuzistan Development Service, unpublished report.

Pannekoek, A. J., "Post-Orogenic History of Mountain Ranges," *Geologische Rundschau,* 50 (1960), 259–273.

Pilgrim, G. E., "Geology of the Persian Provinces of Fars, Kirman, and Laristan," *Mem. Geol. Surv. India,* 48 (1924), 1–118.

Schroeder, J. W., "Essai Sur la Structure de l'Iran," *Ecl. Geol. Helv.,* 37 (1944), 37–81.

Shand, S. J., "A Rift Valley in Western Persia," *Quart. Journ. Geol. Soc. London*, 75 (1919), 245–249.

Shepherd, M. F., E. F. Twerenbold, and F. Sajjadi, *The Geology of the Iraq Border Structures,* Tehran: Iranian Oil Operating Companies, Geol. and Expl. Div., 1961.

Sitter, L. U. de, *Structural Geology,* New York: McGraw-Hill, 1959.

Slinger, F. C. P., and J. G. Crichton, "The Geology and Development of the Gach Saran Field, Southwest Iran," *Proceedings,* 5th World Petrol. Congr. 1959, Sec. 1, No. 18 (1959), 349–375.

Slinger, F. C. P., L. E. T. Parker, and J. F. Watson, "The Mountain Front Geological Survey 1948–49 (Pabda to Behbehan)," Iranian Oil Expl. Prod. Co., *Report* 772 (1949).

Staub, R., "Grundzüge und Probleme Alpiner

Morphologie," *Denkschr. Schw. Naft. Ges.*, 69, Abh. 1 (1934), 183 pp.

Terra, H. de, *Geologische Forschungen im Westlichen K'un-Lun and Karakorum-Himalaya*, Berlin, 1922.

_____, "Himalayan and Alpine Orogenies," *Report*, 16th Internat. Geol. Congr., Washington, 1933, 2 (1936), 859–871.

Thomas, A. N., "The Asmari Limestone of S. W. Iran," *Report*, 18th Internat. Geol. Congr., London, 6 (1950), 35–44.

Thompson, J. H. D., "Drainage Evolution in the Southern Appalachians," Geol. Soc. Amer. *Bulletin*, 50 (1939), 1323–1356.

Ver Steeg, K., "Wind Gaps and Watergaps of the Northern Appalachians, Their Characteristics and Significance," *New York Acad. Sci. Annals*, 32 (1930), 87–220.

Voute, C., "Climate and Landscape in the Zagros Mountains (Iraq)," *Proceedings*, 21st Internat. Geol. Congr., 1960, Copenhagen, Part 4 (1960), 81–87.

Wadia, D. N., *The Geology of India*, London: Macmillan, 1961.

Wright, H. E. Jr., "The Geological Setting of Four Prehistoric Sites in Northeastern Iraq," *Bulletin, Amer. Schools of Oriental Research*, No. 128 (1952), 11–24.

_____, "Pleistocene Glaciation in Kurdistan," *Eiszeitalter und Gegenwart*, 12 (1962), 131–164.

Wright, I. J., "The Newer Appalachians of the South, Part I, Between the Potomac and the New Rivers," *Denison Univ. Bulletin* 34 (1934); *Sci. Lab. Journ.* 29 (1934), 143–250.

_____, "The Newer Appalachians of the South, Part II, South of the New River," *Denison Univ. Bulletin* 36 (1936); *Sci. Lab. Journ.* 31 (1936), 93–142.

Index

Illustrations are indicated in *italics*, footnotes by (n).